PRENTICE HALL
WRITING AND GRAMMAR

Grammar Exercise Workbook

Teacher's Edition

Grade Twelve

PEARSON

Prentice
Hall

Boston, Massachusetts,
Upper Saddle River, New Jersey

Copyright © by Pearson Education, Inc., publishing as **Pearson Prentice Hall, Boston, Massachusetts, 02116.** All rights reserved. Printed in the United States of America. This publication is protected by copyright, and permission should be obtained from the publisher prior to any prohibited reproduction, storage in a retrieval system, or transmission in any form or by any means, electronic, mechanical, photocopying, recording, or likewise. The publisher hereby grants permission to reproduce these pages, in part or in whole, for classroom use only, the number not to exceed the number of students in each class. Notice of copyright must appear on all copies. For information regarding permission(s), write to: Rights and Permissions Department, One Lake Street, Upper Saddle River, New Jersey 07458.

Pearson Prentice Hall™ is a trademark of Pearson Education, Inc.
Pearson® is a registered trademark of Pearson plc.
Prentice Hall® is a registered trademark of Pearson Education, Inc.

ISBN 0-13-361655-X

3 4 5 6 7 8 9 10   10 09

Contents

Note: This workbook supports Chapters 17–27 (Part 2: Grammar, Usage, and Mechanics) of Prentice Hall *Writing and Grammar.*

Diagraming **151**

17.1 **Nouns • Practice 1**

Nouns   A noun is the name of a person, place, or thing. Singular nouns name one person, place, or thing. Plural nouns name more than one. A concrete noun names something you can see, touch, taste, hear, or smell. An abstract noun names something you cannot perceive through your senses. A common noun names any one of a class of people, places, or things. A proper noun names a specific person, place, or thing.

TYPES OF NOUNS		
Singular Nouns	mouse	dish
Plural Nouns	mice	dishes
Concrete Nouns	tomato	bicycle
Abstract Nouns	existence	quality
Common Nouns	day	river
Proper Nouns	Monday	Mississippi River

A collective noun names groups of people or things. A compound noun is composed of two or more words acting as a single unit. Compound nouns may appear in three forms: as separate words, as hyphenated words, or as combined words.

Collective Nouns	Compound Nouns
faculty	office manager
jury	editor-in-chief
team	postmaster

▶ **Exercise 1**   **Recognizing Nouns.**   Underline each noun in the sentences below.

EXAMPLE: My <u>parents</u> took a <u>trip</u> to <u>Vienna</u>.

1. Elections arouse strong feelings in many people.
2. The roof of our barn was damaged in the hurricane.
3. Dubrovnik, a resort in Yugoslavia, is on the Adriatic.
4. My friends were delighted by our success in the long jump.
5. Fortunately, it is a short walk to the library.
6. The committee was impressed by our persistence and determination.
7. The orchestra includes strings, woodwinds, and brass.
8. In the morning the director outlined his plan.
9. Amy offered a good explanation for her failure.
10. Mrs. Hope offered Tom a cruise to the West Indies as a reward.

▶ **Exercise 2**   **Recognizing Collective and Compound Nouns.**   Write *collective* or *compound* next to each noun.

EXAMPLE: sightseeing _____*compound*_____

1. roommate _____
2. class _____
3. dog tag _____
4. typewriter _____
5. committee _____
6. orchestra _____
7. herd _____
8. sister-in-law _____
9. overboard _____
10. highlight _____

17.1 Nouns • Practice 2

> **Exercise 1** **Identifying the Types of Nouns.** Identify each of the following nouns according to whether it (1) names a *person, place,* or *thing,* (2) is *concrete* or *abstract,* (3) is *singular* or *plural,* (4) is *collective,* (5) is *compound,* and (6) is *common* or *proper.*

EXAMPLE: pleasure _____ *(1) thing, (2) abstract, (3) singular, (6) common* _____

1. jump suit _____
2. tomato _____
3. giraffes _____
4. San Francisco _____
5. monkey wrenches _____
6. Lord Peter Wimsey _____
7. herd _____
8. privileges _____
9. hope _____
10. Davis Cup _____
11. stitches _____
12. flock _____
13. White House _____
14. umbrella _____
15. ugliness _____
16. life preservers _____
17. jack-in-the-pulpit _____
18. terrorism _____
19. Pearl Harbor _____
20. sundial _____

> **Exercise 2** **Recognizing Compound Nouns.** If an expression is in the dictionary, write *compound* and give a brief definition. If an expression is not in the dictionary, simply define the expression from common knowledge.

EXAMPLE: word of honor _____ *compound* _____ *solemn promise; oath* _____

1. rain check _____
2. rain puddle _____
3. scarlet fever _____
4. scarlet glow _____
5. scarlet ribbon _____
6. storm warning _____
7. storm window _____
8. dog days _____
9. dog tag _____
10. dog bone _____

Pronouns • Practice 1

Pronouns   A pronoun is a word used to take the place of a noun. The noun it substitutes for is called an antecedent.

PRONOUNS AND ANTECEDENTS
ANTECEDENT   PRONOUN   PRONOUN
Priscilla asked *her* brother if *she* could borrow a sweater.

Study the types of pronouns in the chart and note their uses.

TYPES OF PRONOUNS		
Type	**Uses**	**Examples**
Personal	Refer to particular people, places, or things	I, he, she, it, we, you, they
Indefinite	Refer to people, places, or things without specifying which ones	each, everyone, some, both
Interrogative	Used to ask questions	what, which, who, whom, whose
Demonstrative	Used to point out a particular person, place, or thing	this, that, these, those

▶ **Exercise 1**   **Recognizing Pronouns and Antecedents.**   Underline the personal pronoun in each sentence and circle its antecedent.

EXAMPLE: (Bob) lent Sally his typewriter.

1. Will Ruth bring her stereo to the party?

2. Because of his injury, Ted was unable to play.

3. The doctor said that he would begin first with eye examinations.

4. Jeff, will you please mow the lawn now?

5. With her team about to lose, Betty scored the winning basket.

6. Maimonides completed his first major work in 1168.

7. In the accident the bus lost its rear axle.

8. Allison asked Ted if she could go.

9. When they completed the project, the students went to lunch.

10. How will you feel later, Lee Ann?

▶ **Exercise 2**   **Recognizing Different Types of Pronouns.**   Underline the pronoun in each sentence and tell whether it is *personal, indefinite, interrogative,* or *demonstrative.*

EXAMPLE: Everyone should vote in the election. _____indefinite_____

1. This is much too expensive. _____

2. We have decided to visit Spain next year. _____

3. Whom did Kim ask for directions? _____

4. Has the coach spoken to both of the boys? _____

5. Someone just rang the bell. _____

17.1 Pronouns • Practice 2

Exercise 1 **Recognizing Antecedents.** Write each underlined pronoun and its antecedent on the line. If a pronoun does not have an antecedent, write *none* after the pronoun.

EXAMPLE: Scott turned in his report before it was due.
 his (Scott)   it (report)

1. Jo herself has had clairvoyant experiences at various times in her life. _____

2. The troops trudged through the thick forest. Their throats were parched and they yearned for some refreshment. _____

3. I think nothing is worse than a steak that is well-done. _____

4. All of the graduating seniors must pass proficiency tests. _____

5. Pollution hung in a thick cloud over the city. Its debilitating effects caused the schools to cancel their sports events. _____

6. Amy Lowell is a particularly fine poet. Everyone should read at least one of her poems. _____

7. It is inspirational to me to read stories of people who have overcome severe handicaps and gone on to lead successful lives. _____

8. Listening attentively is a valuable skill. Students should train themselves to do it effectively. _____

9. I asked Marcia what she meant by her mysterious remark. _____

10. Both of the actors gave superior performances. They captured the hearts of their audience. _____

Exercise 2 **Identifying the Different Types of Pronouns.** Identify each underlined pronoun as *personal, reflexive, intensive, demonstrative, relative, interrogative,* or *indefinite.*

EXAMPLE: Television critics worry about its effect on viewers. *personal*

When over 130,000,000 television viewers turned on (1) their sets to watch *Roots,* (2) few had any idea that (3) this was the beginning of a new television era for (4) everyone. Today, docudramas with (5) their colorful dramatizations of historical events make up a substantial portion of (6) each of the networks' programming. But even as American viewers treat (7) themselves to these television triumphs, there are (8) those (9) who denounce (10) them. Critics contend that docudramas mix fact with fiction without telling (11) those (12) who watch (13) them of this. The critics pose some disturbing questions: (14) Who verifies the historical accuracy of these tales? Are the networks doing a disservice by allowing the public to dupe (15) themselves into believing that these distorted accounts are true? (16) Others contend that the critics overstate the seriousness of the problem and insult the viewer (17) who is intelligent enough to distinguish reality from fiction. Nevertheless, the disquieting questions remain. When (18) we realize that the average television set is on for more than six hours a day, we (19) ourselves must ponder the impact these shows may be exerting on us. If we do not, (20) whose version of past events will later fill our textbooks—the Hollywood producers' or the true historians'?

1. _____   6. _____   11. _____   16. _____
2. _____   7. _____   12. _____   17. _____
3. _____   8. _____   13. _____   18. _____
4. _____   9. _____   14. _____   19. _____
5. _____   10. _____   15. _____   20. _____

17.2 **Verbs** (Action Verbs and Linking Verbs) • Practice 1

Action Verbs and Linking Verbs An action verb tells what action someone or something is performing. A linking verb connects its subject with another word that renames or describes the subject.

Action Verbs	Linking Verbs
For years the people *waited*.	Picasso *was* a famous painter.
Our visitors *left* after lunch.	This stew *tastes* delicious.

▶ **Exercise 1** **Identifying Action and Linking Verbs.** Underline each verb. Write *action* or *linking* after it.

EXAMPLE: The river swells near the cove. ____action____

1. Mary Grace seems unusually poised. _____
2. In the morning the freighter sailed. _____
3. In 1066, William the Conqueror landed in England. _____
4. Trenton is the capital of New Jersey. _____
5. In a short time, my sister grew tall. _____
6. After a year, Stan became our captain. _____
7. The magician reached into the velvet bag. _____
8. Unfortunately, the speaker was late. _____
9. My grandfather looks older these days. _____
10. Unnoticed, we slipped out the door. _____

▶ **Exercise 2** **Using Linking Verbs.** From the list below, choose an appropriate linking verb to use in each of the following sentences. You may need to change the form of some verbs.

sound   look   smell   taste   be
grow   turn   feel   become   appear

EXAMPLE: The music ____sounds____ delightful.

1. The train _____ to be late today.
2. Susan _____ our new president.
3. I _____ a better typist quickly.
4. The rhubarb pie _____ too sour.
5. Grandmother doesn't _____ well today.
6. Your new scent _____ fantastic.
7. Sweet cream, unless refrigerated, _____ bad rapidly.
8. Before the game, the team _____ unhappy.
9. In those shoes, he _____ taller.
10. On the phone my father _____ discouraged.

17.2 Verbs (Action Verbs and Linking Verbs) • Practice 2

▶ **Exercise 1** **Identifying Action and Linking Verbs.** Identify each of the underlined verbs in the following sentences as either an *action verb* or a *linking verb*.

EXAMPLE: The apple pie <u>smells</u> delicious. *linking verb*

1. We <u>stayed</u> at charming roadside inns throughout our travels in England. _____
2. The inexperienced actor's mannerisms <u>seemed</u> rehearsed and unnatural. _____
3. Following in the family tradition, Elizabeth <u>became</u> a pharmacist. _____
4. The trail <u>looked</u> perilous to the novice hikers. _____
5. Brussels sprouts <u>taste</u> bitter to me. _____
6. The cat <u>appeared</u> from behind the woodshed. _____
7. I <u>tasted</u> a hint of basil in the soup we were served. _____
8. The canvas on the lawn chair <u>grew</u> pale after being exposed to the sun. _____
9. The people in the odd-looking contraption <u>stayed</u> calm in spite of the crowd's laughter. _____
10. The leaves of the maple tree <u>turn</u> a vibrant shade of red in the fall. _____
11. Because of his nail-biting habit, Harold often <u>appears</u> nervous. _____
12. With its high style and graceful feather, that hat <u>becomes</u> Helen. _____
13. For some unexplained reason, James <u>felt</u> uncomfortable around Marion. _____
14. Peter <u>grows</u> sunflowers and peonies in his backyard. _____
15. The astronomer <u>looked</u> through the new telescope for the first time. _____
16. Despite all her hardships, Gloria <u>remained</u> optimistic for all those years. _____
17. The mice <u>smelled</u> the cheese from two rooms away. _____
18. Grace, a careful shopper, <u>felt</u> each piece of fruit for ripeness. _____
19. During the wild winter storms, Stan <u>remained</u> at home. _____
20. These flowers <u>smell</u> so wonderfully fragrant. _____

▶ **Exercise 2** **Using Action Verbs in Sentences.** From the list below, choose an appropriate action verb to use in each of the following sentences.

EXAMPLE: The train <u>raced</u> past the station.

beckons	calculate	translate	fascinate	hoards
injures	negotiated	participates	quibble	vanquish

1. "Don't _____ over every little detail," said Max.
2. The reckless player _____ someone else in almost every game.
3. Darlene _____ a very good deal for herself.
4. Jack can _____ this story into English for you.
5. With a single, silent gesture, Marilyn _____ to John.
6. The caged birds _____ the kittens.
7. Our team can _____ your team any day!
8. James can _____ the total of all those numbers in his head.
9. Barry _____ in three different after-school clubs.
10. The old miser _____ every extra dollar he gets.

17.2 Verbs (Transitive and Intransitive Verbs) • Practice 1

Transitive and Intransitive Verbs A verb is transitive if it directs action toward someone or something named in the same sentence. A verb is intransitive if it does *not* direct action toward someone or something named in the same sentence.

Transitive	Intransitive
Steve *built* a bookcase.	Jeanne *rowed* across the lake.
Paula *brought* Lucy home.	Grandma *slept* restfully.

> **Exercise 1** **Identifying Transitive and Intransitive Verbs.** Label each underlined verb as *transitive* or *intransitive*.

EXAMPLE: Jennie <u>wiped</u> her windshield carefully. ___*transitive*___

1. We <u>plant</u> an assortment of vegetables every spring. _____
2. The Great Mosque of Samarra <u>has existed</u> since 847. _____
3. Several pages of the document <u>were</u> on file. _____
4. We <u>told</u> the class about the book fair. _____
5. The soloist <u>played</u> Vivaldi's *Mandolin Concerto*. _____
6. Three major religions <u>consider</u> Jerusalem a holy city. _____
7. Smiling, the heroine <u>disappeared</u> into the shadows. _____
8. My aunt always <u>keeps</u> a rescue ladder in her bedroom. _____
9. Mother still <u>talks</u> about President Kennedy. _____
10. All morning the strange rumble <u>grew</u> louder. _____

> **Exercise 2** **Writing Sentences with Transitive and Intransitive Verbs.** Complete the sentences below. For sentences with transitive verbs, add a noun or pronoun toward which the verb directs its action.

EXAMPLE: Transitive: Judy quickly opened the ___*letter.*___
         Intransitive: The victim smiled ___*bravely.*___

1. Intransitive: The principal agreed _____.
2. Transitive: Later, she reached _____.
3. Transitive: Suddenly, the passengers saw a _____.
4. Intransitive: The bus screeched _____.
5. Transitive: The mayor told the _____.
6. Intransitive: At dawn the rooster crowed _____.
7. Intransitive: The team traveled _____.
8. Transitive: Dr. Greer gave the _____.
9. Intransitive: The astronaut spoke _____.
10. Transitive: Take the _____.

17.2 Verbs (Transitive and Intransitive Verbs) • Practice 2

▶ **Exercise 1** **Identifying Transitive and Intransitive Verbs.** Underline the verbs in the following sentences and label each as *transitive* or *intransitive*.

EXAMPLE: We <u>arrived</u> in time for dinner. *intransitive*

1. The wind buffeted the frail sapling. _____
2. At midnight the weary politician conceded the election. _____
3. I was there on Tuesday. _____
4. The glider soared beside the majestic cliffs. _____
5. I made an appointment with the dentist. _____
6. The visitors noticed the new landscaping around our home. _____
7. The agile squirrel scampered up to the top of the tall tree. _____
8. The oil spill polluted the local beaches. _____
9. After his vacation, the President appeared rested. _____
10. The gymnast balanced carefully on the beam. _____
11. The department store advertised its sale in the newspaper. _____
12. The professor lectured to the class. _____
13. The referee penalized the team for the player's foul. _____
14. The timid driver ventured into the busy traffic. _____
15. The carpenter chiseled a pattern in the cabinet door. _____
16. In his answer, Dan quoted William Shakespeare. _____
17. With that music, Inez was transported into another world. _____
18. The doctor inoculated the children against the flu. _____
19. The gentle wind whispered through the tropical trees. _____
20. The use of a seat belt can prevent serious injuries. _____

▶ **Exercise 2** **Using Transitive and Intransitive Verbs.** From the list below, choose an appropriate verb to complete each sentence. Then identify the verb as *transitive* or *intransitive*.

EXAMPLE: After lunch, Ann <u>washed</u> the car. *transitive*

abbreviate	banished	challenge	deteriorate	emphasized
fractured	gloat	whimpers	visualizes	tolerate

1. Diane _____ herself in a very successful career. _____
2. The winners _____ over their victory. _____
3. You cannot _____ that short word. _____
4. Brad and Stu _____ Mick and Jon to a friendly round of golf. _____
5. The boss _____ the importance of promptness and reliability. _____
6. Because of his loud barking, the dog was _____ to the garage. _____
7. Without paint, the exterior of that house will soon _____ in this weather. _____
8. The hungry dog _____ at the back door. _____
9. Sandra _____ her arm during the game. _____
10. "I will not _____ laziness in this class," said Ms. Anderson. _____

17.2 **Verbs** (Verb Phrases) • **Practice 1**

Verb Phrase   A verb that is made up of more than one word is a verb phrase. A verb phrase is formed by adding helping verbs to another verb in a sentence.

VERB PHRASES
The president *will appoint* a committee.
We *could have reached* another decision.
Better prepared, she *might have been chosen* to play a leading role.
I *have* certainly *admired* your work.
She *will* hopefully not *reject* the post.

▶ **Exercise 1**   **Identifying Verb Phrases.**   Underline all parts of the verb phrase in each sentence. Do not underline words that interrupt a verb phrase.

EXAMPLE: I <u>had</u> almost <u>forgotten</u> about the meeting.

1. We should have taken a less congested route.

2. My parents will definitely not give us permission to go.

3. Throughout the Roman period, Ostia had been a leading naval port.

4. Have they opened their presents yet?

5. We could not have gotten a better break in the game.

6. All the stars will appear at the spring festival.

7. By the age of ten, she had almost grown to full height.

8. *The Marriage of Figaro* has been performed twice this season.

9. Undoubtedly, she could not be selected to run.

10. The judges have already made their decision.

▶ **Exercise 2**   **Using Verb Phrases.**   Complete each of the following sentences with an appropriate verb phrase that includes the verb in parentheses.

EXAMPLE: _____ you _____ the new position yet? (accept)
        Have   you   *accepted*   the new position yet?

1. _____ you _____ _____ to the prom? (invite)

2. The office _____ _____ on the second floor. (locate)

3. She _____ already _____ her prize. (receive)

4. Annette _____ _____ _____ _____
   at the news. (surprise)

5. Tomorrow, they _____ _____ to Chicago. (fly)

6. We _____ definitely _____ to remain. (agree)

7. The roof _____ _____ this morning. (repair)

8. They _____ _____ _____ to Cape Cod for years. (go)

9. _____ you _____ the shirts and the pants? (buy)

10. The doctor _____ not _____ you a new prescription. (give)

17.2 **Verbs** (Verb Phrases) • **Practice 2**

▶ **Exercise 1**   **Using Verb Phrases.**   Complete each of the following sentences with an appropriate verb phrase that includes the verb in parentheses.

EXAMPLE: _____ you _____ any of her stories? (read)
              Have   you   _read_   any of her stories?

1. The American Kennel Club _____ _____ dogs into working dogs, sporting dogs, nonsporting dogs, hounds, terriers, and toys. (classified)

2. Euclid _____ _____ _____ the Father of Geometry. (called)

3. The profits from the song "God Bless America" by Irving Berlin _____ _____ to the Scouts. (donated)

4. Next year, professional golfers _____ _____ in at least four big tournaments. (participate)

5. _____ India and Nepal _____ _____ _____ to put their flags atop Mount Everest? (permitted)

6. A person in the Navy with the rank of fleet admiral _____ _____ five stars. (attained)

7. The Jean Hersholt Humanitarian Award _____ always _____ at the Academy Awards. (presented)

8. Liberty Island, home of the Statue of Liberty, _____ formerly _____ at Bedloe's Island. (known)

9. We _____ _____ a new fiscal year next month. (begin)

10. This company _____ _____ _____ bathrobes for over fifty years. (manufacturing)

▶ **Writing Application**   **Writing Sentences with Different Kinds of Verbs.**   Use each of the following verbs in a sentence of your own, following the directions in parentheses. You can change the form of the verb.

EXAMPLE: feel (as a linking verb)
              She feels pleased about her grade.

1. taste (as an action verb)

   _____

2. taste (as a linking verb)

   _____

3. climb (as a transitive verb)

   _____

4. climb (as an intransitive verb)

   _____

5. prevent (with three helping verbs)

   _____

Adjectives • Practice 1

Adjectives   An adjective is a word used to describe a noun or pronoun or to give a noun or pronoun a more specific meaning. Like nouns, adjectives can be proper or compound—that is, they can be made up of more than one word. Proper adjectives are formed from proper nouns and always begin with a capital letter. A pronoun is used as an adjective if it modifies a noun. The chart below summarizes the kinds of pronouns used as adjectives and their use.

Possessive Adjectives		Demonstrative Adjectives	Interrogative Adjectives	Indefinite Adjectives			
				Singular	Plural	Either	
my	its	this	which	another	both	all	most
your	our	that	what	each	few	any	other
his	their	these	whose	either	many	more	some
her		those		neither	several		

▶ **Exercise 1**   **Adding Pronouns Used as Adjectives.**   Fill in each blank with the kind of adjective given in parentheses.

EXAMPLE: I know _____*those*_____ people sitting in the corner. (demonstrative)

1. _____ students were still taking the test. (indefinite)

2. _____ question do you want me to answer? (interrogative)

3. Is this _____ coat or yours? (possessive)

4. There are _____ books I want to read. (indefinite)

5. Jill and Vincent brought _____ new puppy to my house. (possessive)

6. _____ term paper is due next week. (possessive)

7. _____ hat is on the table? (interrogative)

8. This article is more interesting than _____ one. (demonstrative)

9. May I have _____ piece of pie? (indefinite)

10. Are _____ records yours or mine? (demonstrative)

▶ **Exercise 2**   **Using Proper Adjectives in Sentences.**   In the space provided, write a sentence using each word below as an adjective.

EXAMPLE: Parisian _____*Mrs. Townson wore a* **Parisian** *gown.*_____

1. French _____

2. Alaskan _____

3. Latin American _____

4. Himalayan _____

5. Spanish _____

6. Canadian _____

7. Roman _____

8. Elizabethan _____

9. European _____

10. Emersonian _____

17.3 Adjectives • Practice 2

▶ **Exercise 1**   **Identifying Adjectives.**   Write all of the adjectives that modify each underlined noun or pronoun in the following paragraph.

EXAMPLE: Collections of great art <u>treasures</u> have been preserved in many places around the world.

_____great, art_____

Dresden, an East German (1) <u>city</u>, houses some of the greatest art (2) <u>treasures</u> in the world. From the sixteenth (3) <u>century</u> to the eighteenth century, the Saxon (4) <u>electors</u> collected art from the four (5) <u>corners</u> of the globe and brought them to this (6) <u>location</u>. Though the Saxon (7) <u>reign</u> was short-lived, the treasures have not been; most (8) <u>pieces</u> even survived the Allied (9) <u>bombing</u> during World War II. Today the public can view delicate Oriental (10) <u>porcelain</u> and sensitive, moving (11) <u>paintings</u> of great (12) <u>artists</u>. The Green Vault holds precious (13) <u>metals</u> and jewels, the work of the best European (14) <u>artisans</u>. One display contains shining diamond boot (15) <u>buckles</u> and jeweled shirt (16) <u>buttons</u>. To estimate the (17) <u>value</u> of these (18) <u>treasures</u> would prove virtually impossible; (19) <u>many</u> are priceless. For example, at one auction, eight Meissen china (20) <u>pieces</u> sold for $313,720.

1. _____   11. _____
2. _____   12. _____
3. _____   13. _____
4. _____   14. _____
5. _____   15. _____
6. _____   16. _____
7. _____   17. _____
8. _____   18. _____
9. _____   19. _____
10. _____   20. _____

▶ **Exercise 2**   **Putting Adjectives in Order.**   Put the adjectives following each underlined noun in the proper order and write the entire phrase on the line.

EXAMPLE: <u>jacket</u>—down-filled, new, winter, a   _____a new down-filled winter jacket_____

1. <u>sports car</u>—British, that, small, red

_____

2. <u>road</u>—dirt, a, winding, narrow _____

3. <u>vase</u>—lovely, this, hand-painted, Japanese

_____

4. <u>insects</u>—flying, iridescent, many

_____

5. <u>coin</u>—bronze, ancient, the, Roman

_____

6. <u>mouse</u>—field, frightened, the, brown, tiny

_____

7. <u>shirt</u>—green, the, silk _____

8. <u>kitten</u>—Siamese, blue-eyed, little, a

_____

9. <u>library</u>—red, new, brick, our _____

10. <u>stories</u>—mystery, exciting, several _____

17.3 Adverbs • Practice 1

Adverbs   An adverb is a word that modifies a verb, an adjective, or another adverb.

Adverbs Modifying Verbs	
Where? The tuxedos will be delivered *here*.	**When?** According to the plans, our cousins will arrive *tomorrow*.
In what manner? She skates *very* well.	**To what extent?** Diane *nearly* won.
Adverbs Modifying Adjectives	**Adverbs Modifying Adverbs**
To what extent? He is *too* curious.	**To what extent?** She speaks *rapidly*.

> **Exercise 1**   **Recognizing Adverbs and the Words They Modify.**   Underline the adverb in each sentence. In the space provided, tell whether it modifies a *verb*, an *adjective*, or another *adverb*. Some sentences have two adverbs.

EXAMPLE: My brother drives recklessly. ____*verb*____

1. Are your friends still angry? _____

2. The destructive flood stopped there. _____

3. My mother paints really well. _____ _____

4. I think the package was delivered yesterday. _____

5. The shortstop fielded every ball gracefully. _____

6. She has already written to her senator. _____

7. I always organize material carefully. _____ _____

8. The speaker is obviously late. _____

9. She talks incessantly about her boyfriend. _____

10. Your little sister seems very polite. _____

> **Exercise 2**   **Adding Adverbs to Sentences.**   Fill in the blanks below with appropriate adverbs.

EXAMPLE: Everyone in my family spells ____*poorly*____ .

1. Our college applications arrived _____ .

2. They have _____ returned our phone calls.

3. The road _____ changed from three lanes into one.

4. Madeline is _____ finished with her research paper.

5. This digital watch is _____ reliable.

6. Put the new bookcase _____ .

7. She has _____ taken sides against me.

8. Speak _____ when you address the student government.

9. With time short, she shopped _____ .

10. I can _____ understand her reasoning.

17.3 Adverbs • Practice 2

Exercise 1 **Identifying Adverbs.** Each of the following sentences contains from two to four adverbs. Write each adverb and then write the word or words that it modifies.

EXAMPLE: We sailed the boat all afternoon.
_____all (afternoon) afternoon (sailed)_____

1. Yesterday, the architects sketchily explained the plans they have for the office building.
_____

2. A southerly storm approached quickly, drenching the area with an extremely heavy downpour.
_____

3. Almost apologetically, she presented her handmade gift.
_____

4. The roller coaster crazily raced up and down before it eventually released its dizzy passengers.
_____

5. My hand jerked involuntarily, and my glass crashed violently against the floor.
_____
_____

Exercise 2 **Adding Adverbs to Sentences.** Copy the following sentences, adding at least one adverb to each. If necessary, change the wording of the sentence, but do not use the same adverb more than once.

EXAMPLE: Most people have seen the figure of Uncle Sam.
_____Most people have often seen the figure of Uncle Sam._____

(1) Since the War of 1812, the symbol of Uncle Sam has characterized the American government. (2) This famous symbol came from the initials that were stamped on barrels of salted meat by a United States Army meat inspector. (3) Citizens in New York and Vermont liked the nickname and began to use it. (4) Uncle Sam achieved fame in 1813 when he was pictured in a Troy, New York, newspaper. (5) By 1830, Uncle Sam had donned his familiar, splashy costume of stars and stripes. (6) A clown dressed as Uncle Sam delighted crowds during the 1800's and helped to popularize the costume. (7) In 1813, most newspaper cartoonists depicted Uncle Sam as a young man. (8) By 1917, he had grown older. (9) On a poster that was used during the First World War, Uncle Sam pointed his wrinkled finger at the young men across the United States and declared, "I want you." (10) Congress made Uncle Sam an official national symbol in 1961.

1. _____
2. _____
3. _____
4. _____
5. _____
6. _____
7. _____
8. _____
9. _____
10. _____

17.4 # Prepositions • Practice 1

Prepositions A preposition is a word that relates a noun or pronoun that appears with it to another word in the sentence.

FREQUENTLY USED PREPOSITIONS			
about	between	in	over
across	by	into	to
at	before	near	through
among	for	of	under
below	from	on	with

A prepositional phrase begins with a preposition and ends with a noun or pronoun called the object of the preposition.

PREPOSITIONAL PHRASE	
Prepositions	**Objects of Prepositions**
with	my *friends*
between	*us*
next to	the old *building*

► **Exercise 1** **Identifying Prepositions.** Underline each preposition in the sentences below. Some sentences have more than one.

EXAMPLE: In the morning they traveled to the city.

1. She asked for passes to the football game.
2. This agreement is strictly between you and me.
3. They arrived from Spain about ten in the evening.
4. Over the hill is a gas station with a restroom.
5. We spoke for hours about our class reunion.
6. The price of this stereo is below our regular discount price.
7. Go through the corridor into the other building.
8. With great joy, we walked across the stage.
9. I received a special award from the coach.
10. Your hat is under the mirror near the umbrella.

► **Exercise 2** **Identifying Prepositional Phrases.** In each sentence place parentheses around each prepositional phrase. Some sentences have more than one.

EXAMPLE: (At dawn) we drove (to the agricultural fair).

1. The room in the attic is filled with old furniture.
2. The card shop is not far from the park.
3. The cave paintings at Lascaux were discovered in 1940.
4. Near the hotel, you will find a group of craft shops.
5. There are no secrets between Sally and me.
6. I walked through the town in an hour and a half.
7. For years, the author waited for a letter from her son.
8. A group of travelers arrived by air.
9. In high school, I studied the flute with Mr. Poole.
10. They drove through the night to the next town.

17.4 Prepositions • Practice 2

▶ **Exercise 1**   **Identifying Prepositional Phrases.**   Underline the prepositional phrases from the following paragraph and circle each preposition.

EXAMPLE: (During) my vacation I discovered the exciting sport (of) cross-country skiing.

(1) The thrill of cross-country skiing is infecting people around the globe. (2) The sport originated across the Atlantic Ocean in the Scandinavian countries and was brought to the United States by Scandinavian settlers. (3) According to recent figures, more than two million people are now cross-country skiers. (4) Cross-country skiers can compete for prizes in races held around the world. (5) A Norwegian race, the Birkenbeiner, honors two skiers who heroically carried a Norwegian prince to safety amid a civil war in the early thirteenth century. (6) The skiers were called "birch legs" or "birkenbeiner" because of the birch that they wrapped around their legs for warmth. (7) Californians hold the Snowshoe Thompson Race, named after a mail carrier. (8) By means of cross-country skiing, this man regularly carried the mail ninety miles through the Sierras. (9) The most popular cross-country race, however, is probably the one in Sweden called the Vasaloppet. (10) Ten thousand people gather every year for this competition.

▶ **Exercise 2**   **Distinguishing Between Prepositions and Adverbs.**   Identify the underlined word in each sentence as either a *preposition* or an *adverb*. If the word is a preposition, circle its object.

EXAMPLE: They are waiting near the (door) .   *preposition*

1. A college student shimmied up the flagpole. _____
2. The sun went down behind the hill. _____
3. The lights were mistakenly left on overnight. _____
4. When she went away, we left as well. _____
5. The elephant suddenly turned around and charged. _____
6. We remained behind after the others had left. _____
7. A button on my blazer fell off. _____
8. A valley lies below the sea. _____
9. The antique chair was in good condition. _____
10. For dinner the couple went out and had a leisurely meal. _____

▶ **Exercise 3**   **Using Prepositional Phrases.**   Copy the following sentences, adding a prepositional phrase that provides the information requested in the parentheses. The last two sentences require the addition of more than one prepositional phrase.

EXAMPLE: We went to the soccer game. (time)
           We went to the soccer game after school.

1. I longingly watched the sailing vessels. (location)

   _____

2. We postponed the soccer match. (cause)

   _____

3. The snow level topped three feet. (time)

   _____

4. The pungent odor assailed my senses. (possession)

   _____

5. The bats flew erratically. (time, duration)

   _____

Name _____ Date _____

 17.4 # Conjunctions • Practice 1

Conjunctions A conjunction is a word used to connect other words or groups of words. Coordinating conjunctions and correlative conjunctions join similar kinds of words or groups of words that are grammatically alike. Subordinating conjunctions connect subordinate clauses with independent clauses in complex sentences.

COORDINATING CONJUNCTIONS			
and	but	for	nor
or	so	yet	

CORRELATIVE CONJUNCTIONS		
both...and	either...or	neither...nor
whether...or	not only...but also	

FREQUENTLY USED SUBORDINATING CONJUNCTIONS				
after	as soon as	even though	than	when
although	as though	if	though	whenever
as	because	since	unless	wherever
as if	before	so that	until	while

▶ **Exercise 1** **Identifying Conjunctions.** Underline the conjunction in each sentence. Write a *C* if it is coordinating, *CR* if it is correlative, or *S* if it is subordinating.

EXAMPLE: Either I will go, or I will send my sister. _____CR_____

1. Bob arrived late even though he caught the first flight. _____

2. I wanted to play in the homecoming game, but I hurt my knee. _____

3. Not only is he a scholar, but he is also a fine athlete. _____

4. Mother said she would write or phone from Bermuda. _____

5. Hebron and Beersheba were cities in ancient Judah. _____

6. Whether he wins or loses is not really important. _____

7. As soon as the hurricane ended, we began to rescue people. _____

8. Both Whitney and Tiffany agreed to volunteer. _____

9. We visited the science museum while they waited. _____

10. Neither my teacher nor my father liked my idea. _____

▶ **Exercise 2** **Using Coordinating, Correlative, and Subordinating Conjunctions in Sentences.** Complete each sentence. Make sure each subordinating conjunction is followed by a full clause.

EXAMPLE: If _____, I will write you.
If _____*you send me your address*_____, I will write you.

1. Either I _____, or
   I _____.

2. Since _____, I bought a new stereo.

3. Because _____,
   she _____.

4. Both _____
   and _____ phoned yesterday.

5. We hoped to win, but _____.

© **Prentice-Hall, Inc.**   Conjunctions • **17**

17.4 Conjunctions • Practice 2

Exercise 1 **Identifying Conjunctions in Sentences.** Underline the conjunction in each sentence and identify it as *coordinating, correlative,* or *subordinating.*

EXAMPLE: I could not decide <u>whether</u> your answer was right <u>or</u> wrong.   *correlative*

1. The physics instructor explained the theory, but I did not understand it. _____

2. Roger is significantly taller than Doug is. _____

3. You should eat salads since they are good for your digestion. _____

4. I checked several banquet facilities before I finally chose this one. _____

5. Unless you reform, you will be dismissed. _____

6. I burned my tongue, for the soup was still too hot to eat. _____

7. Whenever the shepherd gave the order, the dog began to round up strays. _____

8. Not only can you do some packing, but you can also carry out some boxes. _____

9. Persimmons and pumpkins can be used to make excellent spice cookies. _____

10. Now that the harvest is behind them, the farmers can relax. _____

11. One side of that room divider functions as a bookcase, and the other functions as a china cabinet. _____

12. By cutting down those trees, you endanger not only the spotted owl but also the land itself. _____

13. Although I have been to Seattle many times, I have never visited the Space Needle. _____

14. Jerome had the pasta for dinner, but he did not have any salad. _____

15. We can finish the assignment either right now or after the movie. _____

Exercise 2 **Distinguishing Between Subordinating Conjunctions, Prepositions, and Adverbs.** Identify each underlined word as a *subordinating conjunction, preposition,* or *adverb.*

EXAMPLE: <u>Before</u> we planted seeds, we fertilized the garden.   *subordinating conjunction*

1. Shirley rented a typewriter <u>until</u> the end of the month. _____

2. <u>Where</u> do you keep the silverware? _____

3. They bought more exotic fish <u>after</u> they had experimented with goldfish. _____

4. My relatives had toured Europe four times <u>before</u>. _____

5. You should see Maine, <u>where</u> the thick forests come right to the ocean's edge. _____

6. <u>When</u> did the school board vote on that issue? _____

7. I haven't skied <u>since</u> last February. _____

8. Louis stayed on board <u>till</u> the final warning bell forced him to leave. _____

9. We refinanced the house <u>because</u> we needed money. _____

10. We had dinner <u>before</u> the performance. _____

11. <u>While</u> I was in the shower, the repair person rang the bell. _____

12. We can see a spectacular view <u>if</u> we go to that restaurant at the top of the building. _____

13. The party is on Saturday, but I don't know exactly <u>when</u>. _____

14. Justin arrived at the meeting place <u>before</u> everyone else. _____

15. <u>Where</u> have you been all my life? _____

17.4 Interjections • Practice 1

Interjections   An interjection is a word that expresses strong feeling or emotion. Interjections have no grammatical connection to the sentences in which they appear.

A LIST OF COMMON INTERJECTIONS				
ah	dear	hey	ouch	well
aha	goodness	hurray	psst	whew
alas	gracious	oh	tsk	wow

Interjections are punctuated with either a comma or an exclamation mark. The exclamation mark (!) is used to express strong emotion.

▶ **Exercise 1**   **Identifying Interjections.**   Underline the interjection in each sentence below.

EXAMPLE: "Gracious," said Grandmother, "what will happen next?"

1. "Ouch," said the batter, after fouling a ball off his foot.

2. "Alas! It is almost midnight," cried Cinderella.

3. Well, I think we have only two possible options.

4. Billy commented, "Wow! It's getting late."

5. "Psst," said the stranger. "How do you get to the station?"

6. "Tsk! You should be in class by now," noted the principal.

7. "Hurray!" we shouted. "We have finally won a game."

8. Father confessed, "Oh, I'm afraid we're lost."

9. Whew! Am I glad I've finished my research paper.

10. "Goodness gracious, I'm tired," said my aunt.

▶ **Exercise 2**   **Writing Sentences with Interjections.**   Write an original sentence using each interjection below.

EXAMPLE: Oh dear, _____I wonder why they are late._____

1. "Hurray," said our manager, "_____."

2. Wow! _____.

3. "Ouch!" she cried. "_____."

4. Hey! Wait a minute. _____.

5. My uncle said, "Tsk! _____."

6. Well, _____.

7. Mary exclaimed, "Gee, _____."

8. Aha, now _____.

9. "Tarnation," said Gramps, "_____."

10. It's all over. Alas, _____.

17.4 Interjections • Practice 2

▶ **Exercise 1**   **Identifying Interjections.**   Underline the interjection in each sentence below.

EXAMPLE: Hurray! We won the game.

1. Ah, this house is so warm and cozy.
2. Wow! That hair style looks terrific on you.
3. Aha! So that's where you've been hiding.
4. Whew! This must be the hottest day of the year.
5. Alas, these geraniums seem to be drooping.
6. Well, if you won't call me, I guess I'll have to call you.
7. Dear me! What were you thinking?
8. Goodness! What a wonderful surprise this is!
9. Hey, get away from there!
10. Oh, don't worry about it.

▶ **Exercise 2**   **Using Interjections.**   Write five sentences containing interjections that express the following general emotions. Underline the interjections in your sentences.

EXAMPLE: surprise   *Oh, what was that noise?*

1. indecision

    _____

2. sorrow

    _____

3. urgency

    _____

4. exhaustion

    _____

5. fear

    _____

▶ **Writing Application**   **Using Prepositions and Conjunctions in Sentences.**   Follow the instructions to write five sentences of your own.

EXAMPLE: Write a sentence containing a subordinate conjunction.

     When you have finished reading that book, may I borrow it?

1. Write a sentence containing two prepositions.

    _____

2. Write a sentence containing two coordinating conjunctions.

    _____

3. Write a sentence containing one preposition and one correlative conjunction.

    _____

4. Write a sentence containing two prepositions and one subordinating conjunction.

    _____

5. Write a sentence containing one coordinating conjunction and one subordinating conjunction.

    _____

17.5 Words as Different Parts of Speech

• Practice 1

Words as Different Parts of Speech   The way a word is used in a sentence determines what part of speech it is.

DIFFERENT USES OF A WORD	
As a noun:	The campers built a small *fire*.
As a verb:	Managers may *fire* poor workers.
As an adjective:	*Slaughterhouse-Five* describes a *fire* storm in Dresden.

▶ **Exercise 1**   **Identifying Parts of Speech.**   On each blank at the right, write the part of speech of each underlined word.

EXAMPLES: Before breakfast, I brushed my teeth. ___*preposition*___
             Before she came, she phoned. ___*conjunction*___

1. My older brother always drives too <u>fast</u>. _____

2. She lost three pounds during her <u>fast</u>. _____

3. Trucks are not allowed to use the <u>fast</u> lane. _____

4. Show the <u>group</u> your new cassette deck. _____

5. Our agency only handles <u>group</u> sales. _____

6. Before beginning, <u>group</u> all the ingredients together. _____

7. <u>Since</u> this morning, she hasn't felt well. _____

8. <u>Since</u> I bought the car, I have had nothing but trouble. _____

9. The <u>inside</u> of the jewel box is velvet. _____

10. The <u>inside</u> lane is much faster. _____

▶ **Exercise 2**   **Using Words as Different Parts of Speech.**   Construct sentences of your own using the following words as indicated.

EXAMPLES: Use *storm* as a noun. ___*A sudden storm struck.*___
             Use *storm* as a verb. ___*"Storm the trenches," the major cried.*___

1. Use *light* as an adjective. _____

2. Use *light* as a verb. _____

3. Use *file* as an adjective. _____

4. Use *file* as a verb. _____

5. Use *file* as a noun. _____

6. Use *after* as a preposition. _____

7. Use *after* as a conjunction. _____

8. Use *low* as an adjective. _____

9. Use *low* as an adverb. _____

10. Use *storm* as an adjective. _____

17.5 Words as Different Parts of Speech
• Practice 2

▶ **Exercise 1** Identifying Parts of Speech. Identify the part of speech of each underlined word.

EXAMPLE: <u>Smile</u> at the baby, and you will get a <u>smile</u> in return. ___*verb, noun*___

1. We were <u>bowling</u> with a borrowed <u>bowling</u> ball. _____
2. I went <u>early</u> to catch the <u>early</u> bus. _____
3. <u>Many</u> of us felt that there were <u>many</u> injustices in that law. _____
4. <u>Well</u>, I think I will do <u>well</u> on the upcoming examination. _____
5. Put that package <u>down</u> and come <u>down</u> the steps. _____
6. I <u>left</u> the store and turned <u>left</u>. _____
7. <u>Goodness</u>, I really like to see such <u>goodness</u> praised. _____
8. <u>Post</u> this notice on that <u>post</u>. _____
9. We wanted <u>neither</u> of the choices offered, but <u>neither</u> Jim nor I was in a position to
   bargain. _____
10. We called in a <u>carpet</u> cleaner to clean our dirty living room <u>carpet</u>. _____

▶ **Exercise 2** More Work with Parts of Speech. Identify the part of speech of each underlined word.

EXAMPLE: Vincent Van Gogh was a <u>talented</u> artist. ___*adjective*___

(1) <u>Today</u>, Vincent Van Gogh is recognized as a great artist, (2) <u>but</u> he was not (3) <u>appreciated</u> during his lifetime. In fact, (4) <u>the</u> artist sold (5) <u>only</u> one (6) <u>painting</u> before <u>he</u> died. (7) <u>Amazing!</u> Van Gogh began his (8) <u>artistic</u> career (9) <u>not</u> as a painter but (10) <u>as</u> an art dealer, assisting (11) <u>his</u> uncle. He turned to painting at age twenty-seven and (12) <u>focused</u> his (13) <u>attention</u> on (14) <u>still</u> lifes and landscapes. (15) He soon moved to Paris where he joined a (16) <u>new</u> art movement. (17) <u>Throughout</u> the next few years, Van Gogh (18) <u>experimented</u> (19) <u>widely</u> with new blends of color and new modes of design, creating a (20) <u>series</u> of remarkable paintings.

1. _____   11. _____
2. _____   12. _____
3. _____   13. _____
4. _____   14. _____
5. _____   15. _____
6. _____   16. _____
7. _____   17. _____
8. _____   18. _____
9. _____   19. _____
10. _____   20. _____

18.1 Subjects and Verbs (Complete Subjects and Predicates, Fragments) • Practice 1

Complete Subjects and Complete Predicates   A sentence is a group of words with two main parts: a complete subject and a complete predicate. Together, these parts express a complete thought.

Complete Subjects	Complete Predicates
The weary travelers	staggered into the mining camp.
Business in our society	is based on making a profit.

Fragments   A fragment is a group of words that does not express a complete thought.

Fragments	Complete Sentences
a person with diabetes	A person with diabetes should avoid using sugar.
offered us directions to the mall	The toll taker at the bridge offered us directions to the mall.
in the middle of the film	In the middle of the film, the projector broke.

▶ **Exercise 1**   **Recognizing Complete Subjects and Predicates.**   Draw a vertical line between each complete subject and predicate.

EXAMPLE: Montgomery Center in Vermont | is close to Canada.

1. Waffles and ice cream is a longtime favorite of mine.
2. The parishioners reacted enthusiastically to our appeal.
3. Carrying their gear, the campers departed.
4. The Board of Inquiry reached a unanimous decision.
5. Beethoven's *Creatures of Prometheus* has been recorded many times.
6. My mother uses a recipe for oatmeal cookies passed down through generations.
7. My trip to Madrid and Barcelona has been postponed.
8. The governor, a tall, impressive man, entered the auditorium.
9. Several different flights to Dallas are now available.
10. This Thanksgiving will be a most joyous holiday.

▶ **Exercise 2**   **Distinguishing Between Sentences and Fragments.**   In the blanks below, write *S* for each sentence and *F* for each fragment.

EXAMPLE: Bad weather canceled the flight. ____*S*____

1. The map of the United States. _____
2. Attempted to contact the principal several times. _____
3. At the end of the hearing. _____
4. A salesman telephoned this morning. _____
5. Jeanne's explanation was absurd. _____
6. The jury troubled by inconsistencies in his testimony. _____
7. In spite of every attempt to help the students. _____
8. Strangely, the baby only crawls backwards. _____
9. An angry inspector from the health department. _____
10. Agreed to postpone the decision. _____

18.1 Subjects and Verbs (Complete Subjects and Predicates, Fragments) • Practice 2

Exercise 1 **Recognizing Complete Subjects and Predicates.** Draw a vertical line between each complete subject and predicate.

EXAMPLE: The kitten, a very active Siamese, | walked on the kitchen counters despite being reprimanded.

1. Most of each year's thousands of earthquakes are too small to be noticed.
2. The numbers on the Richter Scale describe the strength of an earthquake.
3. The ancient Greeks had the first public museums.
4. The Charleston Museum in South Carolina is the oldest museum in the United States in continuous existence.
5. The Children's Museum in Boston has a full-size Japanese house, a Latino market, and displays on Native Americans.
6. Millions of children around the world work in factories and fields.
7. More than five million species of living things inhabit our planet.
8. More than 1,000 of the more than 9,000 species of birds are in danger of extinction.
9. The weight of ants on Earth is almost half the weight of all the other insects combined.
10. The habitats of plants and animals are often destroyed by deforestation.

Exercise 2 **Recognizing Complete Subjects and Complete Predicates.** In the following paragraph, draw a vertical line between each complete subject and complete predicate. Some sentences may require more than one line.

EXAMPLE: During the night, | the gently rocking boat | lulled us to sleep.

(1) Morning came quickly. (2) Long before sunrise, the alarm clock rang. (3) Sluggishly, we dragged ourselves from a restful sleep. (4) At five o'clock we left the dock. (5) We were sailing out of the bay on a yacht equipped with every convenience. (6) From bow to stern, the boat measured forty feet. (7) During the night, a fog had crept in. (8) It greatly limited visibility and made the air cold. (9) Sophisticated directional equipment led us through the fog. (10) Inside the cabin, we were warm, dry, and eager to begin deep-sea fishing.

Exercise 3 **Locating and Correcting Sentence Fragments.** Decide whether each item is a sentence or a fragment. If it is a sentence, write *sentence*. If it is a fragment, rewrite it to make it a sentence.

EXAMPLE: In spite of her painful sprained ankle.
She finished the race in spite of her painful sprained ankle.

1. His mother, a gentle, yet strong woman.

2. Stepped from the boat after a rugged trip across the Atlantic.

3. Diane dipped her doughnut into her milk before taking a bite.

4. Into the sky filled with dark thunderclouds.

5. The car's hood, hot from the sun's rays.

18.1 Subjects and Verbs (Simple Subjects and Predicates) • Practice 1

Simple Subjects and Simple Predicates   The simple subject is the essential noun, pronoun, or group of words acting as a noun that cannot be left out of the complete subject. The simple predicate is the essential verb or verb phrase that cannot be left out of the complete predicate. In the chart below each simple subject is underlined once, each simple predicate twice.

SIMPLE SUBJECTS AND SIMPLE PREDICATES	
Complete Subjects	**Complete Predicates**
An important announcement	interrupted the TV program.
The road to Boston	has been flooded by the heavy rains.

▶ **Exercise 1**   **Recognizing Simple Subjects and Predicates.**   Underline the simple subjects once and the simple predicates twice in the sentences below.

EXAMPLE: The reckless athlete endangered his teammates.

1. A box of deluxe chocolates makes an excellent gift.

2. The manila envelope had obviously been opened by someone.

3. At sixteen, Beethoven traveled to Vienna to meet Mozart.

4. Alfred Hitchcock's *Vertigo* is a movie classic.

5. The stamps in Grandfather's collection are extremely valuable.

6. Groups of travelers were stranded by the snowstorm.

7. At the prom, Betty met her old boyfriend.

8. The house on the hill contains a secret passageway.

9. An increasing number of complaints have recently been received.

10. A telltale smudge on the document aroused suspicions.

▶ **Exercise 2**   **Using Simple Subjects and Predicates to Write Sentences.**   Use each simple subject and simple predicate below to write a complete sentence. Draw a vertical line between the complete subject and the complete predicate.

EXAMPLE: rules are _____*Some rules | are hard to enforce.*_____

1. principal announced _____

2. train halted _____

3. report indicated _____

4. recipe uses _____

5. uncle trembled _____

6. package has arrived _____

7. team agreed _____

8. state senator wrote _____

9. grandmother pickled _____

10. swimmer will attempt _____

18.1 # Subjects and Verbs (Simple Subjects and Predicates) • Practice 2

▶ **Exercise 1** **Identifying Subjects and Verbs.** Draw a vertical line between the complete subject and complete predicate of each sentence. Then, underline each subject once and each verb twice.

EXAMPLE: The <u>state</u> with the most people | <u>is</u> California.

1. Some apes have been taught signs for words.
2. Rebecca Latimer Felton was the first woman to serve as a United States Senator.
3. Many of the current television programs are airing sensitive, controversial issues.
4. Members of the Coast Guard rescued the passengers of the sinking ocean liner.
5. People in stressful situations will often show symptoms of fatigue.
6. The pyramids in Egypt have attracted tourists for thousands of years.
7. Two systems of weights and measures coexist in the United States today.
8. The use of the metric system in the United States has been increasing slowly and steadily.
9. The tides are a natural phenomenon influenced by the pull of the moon and the sun.
10. Weather conditions can influence the variations in the high and low tides.

▶ **Exercise 2** **Locating Compound Subjects and Compound Verbs.** Underline the parts of each compound subject once and each compound verb twice. Note that some sentences may have both.

EXAMPLE: The babies <u>kicked</u> their feet and <u>gurgled</u> at each other.

1. We headed south for a mile and then turned east.
2. Shoppers and salespersons felt the tension of the holidays and snapped at one another.
3. Both Sara and Blythe liked the story "The Lie" by Kurt Vonnegut, Jr.
4. Both bees and hummingbirds gather nectar and pollinate flowers.
5. We built, sanded, and stained those tables.

▶ **Writing Application** **Developing Sentences from Subjects and Verbs.** Write five sentences using the following sets of directions. Make sure each of the sentences is complete. Use adjectives, adverbs, prepositional phrases, and conjunctions where appropriate.

EXAMPLE: compound subject + *are*
  Both Steve and Jim are on the honor roll.

1. *fields* + verb phrase

_____

2. compound subject + *were driven*

_____

3. *President-elect* + compound verb

_____

4. compound subject + *surfed and swam*

_____

5. *accountant and lawyer* + verb phrase

_____

18.2 Subjects in Different Kinds of Sentences
(Hard-to-Find Subjects) • Practice 1

Hard-to-Find Subjects   In most sentences the subject comes before the verb. This arrangement is called *normal word order*. In some sentences, however, the verb comes first, and the word order is *inverted*. If there is a problem finding a subject, change the sentence back to normal word order, placing the subject first.

HARD-TO-FIND SUBJECTS	
Problem Sentences	**In Normal Word Order**
Near the road is a *telephone*.	A *telephone* is near the road.
There is a *salesman* at the door.	A *salesman* is at the door.
Here are your *notes*.	Your *notes* are here.
What did you want?	*You* did want what.
Write your congresswoman.	(*You*) write your congresswoman.

▶ **Exercise 1**   **Finding Hard-to-Find Subjects.**   Draw a single line under each subject and a double line under each verb. Include in parentheses any words that are understood or implied.

EXAMPLE: There are several answers to that question.

1. Here is a bushel of apples.

2. Where is the title of your story?

3. What did you buy at the clothing sale?

4. About two miles down the road is a modern hotel.

5. There have been a number of strange reactions to her speech.

6. Between the hospital and the garage is a fast-food restaurant.

7. Tell us in your own words about the accident.

8. There are two interesting routes to Halifax.

9. When has the operation been scheduled?

10. In the back of the drawer are several pens.

▶ **Exercise 2**   **Changing Sentences to Normal Word Order.**   Each sentence below is in inverted word order. Rewrite the sentence, changing it to normal word order. Place a single line under the subject and a double line under the verb.

EXAMPLE: Here are your books.
           Your books are here.

1. Near the window is a box of tissues.

   _____

2. Here are the keys to the safe.

   _____

3. Have you chosen a secretary?

   _____

4. There are three strange men at the door.

   _____

5. What did Pat think of his explanation?

   _____

18.2 Subjects in Different Kinds of Sentences
(Hard-to-Find Subjects) • Practice 2

▶ **Exercise 1**   **Locating Hard-to-Find Subjects.**   Write the subject and verb in each sentence. Include in parentheses any words that are understood or implied. Underline each subject once and each verb twice.

EXAMPLE: Here is my report.   <u>report</u> <u>is</u>

1. On the table lay the unopened letter. _____
2. Are you planning to go to the Thanksgiving Day parade this year? _____
3. Through the speakers came the wonderful sound of blues artist B. B. King. _____
4. There are thousands of foster children in America ready for adoption. _____
5. Which type of singer do you prefer? _____
6. More benefits! _____
7. Where did you buy that granola? _____
8. Here are some tips on fly casting. _____
9. Remember to call me. _____
10. Was Henry Hudson Dutch or British? _____
11. Help! _____
12. Lead us in the Pledge of Allegiance, please. _____
13. There is his social security check. _____
14. Where could I go? _____
15. Are teenagers adequately preparing themselves to become leaders of society? _____
16. Over the mountains trudged the weary but determined pioneers. _____
17. After dinner, finish your homework. _____
18. There are real rattlesnake roundups in Texas. _____
19. Oxygen! _____
20. How much did the first televisions cost? _____

▶ **Writing Application**   **Writing Different Kinds of Sentences with Hard-to-Find Subjects.**   Follow the instructions to write ten sentences with hard-to-find subjects.

1. Write a declarative sentence beginning with *there* or *here* used as an adverb.

_____

2. Write a declarative sentence beginning with *there* as an expletive.

_____

3. Write a declarative sentence with an inverted order.

_____

4. Write an interrogative sentence beginning with a verb.

_____

5. Write an imperative sentence with an understood *you.*

_____

Name _____ Date _____

Complements (Direct and Indirect Objects)
• Practice 1

Direct Objects A *complement* is a word or group of words that completes the meaning of the predicate of a sentence. One of the most common complements, the direct object, is a noun, pronoun, or group of words acting as a noun that receives the action of a transitive verb.

Indirect Objects An indirect object is a noun or pronoun that appears with a direct object and names the person or thing that something is given to or done for.

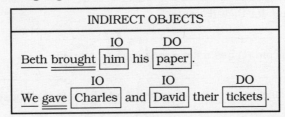

Indirect objects often appear with these transitive verbs: *ask, bring, buy, give, lend, make, promise, show, teach, tell,* or *write.*

▶ **Exercise 1** **Identifying Direct Objects.** Draw a box around each direct object in the sentences below. Some sentences may have a compound direct object.

EXAMPLE: The Senate passed an important ⃞bill⃞.

1. Stew the vegetables in a little beef broth.
2. Jason needs a dictionary and a thesaurus.
3. Which exit do you take from the parkway?
4. I will ask him about the interview.
5. Every morning Father always buys a newspaper.
6. She drinks either tea or coffee.
7. The artist painted a subdued sunset.
8. Can you describe the hotel to us?
9. I will recommend him and her for the two positions.
10. Melody prepared an outstanding graphic for the fair.

▶ **Exercise 2** **Finding Indirect Objects.** Draw a box around each indirect object in the sentences below. Also underline each direct object.

EXAMPLE: I wrote the ⃞governor⃞ a letter.

1. My sister showed the class her award.
2. For his birthday we promised Dad new stereo speakers.
3. Will you give them the bad news?
4. I will teach Susan a new computer game.
5. Why don't you lend Judy and him your old binoculars?

18.3 Complements (Direct and Indirect Objects)
• Practice 2

▶ **Exercise 1** **Recognizing Direct Objects.** Underline each direct object in the sentences below.

EXAMPLE: Sometimes, artists find inspiration for their work in a particular place.

(1) Georgia O'Keeffe spent her early years in the Midwest. (2) Later, she studied art in Chicago and New York. (3) From 1912 to 1914, she supervised art teachers in Amarillo, Texas. (4) From 1916 to 1918, she directed the art professors at a college in Canyon, Texas. (5) O'Keeffe later married Alfred Stieglitz, a famous American photographer. (6) Stieglitz displayed O'Keeffe's paintings in his art gallery. (7) The desert had inspired O'Keeffe. (8) She earned fame for her paintings of the Southwest. (9) Many feature rocks, animal bones, and flowers. (10) From 1949 O'Keeffe made her permanent home near Taos, New Mexico.

▶ **Exercise 2** **Recognizing Indirect Objects.** Write the underlined words in each sentence and identify each as a *direct object*, *indirect object*, or *object of a preposition*.

EXAMPLE: Frank gave his friends vegetables from his garden.
        friends (indirect object)   _vegetables (direct object)_

1. They bought the condominium for their daughter.

_____

2. The university granted the incoming freshman a four-year scholarship.

_____

3. The builder showed the prospective owners some special additions to the house.

_____

4. Beverly Sills sang an aria at the charity ball.

_____

5. Mrs. Phelps taught piano in her home.

_____

6. Eric told his young campers a harrowing bedtime tale.

_____

7. Aunt Harriet described our complete family tree to me.

_____

8. When did they deliver the dining room set to you?

_____

9. Our club made ice cream for the old-fashioned picnic.

_____

10. I ordered you a sweater from the catalog.

_____

11. Sylvia gave her a handmade frame.

_____

12. Marion was within earshot of the conspirators.

_____

13. Enrollment in that class has exceeded our expectations.

_____

14. Enrique proudly handed the teacher his essay.

_____

15. Your eloquent words gave me a chill down my spine.

_____

18.3 Complements (Objective and Subject Complements)
• Practice 1

Objective Complements   An objective complement is an adjective, noun, or group of words acting as a noun that follows a direct object and describes or renames it.

OBJECTIVE COMPLEMENTS
DO   OC Most observers thought the decision incorrect. DO   OC The committee appointed Bill chairperson.

Subject Complement   A subject complement is a noun, pronoun, or adjective that follows a linking verb and tells something about the subject of the sentence. There are two kinds of subject complements: predicate nominatives and predicate adjectives. A predicate nominative is a noun or pronoun that renames or identifies the subject. A predicate adjective is an adjective that describes the subject.

SUBJECT COMPLEMENTS
PN *Predicate Nominative:*   Helen was our coach. PA *Predicate Adjective:*   Your pudding is delicious.

▶ **Exercise 1**   **Recognizing Objective Complements.**   Underline the objective complement in each sentence below. Then write whether it is a *noun* or an *adjective*.

EXAMPLE: Our team thinks the coach unreasonable. ____*adjective*____

1. In this particular case we will keep the files open. _____
2. The class elected Michelle president. _____
3. The inspector thought the plan dangerous. _____
4. The court appointed him executor of the estate. _____
5. After Bob's accident, the coach named Paul captain. _____
6. The college registrar considers her ineligible. _____
7. My sister painted her apartment brown. _____
8. Will our team name Marie spokesperson? _____
9. Most of us found the opera uninteresting. _____
10. The family thought the present inappropriate. _____

▶ **Exercise 2**   **Recognizing Predicate Nominatives and Predicate Adjectives.**   Underline the predicate nominatives and predicate adjectives. Next to each sentence write either *PN* (predicate nominative) or *PA* (predicate adjective).

EXAMPLE: His father is unusually intelligent. ____*PA*____

1. Our counselor often seems distracted. _____
2. Through his own efforts he had become our captain. _____
3. Her chief interest has always been her job. _____
4. The architect's plan for the new theater is impressive. _____
5. Grandmother's old ring must be very valuable. _____

Name _____ Date _____

18.3 Complements (Objective and Subject Complements)
• Practice 2

▷ **Exercise 1** **Using Objective Complements.** Add an objective complement of the type indicated to each of the following sentences.

EXAMPLE: The judges selected that entry ____*the winner*____ .

1. We named our new puppy _____ (noun).
2. The board considered the company's new president _____ (adjective).
3. Unanimously, all my friends in the class appointed me _____ (noun).
4. The editor of the high school magazine appointed Janet _____ (noun).
5. The neighborhood children think my yard is a _____ . (noun).
6. Our organization elected Terry _____ (noun).
7. The new living room curtains make the room _____ (adjective) and _____ (adjective).
8. They named the twins _____ (noun) and _____ (noun).
9. The builders made the housing development a _____ (noun).
10. A court judged the defendant _____ (adjective).
11. We called our new boat the _____ . (noun)
12. The reporter called the scene _____ . (adjective)
13. Alvin thought my new outfit a _____ . (noun)
14. Cynthia declared the news _____ . (adjective)
15. The examiner deemed the accused _____ to stand trial. (adjective)

▷ **Exercise 2** **Identifying Subject Complements.** Underline the subject complement or subject complements in each sentence. Then identify each as a *predicate nominative* or *predicate adjective*.

EXAMPLE: Jean should become a successful college student. ____*predicate nominative*____

1. After my course in astronomy, I became an avid stargazer. _____
2. The rain clouds appeared distant yet forbidding. _____
3. The unruly child grew belligerent and then sullen. _____
4. Those plants to the left are a hybrid. _____
5. Paul Revere was a silversmith and a maker of dentures. _____
6. My quilted comforter felt warm and soft against my skin. _____
7. The air was sweet with the scent of apple blossoms. _____
8. She is both a competent doctor and a devoted mother. _____
9. The juice tasted bitter and warm. _____
10. The vast lawns of the country estate were a vivid green. _____
11. The feudal system was often unfair to the peasants. _____
12. After the invention of the microscope, the existence of microscopic life was surprising to many. _____
13. Richard seems surprisingly aloof today. _____
14. Asparagus with this special sauce is quite a treat. _____
15. The children's governess is Helena Jameson. _____

19.1 Prepositional Phrases and Appositives
(Prepositional Phrases) • Practice 1

Prepositional Phrases   A phrase is a group of words, without a subject and verb, that is used in a sentence as one part of speech. An adjective phrase is a prepositional phrase that modifies a noun or pronoun by telling what kind or which one.

ADJECTIVE PHRASES
The closet *in the den* is empty.
I brought a robe *with pockets.*

An adverb phrase is a prepositional phrase that modifies a verb, adjective, or adverb by pointing out where, when, in what manner, or to what extent.

ADVERB PHRASES
The boat disappeared *during a storm.*
Sandy and Bob drove *across the country.*
Beth arrived late *for work.*

▶ **Exercise 1**   **Identifying Adjective and Adverb Phrases.**   Underline each prepositional phrase in the sentences below. Then circle the word or word each phrase modifies and label the phrase *adjective* or *adverb.*

EXAMPLE: A (seat) on the bus is expensive. _____*adjective*_____

1. The manager is unhappy with Jody's performance. _____
2. After lunch Trish and I visited the library. _____
3. This is an apartment with two full baths. _____
4. A group of traveling actors visited the campus. _____
5. An important conference convened in Ottawa. _____
6. The football coach was angry after the game. _____
7. Ted will give his report on medieval customs. _____
8. Mother is ecstatic about her anniversary present. _____
9. At a later time, we will tell you the entire story. _____
10. Where can I catch the bus to Boston? _____

▶ **Exercise 2**   **Writing Sentences with Adjective and Adverb Phrases.**   Write phrases to complete the following sentences. Then label each phrase as *adjective* or *adverb.*

EXAMPLE: We spoke politely ____*to the detective*____. ____*adverb*____

1. I read *Twelfth Night* _____. _____
2. I bought her birthday present _____. _____
3. Unfortunately, Toby was late _____. _____
4. The library _____ did not have it. _____
5. We had to cancel our trip _____. _____

19.1 Prepositional Phrases and Appositives
(Prepositional Phrases) • Practice 2

▶ **Exercise 1** **Identifying Adjective and Adverb Phrases.** Write the prepositional phrases in the following paragraphs. Then identify each prepositional phrase as *adjective* or *adverb*.

EXAMPLE: The idea of beauty is not identical in all cultures.
      ___of beauty (adjective)___   ___in all cultures (adverb)___

(1) The many cultures of the world have different conceptions of physical beauty. (2) In China, at one time, young girls had their feet bound so that they measured only three or four inches. (3) In some societies today, pins and plugs are inserted through the nose, lips, and ears. (4) In some Eskimo areas of North America, bones are worn through the lips. (5) People of other cultures decorate their bodies with lace-like patterned bumps. (6) The Nuba of Sudan rub mud into small cuts, producing intricate patterns of scars. (7) In parts of Burma, women with long necks are deemed attractive. (8) About their necks the women, therefore, wear increasing numbers of brass spirals. (9) In several Asian societies, people stain their teeth with betel juice because white teeth are thought ugly. (10) Western cultures have also had their share of unusual beauty habits: Corsets, hair dyeing, tattooing, and earpiercing are just a few.

1. _____
2. _____
3. _____
4. _____
5. _____
6. _____
7. _____
8. _____
9. _____
10. _____

▶ **Exercise 2** **Identifying Adjective and Adverb Phrases.** Underline each prepositional phrase in the sentences below. Then circle the word or words each phrase modifies and label the phrase *adjective* or *adverb*.

EXAMPLE: The (food) on the train was delicious.   ___adjective___

1. The cat and the dog slept soundly near the warm radiators. _____
2. The frozen rain made the branches on the trees glisten. _____
3. Happy children rode sleds down the snow—covered streets. _____
4. The icy conditions kept the cars off the streets. _____
5. Katie's mom prepared hot drinks for the chilly children. _____
6. The faucet in the kitchen needs tightening. _____
7. The latest fashions from Paris attracted Sharon's attention. _____
8. Have you ever seen pictures of Norway's fiords? _____
9. Jason sat near Maureen. _____
10. The wedding was held in the hotel's picturesque garden area. _____

19.1 Prepositional Phrases and Appositives
(Appositives and Appositive Phrases) • Practice 1

Appositives and Appositive Phrases   An appositive is a noun or pronoun placed next to another noun or pronoun to identify, rename, or explain it.

APPOSITIVES
My new car, *a Jetstream*, is made of fiberglass.
Father is proud of his profession, *advertising*.

An appositive phrase is a noun or pronoun with modifiers, placed next to a noun or pronoun to add information or details.

APPOSITIVE PHRASES
Jeremy Irons, *a fine British actor*, is my favorite.
We will all attend the concert, *a fund-raising activity meant to benefit neglected children*.

▶ **Exercise 1**   **Identifying Appositives.**   Underline the appositive in each sentence. Circle the noun or pronoun it renames.

EXAMPLE: My (brother) William has just been promoted.

1. I read a fascinating book, *Lincoln*, by Gore Vidal.
2. Miss Touvin, a teacher, leads our Service Council.
3. Brad has an unusual hobby, taxidermy.
4. Her new camera, a Hessinger, is very expensive.
5. The British poet John Donne is still highly regarded.
6. His instrument, the viola, requires great skill.
7. Did you speak to your brother Phil?
8. A British fighter, the Spitfire, probably saved England in the 1940's.
9. Rhonda Evans, a farmer, lives in Vermont.
10. Marty loves playing his favorite instrument, the guitar.

▶ **Exercise 2**   **Identifying Appositive Phrases.**   Underline the appositive phrase in each sentence. Circle the noun or pronoun it renames.

EXAMPLE: My favorite (story), *The Scarlet Ibis* by James Hurst, is available in some anthologies.

1. The Dead Sea Scrolls, ancient writings in Aramaic, stirred many Biblical scholars.
2. His new coat, a garment of cashmere and wool, is quite expensive.
3. I love her special dessert, a dish of berries, bananas, and whipped cream.
4. The graduates, members of the Class of 1995, discussed a reunion.
5. The investigator's files, a record of gambling activities, have been subpoenaed.
6. Lacrosse, a fast-paced, exciting game, is gaining popularity in the United States.
7. I visited my sister's friends, a group of co-eds.
8. You won't believe the first thing you see, a statue of Queen Victoria.
9. The old lamp, a brass hurricane model, is an antique.
10. He has a squalid apartment, two dismal rooms in an attic.

19.1 Prepositional Phrases and Appositives
(Appositives and Appositive Phrases) • Practice 2

▶ **Exercise 1** **Using Appositives and Appositive Phrases to Combine Sentences.** Combine each pair of sentences by turning one into an appositive or appositive phrase.

EXAMPLE: Washington, D.C., is fascinating. It is our capital.
_____Washington, D.C., our capital, is fascinating._____

1. The city of Washington, D.C., was designed by Major Pierre Charles L'Enfant. He was a French architect and engineer.

   _____

2. Tourists flock to Washington, D.C. It is a beautiful city with historic significance.

   _____

3. The white marble Capitol has a large dome on top. The Capitol is the building where Congress meets.

   _____

4. Many visit the White House. It is the President's residence.

   _____

5. The Washington Monument is on the Mall. It is an obelisk.

   _____

6. The Jefferson Memorial is a replica of the Pantheon in Rome. This memorial overlooks the Potomac River.

   _____

7. The Library of Congress is possibly the world's largest library. It has collections that anyone may use.

   _____

8. The National Gallery houses many art treasures. It is one of the largest marble buildings in the world.

   _____

9. Many government officials have residences in Georgetown. Georgetown is a fashionable part of Washington, D.C.

   _____

10. Each September, the President's Cup Regatta is held on the Potomac River. It is an annual motorboat racing contest.

   _____
   _____

▶ **Writing Application** **Using Prepositional and Appositive Phrases.** Use the following instructions to write five sentences of your own. Then underline the prepositional and appositive phrases in your sentences.

EXAMPLE: Write a sentence about a *friend*, using an appositive phrase.
_____Jean, my friend from Chicago, will arrive tomorrow._____

1. Write a sentence about *cars*, using a prepositional phrase.

   _____

2. Write a sentence about *Lincoln*, using an appositive phrase.

   _____

3. Write a sentence about *pie*, using two prepositional phrases.

   _____

4. Write a sentence about *whales*, using an appositive phrase.

   _____

5. Write a sentence about *Mars*, using a prepositional phrase and an appositive phrase.

   _____

19.2 Verbals and Verbal Phrases (Participles and Participial Phrases) • Practice 1

Participles and Participial Phrases A verbal is a word derived from a verb but used as a noun, adjective, or adverb. A participle is a verbal that acts as an adjective. A participial phrase is a participle that is modified by an adverb or adverb phrase or that has a complement. The entire phrase acts as an adjective in a sentence. Participles and participial phrases have three forms: present, past, and perfect.

Kinds of Participles	Forms	Examples
Present Participle	Ends in -ing	*Climbing*, she reached the peak. A *growing* child needs nourishment.
Past Participle	Usually ends in -ed, sometimes -t, -en, or another irregular ending	*Worried*, she consulted a doctor.
Perfect Participle	Includes *having* or *having been* before a past participle.	*Having finished*, she handed in her test. *Having been excused*, he left the table.

▶ **Exercise 1** **Identifying Present, Past, and Perfect Participles.** Underline the participle in each sentence and circle the word it modifies. On the line at the right, write *present*, *past*, or *perfect* to tell which kind it is.

EXAMPLE: Elated, (he) phoned his parents. ___*past*___

1. Having won, the tennis player accepted the trophy. _____

2. Smiling, my sister accepted her award. _____

3. The old man, hesitating, stumbled across the avenue. _____

4. Relieved, she decided to turn over a new leaf. _____

5. Marie strikes everyone as a dedicated young woman. _____

6. Only a chosen few can participate. _____

7. Irritated, the speaker refused to continue. _____

8. Having been paroled, the ex-convict vowed never to commit another crime. _____

9. The old actress, delighted, took another bow. _____

10. Surprised, he began to stumble over his words. _____

▶ **Exercise 2** **Identifying Participial Phrases.** Underline each participial phrase and circle the word it modifies.

EXAMPLE: Troubled by her decision, (she) lay awake.

1. Groping in the drawer, she found her passport.

2. The sailor, running at top speed, reached his ship on time.

3. Told to report at once, I knocked on the principal's door.

4. Tired by her journey, she reached the Al-Azhar Mosque in Cairo.

5. The relentless explorer, broken in spirit, decided to turn back.

6. Jogging rapidly, my cousin circled the dam.

7. The figures, computed with amazing speed, proved accurate.

8. The victors, dancing in the streets, soon exhausted themselves.

9. Dismayed at the news, the old man began to cry.

10. The river, swollen to new heights, finally crested.

19.2 Verbals and Verbal Phrases (Participles and Participial Phrases) • Practice 2

▷ Exercise 1 **Recognizing Participles and Participial Phrases.** Underline the participle or participial phrase in each sentence. Then label it as *present*, *past*, or *perfect*.

EXAMPLE: <u>Led by the captain</u>, the team trotted onto the field.   *past*

1. A scathing attack was delivered by the politician. _____

2. The wheat swaying in the wind was like waves. _____

3. The houses ruined by the fire smoldered until the next morning. _____

4. A giant balloon billowing forth with hot air rose slowly into the sky. _____

5. At the dance, the reserved girl sat in the shadow behind a large philodendron. _____

6. The dignitary representing the President will address the Security Council today. _____

7. Having interviewed several people, the reporter felt ready to write the
   article. _____

8. I listened to the crows cawing continuously in the fields. _____

9. Having been warned, I used a good deal of caution when I approached the guard
   dog. _____

10. The document, yellowed with age, contained the information we needed. _____

11. It took an expert to separate the forged document from the others. _____

12. The audience, applauding loudly, drowned out the announcer's words. _____

13. Having followed the guide for two hours, Hector was very tired. _____

14. The nurse, bandaging the patient's arm, spoke in a calm voice. _____

15. "A house divided against itself cannot stand," said Abraham Lincoln. _____

16. The doctor told Paul that he had a detached retina. _____

17. The water, evaporating quickly, was soon at a very low level. _____

18. Perry, having approached the judge boldly, now seemed at a loss for words. _____

19. The seldom seen opossum is a very strange creature. _____

20. The riot of color quickly glimpsed from the street was what drew Andy into the
    shop. _____

▷ Exercise 2 **Writing Participial Phrases.** Change each underlined verb into a participial phrase and use it in a sentence of your own.

EXAMPLE: The officers were elected.
        The officers <u>elected</u> last year are not living up to their promises.

1. The plane is <u>delayed</u>.

   _____

2. Celia was <u>washing</u> her car.

   _____

3. The district attorney <u>badgered</u> the witness.

   _____

4. The race <u>tired</u> the marathon runner.

   _____

5. The students have <u>collected</u> money.

   _____

Verbals and Verbal Phrases (Gerunds and Gerund Phrases, Infinitives and Infinitive Phrases)

19.2

• Practice 1

Gerunds and Gerund Phrases   A gerund is a verbal that acts as a noun. A gerund phrase is a gerund with modifiers or complements, all acting together as a noun. Gerunds and gerund phrases can be used as subjects, direct objects, indirect objects, objects of prepositions, predicate nominatives, and appositives.

Gerunds	Gerund Phrases
Subject: Smoking is no longer allowed here.	*Subject: Collecting antiques* is her major interest.
Object of a Preposition: He spoke about *drinking.*	*Object of Preposition:* Mr. Haskis told us about *growing different flowers.*
Predicate Nominative: His great joy is *swimming.*	*Direct Object:* She enjoys *baking fruit pies.*
Appositive: Her obsession, *knitting,* annoys us.	*Indirect Object:* Pam gave *bicycling around the lake* one try only.

Infinitives and Infinitive Phrases   An infinitive is a verbal that generally appears with the word *to* and acts as a noun, adjective, or adverb. An infinitive phrase is an infinitive with modifiers, a complement, or a subject, all acting together as a single part of speech.

Infinitives	Infinitive Phrases
Subject: To smile is important when you meet new people.	*Subject: To practice daily* is not easy for most people.
Direct Object: Our team hopes *to win.*	*Direct Object:* We expect them *to be gone all week.*
Adjective: Here is a book *to read.*	*Adjective:* The way *to reach the hospital* is simple.
Adverb: It is often very hard *to change.*	*Adverb:* They struggled *to remain objective.*

▶ **Exercise 1**   **Identifying Gerunds and Gerund Phrases.**   Underline the gerund or gerund phrase in each sentence. In the space provided, tell how it is used.

EXAMPLE: Chewing gum is a bad habit. _____*subject*_____

1. I don't recommend driving too fast. _____

2. She was warned about teasing her sister. _____

3. Her lecture gave dreaming a new perspective. _____

4. Traveling is an important part of this job. _____

5. Her fear, growing old, is shared by many. _____

▶ **Exercise 2**   **Identifying Infinitives and Infinitive Phrases.**   Underline the infinitive or the infinitive phrase in each sentence. In the space provided, tell whether it is used as a *noun, adjective,* or *adverb.*

EXAMPLE: Everyone wants to go swimming. _____*noun*_____

1. Jason tries to eat properly every day. _____

2. The museum to visit is not far from here. _____

3. To graduate from college is her first goal. _____

4. Father is about to read to his grandchildren. _____

5. This is an important document to study. _____

19.2 Verbals and Verbal Phrases (Gerunds and Gerund Phrases, Infinitives and Infinitive Phrases)
• Practice 2

▶ **Exercise 1** **Identifying Gerunds and Gerund Phrases.** Underline the gerund or gerund phrase in each sentence. Then identify its function in the sentence.

EXAMPLE: Taking this shortcut will save time. ___*subject*___

1. Talking during a test is strictly forbidden in this class. _____

2. The librarian began cataloging the newest books. _____

3. His newest hobby, arranging flowers, gives him pleasure. _____

4. A qualification for applicants is having an art degree. _____

5. He left almost immediately after a day of teaching. _____

▶ **Exercise 2** **Identifying Infinitives and Infinitive Phrases.** Underline each infinitive or infinitive phrase. Then identify its part of speech as a *noun*, *adjective*, or *adverb*. If the infinitive or infinitive phrase is used as a noun, further identify its function as a *subject*, *direct object*, *predicate nominative*, *object of a preposition*, or *appositive*.

EXAMPLE: We climbed for three hours to reach the campsite. ___*adverb*___

1. To capture the scene on film required photographic skill. _____

2. The young man had money to burn. _____

3. During the test, Mrs. Linton permitted us to use our dictionaries. _____

4. Her financial goal was to earn one million dollars by age thirty-two. _____

5. The person to see about your complaint has left. _____

▶ **Writing Application** **Writing Sentences Using Verbals.** Change each of the following verbs into the two kinds of verbals indicated in the chart. Then use each one as a verbal phrase in a sentence of your own. Underline the verbal phrases in your sentences.

		Participle	Gerund	Infinitive
1.	confuse	x		x
2.	sail	x	x	
3.	achieve	x		x
4.	undertake		x	x
5.	yearn		x	x

1. _____
   _____

2. _____
   _____

3. _____
   _____

4. _____
   _____

5. _____
   _____

19.3 Adjective Clause • Practice 1

Adjective Clauses   An adjective clause is a subordinate clause that modifies a noun or pronoun by telling what kind or which one. Adjective clauses begin with relative pronouns or relative adverbs.

> **ADJECTIVE CLAUSES**
>
> A magazine *which contains similar information is Scientific Achievement.*
>
> This is the watch *that Mother wants.*
>
> It is they *who are responsible.*

Relative pronouns act as nouns or adjectives within the adjective clauses. Note that in some sentences, such as the third one below, a relative pronoun may be understood.

> **THE USES OF RELATIVE PRONOUNS**
>
> The clown *who is in the center ring* is the funniest. (subject)
>
> The man *whose coat is torn* looks very unhappy. (adjective)
>
> The skirt *(that) I am wearing* is too long. (understood direct object)
>
> This is the friend of *whom I have spoken.* (object of a preposition)

▶ **Exercise 1**   **Identifying Adjective Clauses.**   Underline the adjective clause in each sentence and circle the noun or pronoun it modifies.

EXAMPLE: The (book) which she asked for is too expensive.

1. This is the restaurant which was described in the magazine.
2. The story that she told is hardly plausible.
3. It is Judy whose invitation was lost.
4. Our governor, who has a large private income, travels often.
5. Grandfather saves stamps which portray different animals.
6. Is this the time that we have waited for?
7. A team which doesn't improve should be reorganized.
8. Yes, it is I who wrote the appeal to the President.
9. The book that she read deals with foreign policy.
10. Here are the train tickets that we lost.

▶ **Exercise 2**   **Identifying the Use of Relative Pronouns.**   Identify the use of each of the relative pronouns in Exercise 1 as *subject, direct object, object of a preposition,* or *adjective.*

EXAMPLE: The book which she asked for is too expensive. _____*object of a preposition*_____

1. This is the restaurant which was described in the magazine. _____
2. The story that she told is hardly plausible. _____
3. It is Judy whose invitation was lost. _____
4. Our governor, who has a large private income, travels often. _____
5. Grandfather saves stamps which portray different animals. _____
6. Is this the time that we have waited for?_____
7. A team which doesn't improve should be reorganized. _____
8. Yes, it is I who wrote the appeal to the President. _____
9. The book that she read deals with foreign policy. _____
10. Here are the train tickets that we lost. _____

19.3 Adjective Clause • Practice 2

Exercise 1   **Identifying Adjective Clauses.**   Write each adjective clause, underlining its subject once and verb twice. Then circle the relative pronoun or relative adverb and identify its function in the clause.

EXAMPLE: I applied to the college that my mother attended.
       (that) my mother attended (direct object)

1. We visited the Rockies, which have spectacular scenery.
_____

2. The statement that I just made still reflects my position.
_____

3. The man whose groceries I walked off with was upset.
_____

4. Pavarotti, who sings at the Metropolitan Opera, is a tenor.
_____

5. We made reservations at the hotel where we want to stay.
_____

6. The plane which I will take from Atlanta will stop in Dallas.
_____

7. It snowed on the day when you arrived.
_____

8. The couch that I bought converts into a comfortable bed.
_____

9. The nest that a robin built in our tree has two eggs in it.
_____

10. The book on which she had built her reputation was not her best by any means.
_____

Exercise 2   **Punctuating Adjective Clauses.**   In each sentence, underline the adjective clause and add commas if necessary.

EXAMPLE: We wrote Mr. Gomez, who was our coach last year.

1. Model trains that can carry people have been built.
2. Arthur Ashe who was a successful tennis star was highly intelligent.
3. I devoured the fruit cake the day it arrived.
4. I joined an organization that raises money for charity.
5. People who work hard for their money appreciate its value.
6. I gave my baby sister who was crying some apple juice.
7. I must paint the front porch which has started to peel.
8. The storm that was approaching us was a hurricane.
9. You would enjoy reading the book I just finished.
10. The telephone bill which was very high this month is a source of contention in the family.

19.3 # Adverb Clauses • Practice 1

Adverb Clauses An adverb clause is a subordinate clause that modifies a verb, adjective, adverb, or verbal by telling where, when, in what manner, to what extent, under what conditions, or why. Adverb clauses are introduced by subordinate conjunctions such as *although, since, if, when, while, because,* and *where.*

ADVERB CLAUSES	
Modified Word	**Example**
Verb	*When I finish this letter,* I will begin to prepare the budget.
Adjective	I am lost *if I don't read a newspaper every day.*
Adverb	The committee responded faster *than we anticipated.*
Verbal	Laughing *until tears appeared,* Susan stepped into the lobby.

▶ **Exercise 1** **Identifying Adverb Clauses.** Underline the adverb clause in each sentence and circle the word or words it modifies.

EXAMPLE: I will be (happy) when I have finished this report.

1. The principal was upset after he learned the truth.

2. Sooner than we expected, we received a confirmation of our order.

3. Unless the weather changes rapidly, we will postpone the trip.

4. My brother arrived before we did.

5. We can begin the conference since all the participants have arrived.

6. He will stay until his mission is completed.

7. Although we played brilliantly, we lost the game.

8. The survey was completed faster than we expected.

9. She is happy if everything goes according to schedule.

10. Eat slowly so that you will digest your food better.

▶ **Exercise 2** **Writing Sentences with Adverb Clauses.** Add an appropriate adverb clause to each independent clause below.

EXAMPLE: She didn't have an umbrella _____*when she left the house*_____ .

1. Faster _____, the flood receded.

2. _____, I will save you a seat.

3. She is more unhappy _____.

4. Smiling _____, she rushed to embrace them.

5. I am unable to join you _____.

6. _____, driving can be difficult.

7. _____, I will appear at the rally.

8. The meeting ended much sooner _____.

9. We decided to protest _____.

10. _____, we will try once again.

19.3 Adverb Clauses • Practice 2

> **Exercise 1** **Identifying Adverb Clauses.** Underline the adverb clause in each sentence. Then indicate whether it modifies a *verb, adjective, adverb,* or *verbal*.

EXAMPLE: <u>Although rain had been predicted</u>, the sun shone. ___verb___

1. She developed laryngitis whenever she caught a cold. _____
2. Hobbling on crutches while my foot heals is difficult. _____
3. Our crew rowed faster than our competition did. _____
4. We checked the stock report when the newspaper came. _____
5. The wheels of the train, clanging as they moved, occasionally emitted sparks. _____
6. We hoped to dig the well where the water table was high. _____
7. The oily streets are as slippery as butter is. _____
8. The coffee, gurgling as it perked, had a delicious aroma. _____
9. To wait until a deadline approaches is generally not wise. _____
10. I went to the library since I needed to do research. _____
11. Whenever you want to visit, you will be welcome here. _____
12. Holding the baby while stirring the stew was a pleasure for Ramona. _____
13. The superhero was more powerful than a speeding locomotive was. _____
14. The fire, crackling as new logs were added, kept us warm. _____
15. To do what the majority does is not always the right thing. _____

> **Exercise 2** **Recognizing Elliptical Clauses.** Write each adverb clause, adding in parentheses the understood words.

EXAMPLE: I enjoyed reading this book more than that one.
   ___than (I did) that one___

1. This haircut looks better than the last one. _____
2. Karen Hinton is not as responsible as Millicent Ramat. _____
3. My brother has fewer blond streaks in his hair than red. _____
4. Aunt Delia helps you more than me. _____
5. The child for whom I babysat was as good as gold. _____
6. The last assignment took longer to do than this one. _____
7. I received more praise for my act than criticism. _____
8. My new camera takes better pictures than my old one. _____
9. My parents were as pleased with my grades as I. _____
10. The speech was more inspirational than informative. _____
11. Although tired, Amy insisted on staying up late. _____
12. While getting a haircut, Philip talked about sports with the barber. _____
13. These pies are fresher than those. _____
14. The human heart is bigger than a dog's. _____
15. A dog's sense of smell is more acute than a human's. _____

19.3 Noun Clauses • Practice 1

Noun Clauses   A noun clause is a subordinate clause that acts as a noun.

USES OF NOUN CLAUSES	
Use	**Example**
Subject	*What his proposal will achieve* is anyone's guess.
Direct Object	I hope *that we will hear from you soon.*
Indirect Object	I told *whoever phoned* the news.
Object of a Preposition	Give them funds for *whatever they need.*
Predicate Nominative	A quick promotion is *what she expects.*
Appositive	Her plan, *that we improve the environment*, has much support.

▶ **Exercise 1**   **Identifying Noun Clauses.**   Underline the noun clause in each sentence and tell how it is used.

EXAMPLE: Ted spoke about <u>what he likes</u>. _____*object of a preposition*_____

1. We won't predict what the results will be.

2. How she appeared so suddenly is quite a mystery.

3. We gave whoever volunteered a list of instructions.

4. Grace's songs are about what she truly believes.

5. The company's goals are what we will discuss now.

6. Whichever trip she chooses will be fine with us.

7. Bill's reply, that we remain firm, upset us all.

8. I will discuss the plan with whoever wishes to do so.

9. Her major problem is whether she can go at all.

10. I know how they will react to his allegation.

▶ **Exercise 2**   **Writing Sentences with Noun Clauses.**   Add a noun clause to each sentence below.

EXAMPLE: He wondered ____*what would happen next*____ .

1. This rule, _____, cannot be enforced.

2. _____ is difficult to say that this time.

3. Of course, we hope _____.

4. His reason was _____.

5. The speaker told about _____.

6. We will bring _____ a sandwich and coffee.

7. I know _____.

8. _____ is not easy to predict.

9. They were extremely proud of _____.

10. A trip to a warm climate is _____.

19.3 Noun Clauses • Practice 2

Exercise 1 Identifying Noun Clauses.
Underline each noun clause. Then identify the function of each noun clause as *subject, direct object, indirect object, predicate nominative, object of a preposition,* or *appositive.*

EXAMPLE: A rewarding and interesting career is <u>what everyone wants</u>. ____*predicate nominative*____

1. The system stifled whatever creativity I might have had. _____
2. We gave whoever ate at our restaurant an after-dinner mint. _____
3. Our resolution, that the group be expanded, required money. _____
4. We found that her loquacity was difficult to bear. _____
5. Whoever signs this form must sign all other transactions. _____
6. The tourist inquired about what time the bus was leaving. _____
7. The store sent whoever had charge accounts a statement. _____
8. Her fear is that she will be caught in an elevator. _____
9. Whatever time the baby falls asleep will be his bedtime. _____
10. Give this verification slip to whoever is at the desk. _____

Exercise 2 Identifying Subordinate Clauses.
Identify each underlined clause as *adjective, adverb,* or *noun.*

EXAMPLE: I want to be all <u>that I am capable of becoming</u>.—Katherine Mansfield _____*adjective*_____

1. I have never been hurt by <u>what I have not said</u>.—Calvin Coolidge _____
2. Nothing is enough for the man <u>to whom enough is very little</u>.—Epicurus _____
3. There are things <u>that are important beyond all this fiddle</u>.—Marianne Moore _____
4. It is better to know some of the questions <u>than all of the answers</u>.—James Thurber _____
5. <u>Whoever seeks to set one race against another</u> seeks to enslave all races.—Franklin D. Roosevelt _____

Writing Application Using Subordinate Clauses to Expand Sentences.
Rewrite each sentence, adding the kind of clause indicated.

EXAMPLE: We gave advice to (noun clause).

_____*We gave advice to whoever asked for it.*_____

1. (adverb clause), the Spanish Club will go to Mexico.

_____

2. Our high school band, (adjective clause), played today.

_____

3. Here is the valuable antique (adjective clause).

_____

4. (noun clause) will fit our schedule.

_____

5. Her beautiful smile is (noun clause).

_____

19.4 Sentences Classified by Structure

• Practice 1

The Four Structures of Sentences   English sentences may be classified by the number and kind of clauses they contain.

Kind of Sentence	Number and Kind of Clauses	Examples
Simple	One independent clause	Nicole's trip to Europe was delightful.
Compound	Two or more independent clauses (properly punctuated)	Brad explained his plans for the new park, and the residents reacted enthusiastically.
Complex	One independent clause and one or more subordinate clauses	Whenever I am in Boston, I like to visit Faneuil Hall.
Compound-Complex	Two or more independent clauses and one or more subordinate clauses	I write music as an avocation, and Ellen composes lyrics whenever she has the time.

▷ **Exercise 1**   **Identifying the Structure of Sentences.**   Identify each sentence as (1) *simple*, (2) *compound*, (3) *complex*, or (4) *compound-complex*.

EXAMPLE: Her idea is both practical and original.   ___(1)___

1. Either Sally will speak, or we will send another representative. _____

2. At this time there are several desirable tours available. _____

3. When the warehouse exploded, everyone in the neighborhood was stunned. _____

4. The Battle of the Bulge was Hitler's last great offensive thrust in World War II. _____

5. Since the speaker had arrived, we began the opening ceremonies, but we were soon interrupted by a few late stragglers. _____

6. A four-color process is used in much printing; the four colors employed are blue, yellow, red, and black. _____

7. This is the actual room where Mozart wrote his music. _____

8. Granada in Spain is famous for its Muslim monuments. _____

9. Bradley will play for Portland if he receives a satisfactory contract. _____

10. We prepared the luncheon as soon as we arrived, and we finished none too soon. _____

▷ **Exercise 2**   **Writing Different Types of Sentences.**   Follow the directions below.

1. Write a compound-complex sentence consisting of two independent clauses and one subordinate clause.

_____

_____

2. Write a compound sentence in which the second independent clause follows the word *or*.

_____

3. Write a simple sentence beginning with the expletive *there*.

_____

4. Write a complex sentence which contains an adjective clause.

_____

5. Write a complex sentence which contains a noun clause.

_____

19.4 Sentences Classified by Structure
• Practice 2

Exercise 1   **Identifying the Four Structures of Sentences.**   Identify each sentence as *simple*, *compound*, *complex*, or *compound-complex*.

EXAMPLE: Whoever is the last to leave should lock the door.   _complex_

1. Neither did the winds die, nor did the unbearable heat subside. _____
2. The clerk rang up the sale and then wrapped our purchases for us. _____
3. Though the detectives worked diligently, they could not unravel the mystery. _____
4. When the network produced the special, the critics gave it mixed reviews. _____
5. The peninsula—a long, pencil-like projection—was covered with thick vegetation. _____
6. People who continually complain rarely have many friends. _____
7. We found the entrance to the turnpike quickly, but then we ran out of gas. _____
8. The session was for whatever complaints people wanted to air, and the supervisors heard quite an assortment. _____
9. Leaving the safety of the harbor, we ventured out to sea. _____
10. The room was stuffy, so I opened the window nearest the chair where I sat. _____
11. Either Alicia or Elena will be here at four o'clock. _____
12. The train arrived at the station and left within ten minutes. _____
13. If you leave the food out on the counter, you will attract pests. _____
14. For a boy who dislikes dancing, you certainly go to a lot of dances. _____
15. The moon shone brightly on the breaking waves, and the water was lit up by fluorescence. _____
16. Dan, who had just moved to Manhattan Beach, asked Victoria to come over for a visit, and Victoria was happy to do so. _____
17. The cats were whining, so Cory stopped what she was doing and fed them. _____
18. Would you rather have cats or dogs as pets? _____
19. As soon as I complete the application, I will drop it in the mail. _____
20. Joe picked out some very attractive invitations, and he spent Saturday afternoon writing them. _____

Writing Application   **Writing Sentences with Different Structures.**   Write sentences of your own following the structures listed below.

1. simple sentence

_____

2. simple sentence with compound subject

_____

3. simple sentence containing an appositive phrase

_____

4. compound sentence with a verbal phrase

_____

5. complex sentence with a noun clause

_____

20.1 The Four Functions of Sentences • Practice 1

The Four Functions of Sentences   The four sentence types are *declarative, interrogative, imperative,* and *exclamatory*. A declarative sentence states an idea and ends with a period. An interrogative sentence asks a question and ends with a question mark. An imperative sentence gives an order or direction and ends with a period or exclamation mark. An exclamatory sentence conveys strong emotion and ends with an exclamation mark.

FOUR FUNCTIONS OF SENTENCES
Declarative: Toronto is not far from Buffalo.
Interrogative: Which composer wrote *The Four Seasons*?
Imperative: Renew your driver's license this week.
Exclamatory: What an amazing custom!

▶ **Exercise 1**   **Identifying The Four Functions of Sentences.**   Write *D* for a declarative sentence, *Int.* for an interrogative sentence, *Imp.* for an imperative sentence, and *E* for an exclamatory sentence. Add the proper punctuation marks at the end of each sentence.

EXAMPLE: The Normans invaded England in 1066 ____(.) D____

1. Who knows where the shoulder pads are _____

2. My favorite cake recipe contains pineapple _____

3. Take all the groceries into the kitchen _____

4. What a truly unpleasant situation this is _____

5. The Turks captured Constantinople in 1453 _____

6. How many new members must we recruit this month _____

7. Make certain that you research your paper carefully _____

8. What a horrible turn of events _____

9. Which reference book do you recommend _____

10. Watch out _____

▶ **Exercise 2**   **Writing Original Sentences.**   Complete the work below.

1. Write two declarative sentences. _____

   _____

   _____

2. Write three interrogative sentences. _____

   _____

   _____

   _____

   _____

3. Write three imperative sentences. _____

   _____

   _____

   _____

   _____

4. Write two exclamatory sentences. _____

   _____

   _____

20.1 The Four Functions of Sentences • Practice 2

▶ **Exercise 1**   **Identifying the Four Functions of Sentences.**   Identify each sentence as *declarative, interrogative, imperative,* or *exclamatory.* Then write the end mark for each sentence.

EXAMPLE: As I ran down the street, I heard someone call to me ____*declarative*   (.)____

(1) "Hey, you (2) Slow down for a minute (3) I bet you haven't had breakfast yet (4) Here, how about a new Maxi Muffin"

(5) I stopped in surprise as the grocery clerk tossed a giant muffin to me

(6) "Do you know how important it is to eat a good breakfast" (7) Look over here (8) He pointed to a chart posted in the bread aisle in the store (9) "According to the Doctor's Institute, a good breakfast adds significantly to a person's overall health, and Maxi Muffins contain most of the essential vitamins and minerals we need"

(10) What interesting ideas the chart presented (11) I never realized just how many vitamins a muffin could provide (12) I took a bite of the sample muffin, and began to cough (13) "This is horrible"(14) "Why is it so dry" (15) "Maxi Muffins taste much better with a tall glass of juice"

1. _____   6. _____   11. _____
2. _____   7. _____   12. _____
3. _____   8. _____   13. _____
4. _____   9. _____   14. _____
5. _____   10. _____   15. _____

▶ **Writing Application**   **Writing Sentences with Different Functions.**   Write a sentence for each number in the following chart. Be sure that you use the subject indicated at the left and the function indicated at the top. For example, the first sentence should be a *declarative* sentence about *television.*

	Declarative	Interrogative	Imperative	Exclamatory
Television	1	2		
Politics			3	4
Trivia	5			6
Basketball		7	8	
Subways	9			10

1. _____
2. _____
3. _____
4. _____
5. _____
6. _____
7. _____
8. _____
9. _____
10. _____

20.2 Improving Your Sentences (Sentence Combining) • Practice 1

Sentence Combining   Combine short sentences by using compound subjects or verbs; phrases; or compound, complex, or compound-complex sentences.

Separate Sentences	Combined Sentences
Otis is a very talented guitarist. Alice also plays the guitar very well.	Otis and Alice are both very talented guitarists.
He lost control of his car. It spun around and slammed into a tree.	When he lost control of his car, it spun around and slammed into a tree.
The game had ended. Some of the fans moved quickly toward the exits. Others remained in the stands to celebrate their team's victory.	Once the game had ended, some of the fans moved quickly toward the exits while others remained in the stands to celebrate their team's victory.

▶ **Exercise 1**   **Sentence Combining.**   Combine the sentences in each item into a single, longer sentence.

EXAMPLE: Chuck received an athletic scholarship. He accepted it gratefully.
   When Chuck received an athletic scholarship, he accepted it gratefully. _____

1. Elizabeth Fox is now a district attorney. She is a former congresswoman. _____
   _____

2. Fred is a gifted athlete. He is also a good student. _____
   _____

3. Sandy waited in line for eight hours to buy tickets for the concert. All the tickets were sold before she
   reached the front of the line. _____
   _____

4. Ron slipped and fell into a puddle. He ruined his best pair of pants. _____
   _____

5. The school's football team won easily. The soccer team was defeated. _____
   _____

▶ **Exercise 2**   **More Work with Combining Sentences.**   Follow the directions in Exercise 1.

1. Violet Snodgrass won the talent competition. She is an excellent actress. _____
   _____

2. Tim raced through the airport. He was trying to locate the gate his parents would be coming through. _
   _____

3. Mr. and Mrs. Franklin returned from their vacation. They discovered that their house had been
   broken into. Nothing valuable had been stolen. _____
   _____

4. The wind whistled through the trees. The sound of thunder echoed through the air. The rain steadily
   pounded the ground. _____
   _____

5. School was canceled for the day. There had been a major snowstorm the previous night. Most of the
   students spent the day playing in the snow. _____
   _____

20.2 Improving Your Sentences (Sentence Combining) • Practice 2

> **Exercise 1**   **Sentence Combining.**   Combine each of the following groups of sentences into one longer sentence. Label the method you use as *modifying phrase, appositive, compound verb,* and so on.

EXAMPLE: The plane was due to take off. Nick had not come.
> *Though the plane was due to take off, Nick had not come.   (subordinate clause)*

1. Rust is a popular color. It is often used in home decorating.

   _____

2. She had trouble building the fire. A brisk breeze was blowing.

   _____

3. Our local newspapers were the *Kensington Chronicle* and the *Orinda Record*. Last year they merged.

   _____

4. The dog trotted down the main street. It paused in front of the meat market. It sniffed eagerly.

   _____

5. I ran to answer the phone. I slipped on a magazine. I tripped over the coffee table.

   _____

6. A canoe came around the bend of the shoreline. The weary campers shouted for help.

   _____

7. February was especially cruel that year. Its frigid weather damaged fruit trees and evergreens.

   _____

8. Homemade soup bubbled in the big pot. The boys had not eaten since dawn. They remembered that.

   _____

9. The customs officer opened the suitcase. He saw the toy animals. He smiled.

   _____

10. California and Florida both produce citrus. They vie to see who can grow the best oranges.

   _____

> **Exercise 2**   **Combining Sentences in a Passage.**   Rewrite the following passage, combining some of the sentences.

(1) Rose Ann had always lived in the city. (2) Street sounds, crowds, and motion were normal to her. (3) She thought she would never be content anywhere else. (4) Then one summer she drove across the country. (5) She stayed at small inns in little towns. (6) She saw the many different ways Americans live. (7) Today, Rose Ann has a new career. (8) She is an innkeeper. (9) Her ten-bedroom inn is on a wooded hill above a lazy river.

_____

_____

_____

_____

_____

_____

_____

_____

20.3 Vary Sentences (Expanding Short Sentences, Shortening Long Sentences) • Practice 1

Expanding Short Sentences   Eliminate short, choppy sentences by adding details or combining ideas.

Short Sentences	Expanded Sentences
Frank walked down the street.	Frank walked at an accelerated pace down the dark, deserted city street.
The skydiver jumped out of the plane.	Without hesitating to look down at the ground hundreds of feet below, the skydiver jumped out of the plane.

Shortening Long Sentences   Eliminate long, rambling sentences by regrouping ideas into two or more simpler sentences.

Long, Complicated Sentence	Shorter, Clearer Sentences
Almanacs, which dealt at first only with agricultural affairs, attracted interest early in the Colonial Period and really became an institution with the publication of Benjamin Franklin's *Poor Richard's Almanac* in the Revolutionary Period.	Almanacs, which dealt at first only with agricultural affairs, attracted interest early in the Colonial Period. They really became an institution with the publication of Benjamin Franklin's *Poor Richard's Almanac* in the Revolutionary Period.

▶ **Exercise 1**   **Expanding Short Sentences.**   Improve each of the sentences by adding details.

EXAMPLE: The team won the game.

  The visiting team won the game decisively.

1. Todd's research paper had many faults.

  _____

2. The business district is congested.

  _____

3. Men are repairing the main highway.

  _____

4. Fran drove through the snowstorm.

  _____

5. Dave and Bridget watched the sunset.

  _____

▶ **Exercise 2**   **Shortening Long Sentences.**   Divide each long sentence into two or more sentences.

1. Colorado, a state which produces sugar beets and potatoes as well as coal and silver, really boomed with the discovery of gold in 1859 although it wasn't admitted to the union as the thirty-eighth state until 1876.

  _____

  _____

2. For the annual spring picnic, the senior class voted to have a barbecue at Closter Lake, where there are facilities for swimming, a softball field, and a volleyball court, and a committee was formed to organize the event, but no one could agree on a date for the picnic.

  _____

  _____

20.3 Vary Sentences (Expanding Short Sentences, Shortening Long Sentences) • Practice 2

▶ **Exercise 1**   **Adding Details.**   Rewrite each of the following sentences, adding details to make them longer as well as more interesting. Underline and label your additions.

EXAMPLE: The cat meowed.
    PREP. PHRASE   ADJ. ADJ.   ADV.   PREP. PHRASE
    For three hours, the lost tiger cat meowed loudly on our doorstep.

1. Selma looked at each of her friends.

   _____

2. We wore purple caps and gowns.

   _____

3. Confusion as well as excitement filled the air.

   _____

4. We filed in.

   _____

5. The principal called the first name.

   _____

▶ **Exercise 2**   **Adding Details and Combining Ideas.**   Rewrite the passage to correct a series of short, choppy sentences. Add details and join ideas to make longer sentences.

(1) The race was over. (2) Sally stumbled to the post. (3) It had been a long five miles. (4) No one had expected her to finish, or even "place." (5) She had shown them. (6) She had worked out for weeks. (7) She had used her training. (8) She had depended on her confidence. (9) She had given all of her energy to this goal. (10) She had now won a personal victory as well as a public one.

_____

_____

_____

_____

▶ **Exercise 3**   **Simplifying Long Sentences.**   On the back of this sheet, rewrite the following passage by eliminating the rambling sentences. In some of the sentences, separate the thoughts to form sentences with fewer clauses. In others, separate and regroup the ideas. Make sure that the lengths of sentences are varied.

(1) In moving, almost everything that is familiar to a child, except of course members of the family, disappears, leaving the child with a feeling of loss and perhaps without a sense of identity in the new surroundings, and many children at such times attach themselves to certain objects such as a blanket, stuffed animal, or favorite toy, which they have carried with them, because it can serve as a source of comfort and security.

(2) Such attachments can be sensitive stages in a child's development because when the child has become dependent on one particular object, he or she may then resist new things, often holding desperately to the familiar old ones, fearing the type of loss first felt during the move to a new home.

20.3 Vary Sentences (Using Different Sentence Openers and Structures) • Practice 1

Using Different Sentence Openers and Structures Avoid monotony in your writing by varying sentence openers and sentence structure.

DIFFERENT SENTENCE OPENERS
Adjectives: Tired and depressed, she burst into tears.
Participial Phrase: Crossing the finish line, he raised his arms.
Infinitive Phrase: To find a route, she consulted a map.
Adverb Clause: Since they left, nothing is the same.
Subject/Appositive: Mrs. Greene, our counselor, led the discussion.
Transitional Phrase: For that reason, we decided to stay.
Inverted Order: Around and around whirled the dancers.

DIFFERENT SENTENCE STRUCTURES
Simple: The game was canceled.
Compound: The game was canceled, so we went to the movies.
Complex: Since the game was canceled, we went to the movies.
Compound-Complex: When the game was canceled, we went to the movies, but we did not enjoy the show.

▶ **Exercise 1** **Writing Sentences with Different Openers.** Rewrite each sentence below so that it begins with the construction given in parentheses.

EXAMPLE: Bob left the office; he was finished for the day. (participial phrase)

   Finished for the day, Bob left the office.

1. Marni checked the telephone directory to get the number. (infinitive phrase)

   _____

2. My new CD player is a compact model, but it has superb stereo speakers. (appositive)

   _____

3. The committee approved the plan although I disagreed. (adverb clause)

   _____

4. Mary accepted the award; she was smiling happily. (participial phrase)

   _____

5. The weary hikers trudged up the hill. (inverted order)

   _____

▶ **Exercise 2** **Varying Sentence Structure.** Rewrite each set of simple sentences below to create the sentence structure given in parentheses.

EXAMPLE: Joey tied the boat to the dock. Anna cleaned the fish. (complex)

   While Joey tied the boat to the dock, Anna cleaned the fish.

1. The crowd was small. It inspired the team. (complex)

   _____

2. We knocked several times. No one answered. (compound)

   _____

3. I'm baby-sitting for Emma. She is a charming child. We have fun together. (compound-complex)

   _____

4. Meet me at my locker. We can walk home together. (complex)

   _____

20.3 Vary Sentences (Using Different Sentence Openers and Structures) • Practice 2

▶ **Exercise 1** **Using Different Sentence Openers.** Rewrite the beginning of each sentence below. Use as many different openers as you can, and label the type of opener in each case.

1. Many new houses in the West, in contrast, do not have attics or basements.

_____

2. The child got lost in the crowd at the fair.

_____

3. He sprained his ankle, dashing for a bus.

_____

4. They felt that they could not leave the place until they had fulfilled their obligations.

_____

5. The Red Cross in its Basic First Aid Course teaches three methods to stop bleeding.

_____

6. Mavis was careful not to overwater the begonia to avoid rotting the plant's roots.

_____

7. A six-cylinder engine uses less fuel, not surprisingly, than does one with eight cylinders.

_____

8. The dog, lonely and sad, watched me through the window.

_____

9. Antique jewelry and furniture are smart investments because they appreciate in value rather than

depreciate.

_____

10. A faint glimmer appeared through the window.

_____

▶ **Exercise 2** **Using Different Sentence Structures.** Rewrite the following passage so that it contains simple, compound, complex, and compound-complex sentence structures. After each sentence, identify its structure in parentheses.

(1) I entered the forest as the sun began to set. (2) The shadows were long. (3) I followed a seldom-used path. (4) I felt restless. (5) I had started walking. (6) The forest was cool. (7) The dark branches dropped with the weight of green summer foliage. (8) The leaves fluttered. (9) The brush crackled beneath my feet.
    (10) I turned to the left. (11) I walked into a clearing. (12) The grass was short and peppered with dark-colored flowers. (13) I climbed onto a rock. (14) I faced the west. (15) The sun was disappearing into a honey sunset swirl. (16) The clouds shimmered orange. (17) A cool breeze blew the leaves, my hair, and the grass. (18) The sun melted into the trees and soon dropped out of sight. (19) My restlessness was gone. (20) I was at peace.

_____

_____

_____

_____

_____

_____

_____

20.3 Vary Sentences (Using Different Types of Sentences)
• Practice 1

Using Different types of Sentences   Consider using different types of sentences to achieve special kinds of emphasis for your ideas.

DIFFERENT SENTENCE TYPES		
Type	**Characteristics**	**Example**
Loose	Main idea is presented at the beginning; follows the regular subject-verb-complement order	The manager *explained* the proposal to his staff.
Periodic	Main idea is presented at the end	After an unusual two hour delay, the *train finally arrived.*
Balanced	Main ideas are presented in parallel phrases or clauses	*Our first option is to begin* building at once; *our second option is to wait* for an additional loan.
Cumulative	Main idea is surrounded by layers of detail	*If the senator decides to run again,* he will be elected with one of the largest pluralities on record.

▶ Exercise 1   **Identifying Different Types of Sentences.**   Label each sentence below *L* for loose, *P* for periodic, *B* for balanced, or *C* for cumulative.

EXAMPLE: Early the next morning, the rescue began. ____*P*____

1. Foreign cars get better mileage, but American cars ride better. _____

2. When the votes were tabulated, Mrs. Lester was elected with a higher total number of votes than her managers expected. _____

3. My parents intend to visit Central America next summer. _____

4. At the height of his power and popularity, he resigned. _____

5. I shower in the morning; my sister showers at night. _____

▶ Exercise 2   **Writing Different Types of Sentences.**   Follow the directions below.

1. Write a loose sentence.

_____

_____

2. Write a periodic sentence.

_____

_____

3. Write a balanced sentence. Punctuate it with a comma and a coordinating conjunction.

_____

_____

4. Write a balanced sentence. Punctuate it with a semicolon.

_____

_____

5. Write a cumulative sentence.

_____

_____

20.3 Vary Sentences (Using Different Types of Sentences)
• Practice 2

▶ **Exercise 1** **Identifying Types of Sentences.** Identify each of the following sentences as loose, periodic, balanced, or cumulative.

1. A sloop was loitering in the distance, dropping slowly down with the tide, her sail hanging uselessly against the mast . . .—Washington Irving. _____

2. Let us never negotiate out of fear [but] let us never fear to negotiate.—John F. Kennedy _____

3. Whenever the rain hangs a gray curtain around the house and pitter-patters on the leaves, I am lulled to sleep. _____

4. We chose to sit on the far side of the stadium for the big game because that side was in the shade. _____

5. The energetic came, eager to put their hands to work; the lazy [came], hoping to live with no work at all.—Eric Sevareid. _____

▶ **Exercise 2** **Practicing with Different Types of Sentences.** Examine magazine articles and short stories to find different types of sentences. Find *two* loose, *two* periodic, *two* balanced, and *two* cumulative sentences. Using them as models, write (1) *two* loose, (2) *two* periodic, (3) *two* balanced, and (4) *two* cumulative sentences. Label each sentence.

1. _____
   _____

2. _____
   _____

3. _____
   _____

4. _____
   _____

5. _____
   _____

6. _____
   _____

7. _____
   _____

8. _____
   _____

20.3 Vary Sentences (Using Different Sentence Patterns and Professional Models) • Practice 1

Using Different Sentence Patterns   Use parallel structures within a sentence and in groups of sentences to point out relationships among ideas.

> **PARALLEL STRUCTURES WITHIN A SENTENCE**
>
> The dramatist agreed *to write a one-act play, to help select the performers*, and *to arrange for production in a local theater.*

Use a contrasting structure to emphasize an idea or to present a concluding thought.

> **CONTRASTING STRUCTURE WITHIN A SENTENCE**
>
> Unable to get support of the media, abandoned by local politicos, and thwarted by the state legislature, *the governor resigned.*

Using Professional Models   Examine and learn from the kinds of sentences that professional writers use.

▷ **Exercise 1**   **Writing Sentences with Parallel Structures.**   Follow the directions below.

EXAMPLE: Write a sentence with three parallel verbs.

> *After breakfast she cleaned the house, did some local shopping, and hopped on a bus to the library.*

1. Write a sentence that ends with three prepositional phrases. _____

   _____

2. Write a sentence with three or four parallel verbs. _____

   _____

3. Write a sentence that begins with two participial phrases connected by *and.* _____

   _____

4. Write a sentence that ends with three infinitive phrases. _____

   _____

5. Write a sentence with two parallel adverb clauses. _____

   _____

▷ **Exercise 2**   **Writing a Paragraph with a Contrasting Structure.**   Write a paragraph describing a recent news event. Begin with three to five sentences of normal word length. Then conclude with a brief sentence of no more than six words.

_____

_____

_____

_____

_____

20.3 Vary Sentences (Using Different Sentence Patterns and Professional Models) • Practice 2

▶**Exercise 1**   **Using Structural Similarities.**   Write several sentences or a passage in which you use structural similarities to underscore relationships among ideas.

_____

_____

_____

_____

_____

_____

▶**Exercise 2**   **Using Structural Differences.**   Write a passage with a pattern that readers will find appropriate and comfortable. Then break the pattern with a contrasting sentence structure.

_____

_____

_____

_____

_____

_____

_____

▶**Exercise 3**   **Using Models of Professional Writing.**   Find passages that you have read and enjoyed. Make copies of three passages with striking sentence patterns. Use any of the models to write a passage of your own on any topic. Use the types of sentences that the writer used, and follow a pattern similar to that in the model.

_____

_____

_____

_____

_____

_____

_____

_____

_____

_____

_____

20.4 # Fragments and Run-ons (Fragments) • Practice 1

Fragments Do not capitalize and punctuate phrases, subordinate clauses, or words in a series as if they were complete sentences.

Fragments	Complete Sentences
at the approach of sunset	We returned to shore *at the approach of sunset.*
disturbed by the shouting	Everyone was *disturbed by the shouting.*
a car, a bus, or a plane	You have a choice of *a car, a bus, or a plane.*
when she spoke to us later	*When she spoke to us later,* she changed her mind.
which is in the next county	Christy's, *which is in the next county,* is a fine restaurant.

▶ **Exercise 1** **Distinguishing Between Fragments and Complete Sentences.** Write *F* if the group of words is a fragment and *S* if it is a complete sentence.

EXAMPLE: Waiting for hours at the bus terminal. ___*F*___

1. The northern road from Barcelona. _____

2. Whether he intends to follow through on his threat. _____

3. The committee discussed a school anniversary celebration. _____

4. Within minutes of the appearance of the first flash. _____

5. A glass of orange juice, Belgian waffles, and coffee. _____

6. Frightened by an early morning phone call. _____

7. Unfortunately, the package was shipped to the wrong address. _____

8. She likes to read novels of espionage. _____

9. Which can be found in any reputable reference book. _____

10. Asked for and received a second opportunity. _____

▶ **Exercise 2** **Changing Fragments into Complete Sentences.** Each group of words below is a fragment. Add whatever is necessary to make it into a complete sentence. Then draw a single line under the subject, and a double line under the verb of the independent clause.

EXAMPLE: Adjusting the turntable again.
Adjusting the turntable again, I finally got it right.

1. reaching the stop sign _____

2. a chisel, a hammer, and headless nails _____

3. if you phone her _____

4. between you and me _____

5. frozen together _____

6. in the reference section of the school library _____

7. since she fell _____

8. with rubber cement _____

9. which Mother wanted _____

10. in the file cabinet _____

20.4 **Fragments and Run-ons** (Fragments) • **Practice 2**

▶ **Exercise 1** **Distinguishing Between Fragments and Complete Sentences.** Write *F* if the group of words is a fragment and *S* if it is a complete sentence.

EXAMPLE: After we left the supermarket. _____*F*_____

1. Grateful at having been allowed to go to the circus. _____
2. Please be quiet. _____
3. The long, strange shadows of the bare aspen, growing longer as dusk approached. _____
4. Just then, their eyes met. _____
5. Gently wiping away the tiny tears on the baby's cheeks. _____
6. Not wishing to join a fraternity and happy to remain independent. _____
7. I would rather have an apricot tree than a plum. _____
8. Tripped over the ever-underfoot cat. _____
9. After spending the entire morning and part of the afternoon in the garden. _____
10. The geese, flying high and heading toward their winter home. _____

▶ **Exercise 2** **Identifying and Correcting Fragments.** If an item does not contain a fragment, write *correct*. If the item contains a fragment, rewrite it to make one or more complete sentences.

EXAMPLE: Pleased by the applause of the audience. The violinist played an encore.
_____*Pleased by the applause of the audience, the violinist played an encore.*_____

1. Their faces shining with delight at seeing the movie star.

   _____

2. I wanted one thing. To take a long nap.

   _____

3. The committee was impressed by this application. Which we received just yesterday.

   _____

4. I enjoy working with my hands.

   _____

5. Traffic lights flashing erratically as the cars jammed in the intersection, unsure whose turn it was to proceed.

   _____

6. The apples cooked. With their sweet juices bubbling away.

   _____

7. Just as Mr. Chao said goodbye.

   _____

8. Classified ads filled the pages of the newspaper.

   _____

9. A report to write and math to do before tomorrow.

   _____

10. The silhouettes of the trees against the light of the moon.

    _____

20.4 Fragments and Run-ons (Run-ons) • Practice 1

Run-ons A run-on sentence consists of two or more complete sentences that are not properly joined or separated. Use punctuation, conjunctions, or other means to separate the parts of a run-on sentence correctly.

Run-on Sentences	Properly Punctuated Sentences
Jason plays football, Jeff prefers soccer and track.	Jason plays football, and Jeff prefers soccer and track.
The first bus was an hour late the second was on time.	The first bus was an hour late; the second was on time.
Jo Ann never cared for city life, I just don't know why.	Jo Ann never cared for city life. I just don't know why.

▷ **Exercise 1** **Distinguishing Between Run-ons and Properly Punctuated Sentences.** If the sentence is a run-on, write *RO*; if the sentence is correct, write *S*.

EXAMPLE: The road curved sharply, she swerved into a fence. ___*RO*___

1. Dave is a computer whiz, he is also a crackerjack programmer. _____

2. Brahms wrote four symphonies each one is superb. _____

3. From the oven came an aroma of chocolate and honey. _____

4. Mickey is an expert seamstress, she makes her own clothes. _____

5. Some companies manufacture special security envelopes. _____

6. Charles researched the topic, and later he wrote the brief. _____

7. There are three possibilities I don't like any of them. _____

8. Steve has grown massive, his doctor wants him to lose weight. _____

9. Zimbabwe used to be called Rhodesia, its old capital Salisbury is now called Harare. _____

10. Judy types daily she is trying to finish a research paper. _____

▷ **Exercise 2** **Changing Run-ons into Properly Punctuated Sentences.** Rewrite each run-on so that it is correct.

EXAMPLE: I play second base, Bill is the shortstop.
       I play second base, and Bill is the shortstop.

1. There are two choices I will explain them both.

_____

2. The new mall will contain sixty shops enclosed parking will be nearby.

_____

3. Cabbage can be prepared in many ways, my favorite is stuffed cabbage.

_____

4. Carl Sagan wrote *Cosmos* he also was the author of *Broca's Brain*.

_____

5. Ice, of course, is dangerous, last winter Father slipped and fell.

_____

20.4 Fragments and Run-ons (Run-ons) • Practice 2

▶ **Exercise 1**   **Identifying and Correcting Run-ons.**   If a sentence is a run-on, correct it. If it is correct as written, write *correct*.

EXAMPLE: I want to study genetics it is a developing science.
_____*I want to study genetics, a developing science.*_____

1. I looked down, I saw that the well was apparently dry.
   _____

2. We read the Preamble to the Constitution, our group felt anew the power of those words.
   _____

3. The boy had trouble with the decimal point when multiplying he always put it in the wrong place.
   _____

4. The thermometer broke, the mercury spilled onto the floor.
   _____

5. I mislaid my car keys, my house keys were also gone.
   _____

6. It is against the law to litter, nevertheless, people do it.
   _____

7. Ann threw away the check, but she eventually recovered it.
   _____

8. I generally like the climate of the area where I live I do not enjoy subfreezing winter temperatures.
   _____

9. Everyone should be polite, however many people are rude.
   _____

10. I made my own chili to eat it one needs an iron stomach.
    _____

▶ **Writing Application**   **Avoiding Fragments and Run-ons.**   Write the paragraph, correcting all fragments and run-ons. Use the back of this sheet if you need more space.

EXAMPLE: Mosquitoes are pests, they are difficult to control.
_____*Mosquitoes are pests that are difficult to control.*_____

   (1) Mosquitoes, those nasty little insects whose bites cause our skin to swell and itch. (2) They inhabit every state in the Union and most areas of the world. (3) Actually, the bites should not be considered mere irritants they lead to many deaths every year. (4) These insects transmit many ailments. (5) Temporary insanity, filariasis, and many types of viral and bacterial infections. (6) Of course, mosquitoes must bite to survive, the females need the protein from the blood to produce their eggs. (7) The females weigh one ten-thousandth of an ounce when unfed, they triple that after a single bite. (8) Among nature's greatest achievements, the two intricate pumps inside the female's head. (9) Only one bite is necessary, they draw enough blood to produce seventy-five eggs. (10) Much has been done to halt the growth of mosquitoes, nothing, however, completely eradicates these insects.

_____

_____

_____

_____

_____

20.5 Misplaced and Dangling Modifier • Practice 1

Misplaced Modifiers A misplaced modifier seems to modify the wrong word in a sentence. It should be placed as close as possible to the word it modifies.

MISPLACED MODIFIERS	
Misplaced	**Improved**
Gloria purchased a wristwatch in Chicago *with a leather band.*	In Chicago Gloria purchased a wristwatch *with a leather band.*
The map is in the hall closet *that you need.*	The map *that you need* is in the hall closet.

Dangling Modifiers A dangling modifier seems to modify the wrong word or no word at all because the word it should modify has been omitted from the sentence.

DANGLING MODIFIERS	
Dangling	**Improved**
Reading the first paragraph, the book was too difficult.	*Reading the first paragraph,* I realized the book was too difficult.
While scoring the winning goal, his father's cheer could be heard clearly.	*While scoring the winning goal,* he heard his father's cheer clearly.

> **Exercise 1** **Recognizing Misplaced Modifiers.** Underline each misplaced modifiers.

EXAMPLE: The patrol car usually waits near the station <u>with the loud horn.</u>

1. The old woman bumped into the bench walking her dog.

2. Marie gave her TV to her younger sister with remote control.

3. The lithograph was a genuine Chagall that was stolen.

4. The girls fled from the dormitory noticeably upset.

5. Bill wants a hamburger and coffee cooked well done.

6. Apricots have a better flavor that come from California.

7. Father bought new glasses in the city with bifocals.

8. The oak tree was hit by lightning with a forked trunk.

9. Grandma called the police frightened by the strange noise.

10. The city has to be Boston with the large outdoor fruit and vegetable market.

> **Exercise 2** **Recognizing Dangling Modifiers.** Underline each dangling modifier. If a sentence has no dangling modifier, leave it unmarked.

EXAMPLE: <u>Turning the corner,</u> a beautiful sunset could be seen.

1. Closing the car trunk, her keys had been misplaced.

2. Announcing the winners, Bob spoke in a hushed voice.

3. Reaching the intersection, an accident blocked the next street.

4. While opening the package, a mistake was inadvertently made.

5. Raising his baton, the conductor began the symphony.

20.5 Misplaced and Dangling Modifier • Practice 2

▶ **Exercise 1** **Identifying and Correcting Misplaced Modifiers.** Write each sentence, correcting the misplaced modifier.

EXAMPLE: Swinging from the branches, we saw two monkeys.

_____*We saw two monkeys swinging from the branches.*_____

1. We saw the seagulls sitting at the sidewalk café.

_____

2. We arranged to have a pizza made by phone.

_____

3. Whirling round and round, we saw our clothes in the drier.

_____

4. The grandfather clock awoke me chiming out the hour.

_____

5. Under the couch, he found the dollar.

_____

▶ **Exercise 2** **Identifying and Correcting Dangling Modifiers.** If a sentence contains a dangling modifier, rewrite it. If a sentence is correct, write *correct*.

EXAMPLE: Having finished the assignment, the hour was late.

_____*Having finished the assignment, I realized how late it was.*_____

1. To eat before the game, dinner must be ready within fifteen minutes.

_____

2. While laughing, the chicken bone stuck in her throat.

_____

3. Checking all the stations, the assembly line was running smoothly.

_____

4. Having lost my hat, I missed the bus I wanted.

_____

5. Falling on the stairs, my jaw was dislocated.

_____

▶ **Writing Application** **Avoiding Misplaced and Dangling Modifiers.** Fill in each blank with the kind of phrase or clause indicated, being careful to avoid using any misplaced or dangling modifiers.

EXAMPLE: I still remember the day _____*I still remember the day that I started kindergarten.*_____ (adjective clause)

1. When carving the turkey, _____. (independent clause)

2. _____, the jockey rode the horse to victory. (participial phrase)

3. The huge rock _____ threatened the houses in the area. (adjective phrase)

4. Standing speechless before the group, _____. (independent clause)

5. _____, Paula's aunt gave her a family album. (subordinate clause)

20.6 Faulty Parallelism • Practice 1

Recognizing the Correct Use of Parallelism   Parallelism is the placement of equal ideas in words, phrases, or clauses of similar types.

PARALLEL WORDS, PHRASES, AND CLAUSES
Words: This room seems *bright, spacious,* and *suitable.*
Phrases: *Gathering the best spices* and *mixing them carefully* are important if you want this recipe to work.
Clauses: I have no patience with *what you said* or with *what you did.*

Correcting Faulty Parallelism   Correct a sentence containing faulty parallelism by rewriting it so that each parallel idea is expressed in the same grammatical structure. Faulty parallelism can involve words, phrases, and clauses in a series as well as comparisons.

CORRECTING FAULTY PARALLELISM
Nonparallel: My sister likes *to jog, to swim,* and *dance.*
Parallel: My sister likes *to jog, to swim,* and *to dance.*
Nonparallel: He prefers a *sandwich* to *eating a full meal.*
Parallel: He prefers *a sandwich* to *a full meal.*

▶ **Exercise 1**   **Recognizing Parallel Structure.**   In each sentence below, underline the parallel structures.

EXAMPLE: I walk <u>to school</u> and then <u>to work.</u>

1. A person who gives to charity and who helps others is rare indeed.
2. In his career he has been an accountant, an expediter, and a consultant.
3. Growing very slowly and then bursting into glorious color is a characteristic of that tropical plant.
4. I have had virtually no peace since my daughter left and since my oldest son returned.
5. After the accident, she sobbed, whimpered, and collapsed.
6. Maggie always sings in the shower, at the breakfast table, and at most other times.
7. We try to jog daily and to hike on weekends.
8. Her hobbies include refinishing furniture, repairing clocks, and constructing floral displays.
9. Ms. Ames, Mr. Paulson, and Dr. Phillip will all present seminars at the convention.
10. She was fascinated to learn that Joel writes sonnets and that I design mobiles.

▶ **Exercise 2**   **Recognizing Faulty Parallelism.**   Next to each sentence below write *FP* if there is faulty parallelism and *C* if the sentence is correct.

EXAMPLE: I enjoy reading magazines rather than to clean my room.   *FP*

1. Exercising every day, eating the right foods, and to get enough sleep can help a person stay healthy. _____
2. My mother would rather bake fresh bread than buying a packaged loaf. _____
3. I expect to drive to Providence, to see two friends, and to return this evening. _____
4. My teacher prefers a simple list of ideas to preparing a complicated Harvard outline. _____
5. She would rather return to our hotel than going to the stadium. _____

20.6 Faulty Parallelism • Practice 2

▶ **Exercise 1** **Correcting Faulty Parallelism.** Rewrite each sentence to correct the faulty parallelism.

EXAMPLE: She not only plays soccer but also basketball.

　　　　She plays not only soccer but also basketball.

1. The new employee was lazy, insolent, and often came late.

   _____

2. I think the plants did well because they were fertilized rather than because of my talks to them.

   _____

3. Ken either will go to the parade or to the Egyptian museum.

   _____

4. I hate weeding as much as having shots upsets me.

   _____

5. He both wanted to keep his job and to move to the country.

   _____

6. Going home is better than to stay here.

   _____

7. I would choose reading a book over a television show.

   _____

8. His old tennis shoes were dirty, laceless, and smelled.

   _____

9. The coach tells me that I bat well, but I field poorly.

   _____

10. Laughing together, sharing one another's problems, and to overlook faults—these make true friends.

   _____

▶ **Writing Application** **Writing Sentences Containing Parallel Structures.** Follow the instructions in parentheses to revise each sentence, making sure the revisions contain parallel structures.

EXAMPLE: If you have completed all the assignments, you will do well on the test. (Add another adverb clause.)

　　　　If you have completed all the assignments and if you have reviewed your notes carefully, you will do well on the test.

1. Gathering honey, the bees worked diligently. (Add another participial phrase.)

   _____

2. I listened to the melody floating through the air. (Add another independent clause.)

   _____

3. I love gardening. (Compare gardening to something else.)

   _____

4. I will participate in the log rolling contest. (Add two more prepositional phrases.)

   _____

5. I was pleased by the game we played. (Add another prepositional phrase that is modified by an adjective clause.)

   _____

20.7 # Faulty Coordination • Practice 1

Recognizing Faulty Coordination   Use *and* or other coordinating conjunctions only to connect related ideas of equal importance.

FAULTY COORDINATION
Leonard Warren was perhaps the greatest of all baritones, *and* he loved to play chess. Wilson is our top computer analyst, *and* he lives not far from our main office.

Correcting Faulty Coordination   Revise sentences with faulty coordination by putting unrelated ideas into separate sentences or by putting a less important or subordinate idea into a subordinate clause or a phrase.

CORRECTING FAULTY COORDINATION
Faulty: Amelia Earhart won the love of many Americans through her courageous early flights, *and* she never returned from her last flight.
Better: Amelia Earhart won the love of many Americans through her courageous early flights. She never returned from her last flight.

▶ **Exercise 1**   **Recognizing Faulty Coordination.**   For the five sentences below in which coordination is used correctly, write *C*. For the others, write *F* for faulty.

EXAMPLE: New housing is out of the reach of most young couples today, and my grandparents once owned a new home.   ___F___

1. Our first report was not complete, but the second is much better. _____

2. Charles Goodyear invented a vulcanization process for rubber, and I need a new pair of front tires. _____

3. The 14th Amendment to the Constitution was ratified in 1868, and we need a new constitution for our club. _____

4. My grandfather always enjoyed puttering around the house, and he now lives in Montana. _____

5. Nellie Tayloe Ross became the first woman governor of a state in 1925, and later she served as the first woman director of the United States Mint. _____

▶ **Exercise 2**   **Correcting Faulty Coordination.**   Correct the faulty coordination in the sentences below.

EXAMPLE: It was obvious that the Johnsons needed more closet space, and they had six children.
   It was obvious that the Johnsons, who had six children, needed more closet space.

1. World War II brought out a high degree of patriotism, and the war lasted for half a decade.

_____

2. I have read a number of mystery stories, and all of them have been popular for years.

_____

3. Our principal has just instituted a new behavior code, and she is married and has two children.

_____

4. Australia is located in the Southern Hemisphere, and most countries are located in the Northern Hemisphere.

_____

5. I plan to study architecture in college, but I also have a nervous stomach.

_____

20.7 Faulty Coordination • Practice 2

▶ **Exercise 1** **Recognizing Faulty Coordination.** For the six sentences in which *and* is used improperly, write *faulty*. For the sentences in which *and* is used properly, write *correct*.

EXAMPLE: I took the examination, and I passed it. ____correct____

1. The spaniel has been snapping and barking at approaching strangers, and her puppies were born last night. _____

2. Oak trees lined the street, and it was called Grand Avenue. _____

3. The children jumped into the unheated pool and squealed as they hit the water, and immediately they hopped out and dried themselves off and decided to forgo the swim. _____

4. The outside of my house is freshly painted, and the inside is newly redecorated. _____

5. I remembered that I had read the book a long time ago, and I saw the movie last night. _____

▶ **Exercise 2** **Correcting Faulty Coordination.** Rewrite each sentence, correcting the faulty coordination.

EXAMPLE: Learning to parallel park was difficult for me, and I finally mastered the technique.
_____*Although learning to parallel park was difficult for me, I finally mastered the technique.*_____

1. I slowly climbed to the lookout point, and reaching the top provided me with a spectacular view.

_____

2. The car is dented, and it has room for six.

_____

3. The truck had a full load, and it slowed down going uphill.

_____

4. I turned on the television, and a commercial promptly showed up, and I turned the channel looking for something better, and commercials were on wherever I turned.

_____

_____

5. Evan has a new wool pullover, and he plans to wear it to the beach where the nights get cold.

_____

▶ **Writing Application** **Avoiding Faulty Coordination in Sentence Combining.** Combine each pair of sentences, avoiding faulty coordination.

EXAMPLE: Gorillas look ferocious. They are really very gentle.
_____*Although gorillas look ferocious, they are really very gentle.*_____

1. I lost the gold charm. It had been a gift from my father.

_____

2. Daydreams invade the day. Nightmares haunt the darkness.

_____

3. Millions of bats inhabit one particular cave. They journey each night to a lake over a hundred miles away.

_____

4. I enjoy thumbing through encyclopedias. They contain fascinating articles.

_____

5. The ice was left out. It melted all over the countertop.

_____

21.1 # Verb Tenses (The Six Verb Tenses, The Four
Principal Parts) • Practice 1

Verb Tenses A tense is a form of a verb that shows the time of an action or state of being. There are six different tenses, each with a basic and a progressive form. The present and past tenses also have an emphatic form.

Tenses	Basic Forms	Progressive Forms	Emphatic Forms
Present	I see	I am seeing	I do see
Past	I saw	I was seeing	I did see
Future	I will see	I will be seeing	
Present Perfect	I have seen	I have been seeing	
Past Perfect	I had seen	I had been seeing	
Future Perfect	I will have seen	I will have been seeing	

The Four Principal Parts A verb has four principal parts: the present, the present participle, the past, and the past participle.

THE FOUR PRINCIPAL PARTS			
Present	**Present Participle**	**Past**	**Past Participle**
propel	propelling	propelled	(have) propelled
take	taking	took	(have) taken

▶ **Exercise 1** **Recognizing Tenses and Forms of Verbs.** Underline the verb or verb phrase in each sentence below. Then write the tense and form of the verb.

EXAMPLE: The Pandas were winning in the first quarter. ___*past progressive*___

1. I often study in the library. _____

2. The governor will be speaking to the Chamber of Commerce today. _____

3. The train arrived an hour late. _____

4. A few of the members did support my proposal. _____

5. We had been planning a picnic. _____

6. Lenore has finished her term paper already. _____

7. By the end of the run, the play will have had 12,500 performances. _____

8. Most of my friends do take their schoolwork seriously. _____

9. Some candidates will promise anything at election time. _____

10. I am having a hard time understanding Max's anger. _____

▶ **Exercise 2** **Recognizing Principal Parts.** On the lines below, write the principal part used to form the verb in each sentence above. Then write the name of that principal part.

EXAMPLE: ___*winning*___   ___*present participle*___

1. _____
2. _____
3. _____
4. _____
5. _____

6. _____
7. _____
8. _____
9. _____
10. _____

21.1 Verb Tenses (The Six Verb Tenses, The Four Principal Parts) • Practice 2

▶ **Exercise 1**   **Recognizing Verb Tenses and Their Forms.**   Identify the tense of each verb and its form if the form is not basic.

EXAMPLE: We have been running. ___*present perfect progressive*___

1. I did investigate. _____
2. He was waiting._____
3. I had been studying._____
4. He will have left. _____
5. We listened. _____
6. They have been walking. _____
7. She will forget. _____
8. They float. _____
9. I will have finished. _____
10. I accept. _____
11. She was limping. _____
12. He had been typing. _____
13. They do understand. _____
14. I will have been running. _____
15. You have failed. _____
16. I am going. _____
17. She helped. _____
18. It had disappeared. _____
19. He will come. _____
20. We will have decided. _____
21. I did wonder. _____
22. She was studying. _____
23. We had been trying. _____
24. You will have gone. _____
25. We visited. _____
26. They have been playing. _____
27. I will return. _____
28. They fly. _____
29. He will have begun. _____
30. I agree. _____

▶ **Exercise 2**   **Recognizing Principal Parts.**   Identify the principal part used to form each verb in Exercise 1.

EXAMPLE: We have been running. ___*present participle*___

1. _____
2. _____
3. _____
4. _____
5. _____
6. _____
7. _____
8. _____
9. _____
10. _____
11. _____
12. _____
13. _____
14. _____
15. _____
16. _____
17. _____
18. _____
19. _____
20. _____
21. _____
22. _____
23. _____
24. _____
25. _____
26. _____
27. _____
28. _____
29. _____
30. _____

21.1 Verb Tenses (Regular and Irregular Verbs)
• Practice 1

Regular and Irregular Verbs A regular verb is one whose past and past participle are formed by adding *-ed* or *-d* to the present form.

PRINCIPAL PARTS OF REGULAR VERBS			
Present	**Present Participle**	**Past**	**Past Participle**
invent	inventing	invented	(have) invented
allege	alleging	alleged	(have) alleged
frighten	frightening	frightened	(have) frightened

An irregular verb is one whose past and past participle are not formed by adding *-ed* or *-d* to the present form.

PRINCIPAL PARTS OF IRREGULAR VERBS			
Present	**Present Participle**	**Past**	**Past Participle**
cost	costing	cost	(have) cost
catch	catching	caught	(have) caught
leave	leaving	left	(have) left
become	becoming	became	(have) become
break	breaking	broke	(have) broken
swim	swimming	swam	(have) swum

▶ **Exercise 1** **Writing the Principal Parts of Irregular Verbs.** Add the missing principal parts.

EXAMPLE: ring ____*ringing*____ ____*rang*____ ____*(have) rung*____

1. _____ drinking _____ _____
2. grow _____ _____ _____
3. bite _____ _____ _____
4. _____ _____ flew _____
5. _____ hurting _____ _____
6. _____ _____ _____ (have) slain
7. _____ speaking _____ _____
8. draw _____ _____ _____
9. _____ _____ _____ (have) frozen
10. _____ _____ rode _____

▶ **Exercise 2** **Choosing the Correct Form of Irregular Verbs.** Fill in each blank with the correct verb form from those given in parentheses.

EXAMPLE: Tanya has not yet ____*chosen*____ her courses for next year. (chose, chosen)

1. Several large branches have _____ across the driveway. (fell, fallen)
2. I'm not sure I _____ the car door. (shut, shutted, shutten)
3. I have _____ my applications to three colleges. (send, sended, sent)
4. The neighbors _____ a huge party last night. (gave, given)
5. In the course of the experiment, the test tube _____. (burst, busted)

21.1 Verb Tenses (Regular and Irregular Verbs)
• Practice 2

▷ **Exercise 1** **Learning the Principal Parts of Irregular Verbs.** Write the present participle, the past, and the past participle of each verb.

EXAMPLE: become ___*becoming*___ ___*became*___ ___*become*___

1. break _____
2. put _____
3. ring _____
4. teach _____
5. choose _____
6. lay _____
7. spread _____
8. tear _____
9. bite _____
10. shut _____

11. fight _____
12. eat _____
13. swing _____
14. shake _____
15. sing _____
16. bind _____
17. arise _____
18. grind _____
19. shine _____
20. stride _____

▷ **Exercise 2** **Choosing the Correct Forms of Irregular Verbs.** Fill in each blank with the correct verb form from those given in parentheses.

1. It must have _____ into the house last night. (creeped, crept)
2. I have _____ a note for Bob to take to school. (written, wrote)
3. The debris had been _____ onto the shore. (flung, flinged)
4. A Dalmatian _____ into the limousine. (sprang, sprung)
5. The apparition supposedly had _____ a black horse. (ridden, rode)
6. I have _____ to deliver a message. (come, came)
7. Carol had _____ her promise again. (broke, broken)
8. He has always _____ a ball very well. (thrown, throwed)
9. The horse had stumbled, _____, and thrown its rider to the ground. (fallen, fell)
10. I have _____ all the candles out with one breath. (blowed, blown)
11. She has _____ into town for the afternoon. (went, gone)
12. He had _____ before we went to the game. (eaten, ate)
13. As the heat intensified, the windows _____. (busted, burst)
14. You have _____ those jeans all week. (wore, worn)
15. You should have _____ cooler clothes. (brung, brought)
16. I _____ several times at the auction. (bid, bidded)
17. The concert _____ before everyone had arrived. (began, begun)
18. She had _____ a piece of cloth and wrapped his hand. (tore, torn)
19. Cristina _____ alto in the church choir. (sang, sung)
20. He had _____ the pain without a murmur. (bore, borne)
21. The icy rain _____ on the Eskimos' parkas. (freezed, froze)
22. Uncle Marty had _____ all the candy away. (gave, given)
23. She had _____ in the relay race last year. (ran, run)
24. Karen _____ the ball. (catched, caught)
25. He had _____ a compass but forgot to consult it. (taken, took)

21.1 Verb Tenses (Verb Conjugation) • Practice 1

Verb Conjugation A conjugation is a complete list of the singular and plural forms of a verb. A short conjugation lists just the forms that are used with a single pronoun. Note that the verbs used with *you* are also used with *we* and *they*. The verbs used with *she*, likewise, are also used with *he* and *it*.

SHORT CONJUGATIONS

Basic, Progressive, and Emphatic Forms	run (with *I*)	run (with *you*)	run (with *she*)
Present	I run	you run	she runs
Past	I ran	you ran	she ran
Future	I will run	you will run	she will run
Present Perfect	I have run	you have run	she has run
Past Perfect	I had run	you had run	she had run
Future Perfect	I will have run	you will have run	she will have run
Present Progressive	I am running	you are running	she is running
Past Progressive	I was running	you were running	she was running
Future Progressive	I will be running	you will be running	she will be running
Present Perfect Progressive	I have been running	you have been running	she has been running
Past Perfect Progressive	I had been running	you had been running	she had been running
Future Perfect Progressive	I will have been running	you will have been running	she will have been running
Present Emphatic	I do run	you do run	she does run
Past Emphatic	I did run	you did run	she did run

▶ **Exercise 1** **Conjugating Basic and Progressive Forms.** Write a short conjugation for each item.

1. win (with *I*)
2. go (with *he*)
3. ride (with *we*)
4. love (with *they*)

_____ _____ _____ _____
_____ _____ _____ _____
_____ _____ _____ _____
_____ _____ _____ _____
_____ _____ _____ _____
_____ _____ _____ _____
_____ _____ _____ _____
_____ _____ _____ _____
_____ _____ _____ _____
_____ _____ _____ _____
_____ _____ _____ _____
_____ _____ _____ _____
_____ _____ _____ _____
_____ _____ _____ _____

▶ **Exercise 2** **Supplying the Correct Verb Form.** Fill in each blank with the form of the verb given in parentheses.

EXAMPLE: We ____*were hoping*____ for your cooperation. (hope, *past progressive*)

1. Tony _____ a Giants' fan all his life. (be, *present perfect*)

2. We _____ New Mexico this summer. (visit, *future progressive*)

3. You _____ to help us. (promise, *past emphatic*)

4. Tomorrow we _____ here a month. (live, *future perfect progressive*)

5. We _____ soundly in spite of the noise. (sleep, *past*)

21.1 Verb Tenses (Verb Conjugation) • Practice 2

▶ **Exercise 1** **Conjugating Verbs.** Conjugate the verbs below in the forms indicated in parentheses. Use the back of this sheet to complete the first conjugation.

1. plan (basic)

2. break (emphatic)

_____   _____
_____   _____
_____   _____
_____   _____
_____   _____
_____   _____
_____   _____
_____   _____
_____   _____
_____   _____
_____   _____

▶ **Writing Application** **Using Different Tenses.** Use each verb in a sentence of your own.

EXAMPLE: Future perfect of *finish*
        I will have finished the project by tomorrow.

1. Past perfect of *borrow*

_____

2. Present progressive of *land*

_____

3. Future perfect of *spring*

_____

4. Present of *burst*

_____

5. Past progressive of *intend*

_____

6. Future progressive of *wear*

_____

7. Past emphatic of *try*

_____

8. Future of *investigate*

_____

9. Present progressive of *swim*

_____

10. Past of *lose*

_____

Name _____   Date _____

21.2 The Correct Use of Tenses (Present, Past, and Future Time) • Practice 1

Present, Past, and Future Time   The three forms of the present tense show present actions or conditions as well as various continuous actions or conditions. The seven forms that express past time show actions or conditions beginning in the past. The four forms that express future time show future actions or conditions.

USES OF TENSE IN PRESENT TIME		
Verb Forms	**Use**	**Examples**
Present	present event	I *have* a headache.
	recurring event	Lou often *misses* the bus.
	constant event	The sun *rises* in the east.
Pres. Progressive	continuing event	Pam *is putting* the baby to bed.
Pres. Emphatic	emphasized event	We *do need* milk.
USES OF TENSES IN PAST TIME		
Past	completed event	Everyone *was* hungry.
Present Perfect	complete (indefinite time)	Ed *has finished* his homework.
	continuing to present	The owner *has offered* a reward.
Past Perfect	completed before	The snow *had stopped* before we began our trip.
Past Progressive	continuing past event	The wind *was blowing* from the west.
Present Perfect Progressive	continuing to present	The police *have been investigating* for several months.
Past Perfect Progressive	continuous before another past event	Carol *had been studying* when the power went off.
Past Emphatic	emphasized event	I *did give* you the phone message.
USES OF TENSES IN FUTURE TIME		
Future	future event	Dinner *will be* ready in a few minutes.
Future Perfect	future event before another future event	The agent *will have mailed* your tickets before the end of the week.
Future Progressive	continuing future event	The show *will be playing* for another week.
Future Perfect Progressive	continuous before another future event	In January we *will have been living* in this house for seven years.

▶ **Exercise 1**   **Identifying Tenses.**   Underline each verb that shows present time. Circle each verb that shows past time. Put parentheses around verbs that show future time.

EXAMPLE: The press is following the case very closely. _____

1. In her youth, the pianist had studied with a famous composer. _____

2. The committee will have made its decision by tomorrow. _____

3. We did try to reach you last weekend. _____

4. Ed has been studying harder this term. _____

5. Crustaceans have the ability to regenerate lost claws. _____

6. This time next week, we will be lying on the beach in Jamaica. _____

7. A heavy fog was rolling in. _____

8. The travel agent will make all the reservations. _____

9. The contestant had answered only one question by the end of the show. _____

10. The train will be leaving from Track 8. _____

▶ **Exercise 2**   **Identifying Uses of Verbs.**   On the rule following each sentence in Exercise 1, write the use of the verb tense, using the labels in the chart.

EXAMPLE: The press is following the case very closely. *continuing event*

The Correct Use of Tenses (Present, Past, and Future Time) • 77

21.2 The Correct Use of Tenses (Present, Past, and Future Time) • Practice 2

Exercise 1   **Identifying the Uses of Tense in Present Time.**   Identify the use of the verb tense in each sentence, using the labels in the chart on the preceding page.

1. These tight shoes hurt my feet. _____

2. Diane is doing remarkably well on her diet. _____

3. The author had written many short stories by the time he reached his thirtieth
   birthday. _____

4. The sky is becoming overcast. _____

5. Halley's comet returns every seventy-six years. _____

6. I have forgotten most of the details. _____

7. A flight from Chicago will arrive later in the afternoon. _____

8. Jim is in Detroit. _____

9. My father is building a log cabin in the mountains. _____

10. Carolyn reads at least one novel a week. _____

Exercise 2   **Using Tense in Past Time.**   Write the indicated form of each verb in parentheses.

1. I _____ you to deliver these packages. (ask—*past*)

2. Our school _____ the honor system. (adopt—*present perfect*)

3. The students _____ the new film. (discuss—*past progressive*)

4. His hair _____ white for many years. (be—*present perfect*)

5. Alexander Dumas _____ plays before he began writing *The Three Musketeers*.
   (write—*past perfect*)

6. John _____ more diligently this semester. (study—*present perfect progressive*)

7. The angry customer _____ on a refund. (insist—*past emphatic*)

8. Someone _____ a package on his desk. (leave—*past perfect*)

9. Ricky _____ throughout Europe. (travel—*present perfect*)

10. Joan _____ the keys behind the desk. (find—*past*)

Exercise 3   **Using Tense in Future Time.**   Underline the correct verb in parentheses to complete each sentence.

1. By nightfall I (will have planted, will have been planting) over a hundred disease-resistant elms.

2. I (will be, will have been) disappointed if all my friends are away for the summer.

3. If Ms. Ramon teaches this class, her enthusiasm (will motivate, will have motivated) the students.

4. No pets (will have been allowed, will be allowed) in this new condominium.

5. Ginger (will be, will have been) in Brazil next summer.

6. By Tuesday, they (will be exploring, will have been exploring) the coast of Antarctica for nearly a
   month.

7. Tomorrow I (will fly, will have flown) to London.

8. By the time we stop, we (will have been driving, will be driving) over ten hours.

9. The coach told us that we (will practice, will have practiced) on Sunday.

10. The polls cannot say for sure who (will have won, will win) the election.

21.2 The Correct Use of Tenses (Sequence of Tenses, Modifiers That Help Clarify Time) • Practice 1

Sequence of Tenses   When showing a sequence of events, do not shift tenses unnecessarily. The tense of a verb in a subordinate clause should follow logically from the tense of the main verb.

SEQUENCE OF TENSES		
Main Verb	**Subordinate Verb**	**Type of Events**
I *know*	that you *are going* to Boston.	Simultaneous events
I *know*	that you *will help.*	Sequential events
I *knew*	that I *was* not wrong.	Simultaneous events
I *knew*	that the phone *had rung.*	Sequential events
We *will see*	if he *knows* the answer.	Simultaneous events (present used as future)
You *will see*	that you *have chosen* well.	Sequential events

The form of a participle or infinitive should set up a logical time sequence in relation to the main verb.

SIMULTANEOUS EVENTS		
Present	*Hearing* a siren, we *pull* over.	I *want to pay* you a visit.
Past	*Hearing* a siren, we *pulled* over.	I *wanted to pay* you a visit.
Future	*Hearing* a siren, we *will pull* over.	I *will want to pay* you a visit.
SEQUENTIAL EVENTS		
Present	*Having eaten*, we *leave* the table.	We *are* glad *to have been asked.*
Past	*Having eaten*, we *left* the table.	We *were* glad *to have been asked.*
Future	*Having eaten*, we *will leave* the table.	We *will be* glad *to have been asked.*

Modifiers That Help Clarify Tense   Use modifiers that indicate time to help clarify tense.

▶ **Exercise 1**   **Using the Correct Tense.**   Begin or complete each of the following sentences with words of your own choice. Make sure that the verb you use works well with the other verb.

EXAMPLE: We will go to school after _____*we have eaten breakfast.*_____

1. John feels that _____.

2. _____ that we had more time to complete this project.

3. I wrote to Steven while _____.

4. Tina sat at her desk and _____.

5. It has been several years since _____.

▶ **Exercise 2**   **Adding Modifiers to Help Clarify Tense.**   Complete each of the sentences below by writing a modifier that clarifies time.

EXAMPLE: My parents are going to Europe _____*next month*_____.

1. Phyllis has asked me to help her with her math homework _____.

2. The Tiers won the World Series _____.

3. My English class is _____ very interesting.

4. The _____ winters have been very long and cold.

5. _____, my father wakes up at 6:00.

21.2 The Correct Use of Tenses (Sequence of Tenses, Modifiers That Help Clarify Time) • Practice 2

▶ **Exercise 1** Using the Correct Forms of Subordinate Verbs, Participles, and Infinitives. Rewrite each sentence, following the instructions in parentheses.

1. Our captain chose John for the team. (Add a phrase containing the perfect participle of *see*.)

_____

2. Eventually he wrote to his congressman. (Add a subordinate clause containing the past perfect of *try*.)

_____

3. My plan is that I will leave before the evening train departs. (Change *will leave* to a perfect infinitive.)

_____

4. She is afraid. (Add a subordinate clause containing the present perfect of *hear*.)

_____

5. Joel liked watching the storm clouds gather. (Change *watching* to a present infinitive.)

_____

6. The ballerina retired gracefully. (Add a phrase containing the perfect participle of *dance*.)

_____

7. Lisa is working industriously at her new job as a law clerk in the city. (Add a subordinate clause containing the present of *earn*.)

_____

8. She was glad she had gained experience in the field of electronics. (Change *gained* to a perfect infinitive.)

_____

9. The conductor listened to the cacophony in angry silence. (Add a phrase containing the perfect participle of *expect*.)

_____

10. You will notice the difference. (Add a subordinate clause containing the present perfect of *observe*.)

_____

▶ **Exercise 2** Correcting Errors in Tense. Rewrite the following paragraph, correcting unnecessary shifts in tense.

(1) In the mid-1870's, General George Custer was receiving permission to explore the possibility of establishing a military post in the Black Hills. (2) The Northern Plains tribes were owning the territory, which, according to rumor, is rich in gold. (3) With him Custer takes geologists who did find this precious metal. (4) Soon after, hordes of prospectors have invaded the land, violating the treaty. (5) The Indians had objected and the government was sending soldiers, supposedly to force the miners' departure.

_____

_____

_____

_____

_____

_____

21.3 The Subjunctive Mood • Practice 1

The Correct Use of the Subjunctive Mood   Use the subjunctive mood (1) in clauses beginning with *if* or *that* to express an idea contrary to fact or (2) in clauses beginning with *that* to express a request, a demand, or a proposal.

USES OF THE SUBJUNCTIVE	
Ideas Contrary to Fact	**Requests, Demands, Proposals**
I wish that today *were* Friday.	They requested that he *leave*.
If I *were* rich, I would buy a yacht.	I demand that the package *be* ready.

Auxiliary Verbs That Help Express the Subjunctive Mood   *Could, would,* or *should* can be used to help a verb express the subjunctive mood. In the chart below, sentences on the left contain the past subjunctive form of the verb *be: were*. Sentences on the right have been reworded with *could* and *would*.

THE SUBJUNCTIVE MOOD EXPRESSED THROUGH AUXILIARY VERBS	
If you *were* to help me, I would finish by noon.	If you *could* help me, I would finish by noon.
If you *were* more careful, the paint would not have spilled.	If you *would* be more careful, the paint would not have spilled.

> **Exercise 1**   **Using the Subjunctive Mood.**   Rewrite each sentence, changing the verb that should be in the subjunctive mood to its correct form.

EXAMPLE: If I was in your place, I would be nervous.
        If I were in your place, I would be nervous.

1. It is essential that the committee keeps its findings secret.

   _____

2. The law requires that you are eighteen in order to vote.

   _____

3. The librarian asks that all books are back before vacation.

   _____

4. I wish that I was going along.

   _____

5. If I was rich, I could afford a yacht.

   _____

> **Exercise 2**   **Using Auxiliary Verbs to Express the Subjunctive Mood.**   Each of the following sentences contains a subjunctive verb used correctly. Rewrite each sentence, using an auxiliary verb to help express the subjunctive mood.

EXAMPLE: If you were to leave, I would be unhappy.
        If you should leave, I would be unhappy.

1. If I were neater, I would not have to rewrite this paper.

   _____

2. The kitchen would be cooler if you were to turn off the oven.

   _____

3. If you were to go to New York City, what would you want to see?

   _____

4. I would make a roast if you were to stay for dinner.

   _____

5. We would not be so rushed if you were to start earlier.

   _____

21.3 The Subjunctive Mood • Practice 2

▶ **Exercise 1**   **Using the Subjunctive Mood.**   Rewrite each sentence, changing the verb that should be in the subjunctive mood to the subjunctive mood.

EXAMPLE: She wished that she was rich.

_____ *She wished that she were rich.* _____

1. He wishes that he was a few inches taller.

_____

2. The judge insists that the reporter remains outside.

_____

3. I prefer that she waits in the lobby.

_____

4. They stared at me as if I was a ghost.

_____

5. I move that the minutes from the meeting are read.

_____

▶ **Exercise 2**   **Using Auxiliary Verbs to Express the Subjunctive Mood.**   Rewrite each sentence, using an auxiliary verb to express the subjunctive mood.

EXAMPLE: He demanded that the ransom be paid.

_____ *He demanded that the ransom should be paid.* _____

1. This meeting would run more smoothly if he were friendlier.

_____

2. She wishes that Kate were relaxed and comfortable.

_____

3. If Noreen were to invite you, would you attend?

_____

4. The house would be warmer if you were to heat it better.

_____

5. I would go to the library if I were to get home earlier.

_____

▶ **Writing Application**   **Writing Sentences in the Subjunctive Mood.**   Write a sentence using each item, making sure each sentence contains a verb in the subjunctive mood.

1. require that

_____

2. I suggest

_____

3. as if

_____

4. that she be

_____

21.4 Voice • Practice 1

Active and Passive Voice   Voice is a form of a verb that shows whether the subject is performing the action. A verb is active if its subject performs the action. A verb is passive if its action is performed upon the subject. A passive verb is made from a form of *be* plus the past participle of a transitive verb.

Active Voice	Passive Voice
The early frost *damaged* the crops.	The crops *were damaged* by early frost.

Using Active and Passive Voice   Use the active voice whenever possible. Use the passive voice to emphasize the receiver of an action rather than the performer of an action. Also use the passive to point out the receiver of an action whenever the performer is not important or not easily identified.

Emphasizing the Receiver	Performer Unknown or Unimportant
Only Reggie *was amazed* by her actions after class.	This cheese *was imported* from Denmark. One name *was omitted* from the list.

▶ **Exercise 1**   **Distinguishing Between Active and Passive Voice.**   After each sentence, write *active* or *passive* to describe the verb.

EXAMPLE: The ingredients should be blended slowly. ____*passive*____

1. Four large pizzas were delivered to us by mistake._____

2. The new law protects consumers from unscrupulous dealers. _____

3. After some argument, Sandy agreed to rewrite the last act. _____

4. The nominee was elected by a voice vote. _____

5. The wind blew down several trees in the neighborhood. _____

▶ **Exercise 2**   **Using the Active and Passive Voice.**   Write *weak* after each of the passive sentences below that would be more forceful in the active voice. Write *acceptable* after each sentence that makes good use of the passive voice.

EXAMPLE: Flight 21 has been delayed because of bad weather. ____*acceptable*____
          The party was enjoyed by everyone. ____*weak*____

1. Browning's first book of poems was published anonymously. _____

2. My composition was given a C by Mrs. Morrison. _____

3. Tryouts will be held on Friday at 4 P.M. _____

4. The performance will be repeated tomorrow night. _____

5. The shoreline was battered by Hurricane Ida. _____

21.4 Voice • Practice 2

▶ **Exercise 1** **Distinguishing Between the Active and Passive Voice.** Identify each verb as *active* or *passive.*

1. The winning essays were selected for their originality and lucidity. _____

2. Our bread truck delivers as quickly as possible. _____

3. Murphy has been chosen for the task. _____

4. Carefully he removed the glass from the picture window. _____

5. They prepared for any eventuality. _____

6. Fry the eggs on one side only. _____

7. The last sentence in the contract has been reworded. _____

8. Formal gowns will be worn at the dance. _____

9. My reflection stared back at me from the mirror. _____

10. The dog was being rewarded for his quick response. _____

11. She threw a handful of herbs into the pot. _____

12. Hundreds of applications were received. _____

13. His numerous complaints are being ignored. _____

14. These pants have shrunk at least two sizes. _____

15. A single guppy energetically swam around the large tank. _____

16. Pools of water were lying beneath the broken spouts. _____

17. The tigers will have been fed by noon. _____

18. Kay's seeming indifference is misconstrued by her friends. _____

19. They discussed their views with the President. _____

20. A cold compress was quickly applied to the wound. _____

▶ **Exercise 2** **Using the Active Voice.** Rewrite each of the ten sentences in Exercise 1 that have passive voice verbs. Change or add words as necessary in order to put each verb into the active voice.

1. _____

2. _____

3. _____

4. _____

5. _____

6. _____

7. _____

8. _____

9. _____

10. _____

22.1 Case (The Three Cases) • Practice 1

The Three Cases Case is the form of a noun or pronoun that indicates its use in a sentence. The three cases are the nominative, the objective, and the possessive. Pronouns have different forms for all three cases. Nouns change form only in the possessive case.

Case	Use in Sentence	Forms
Nominative	subject, predicate nominative	I; you; he, she, it; we; they; player, players
Objective	direct object, indirect object, object of a preposition	me; you; him, her, it; us; them; player, players
Possessive	to show ownership	my, mine; your, yours; his; her, hers; its; our, ours; their, theirs; player's, players'

▶ **Exercise 1** **Identifying Case.** Write the case of each underlined noun or pronoun in the following sentences.

EXAMPLE: The sandwich with a toothpick in it is yours. _____*possessive*_____

1. Kevin borrowed some money from Jake and me. _____

2. We promised to visit again soon. _____

3. The first person we asked was she. _____

4. The producers' investment earned them a handsome profit. _____

5. Alice maintains that the idea was hers alone. _____

6. Their right to the property is incontestable. _____

7. The hot-air balloon lifted its cargo high above the spectators. _____

8. Did you follow Aunt Vera's recipe exactly? _____

9. Did you buy these pies or make them yourself? _____

10. The house with the flagpole in front is ours. _____

▶ **Exercise 2** **Recognizing the Use of Nouns and Pronouns.** After each number, write the use of each underlined noun or pronoun in Exercise 1: *subject, predicate nominative, direct object, indirect object, object of a preposition,* or *to show ownership.*

EXAMPLE: _____*to show ownership*_____

1. _____

2. _____

3. _____

4. _____

5. _____

6. _____

7. _____

8. _____

9. _____

10. _____

22.1 **Case** (The Three Cases) • **Practice 2**

▷ **Exercise 1** **Identifying Case.** Write the case of each underlined pronoun. Then write its use.

EXAMPLE: The letter was addressed to <u>me</u>. _____objective (object of a preposition)_____

1. <u>My</u> parents are strict and never waver in their decisions. _____
2. My friends and I gave <u>him</u> a pet snake. _____
3. His most receptive listeners were <u>we</u> and they. _____
4. Mrs. Stapleton gave <u>us</u> an interesting assignment. _____
5. The company has decided to hire <u>her</u>. _____
6. Visiting the botanical gardens was <u>his</u> idea. _____
7. Their references establish <u>them</u> as good credit risks. _____
8. The caretaker and his wife's cottage are empty; <u>they</u> apparently have departed without notice.

   _____
9. I will send <u>them</u> a map to our new house. _____
10. This restaurant will not let <u>us</u> enter without jackets. _____
11. The prettiest garden is <u>theirs</u>. _____
12. <u>You</u> must accept my apology. _____
13. <u>Yours</u> is not the best answer, nor is it the worst. _____
14. The school awarded <u>her</u> a scholarship. _____
15. The only one who qualified was <u>she</u>. _____
16. <u>Their</u> assimilation into the new culture was very quick. _____
17. Without hesitating, <u>she</u> answered all of the questions. _____
18. The elevator ride left <u>me</u> with an upset stomach. _____
19. <u>He</u> dazzled the audience with his magical feats. _____
20. No one knew how <u>they</u> had got inside the building. _____

▷ **Exercise 2** **Using Pronouns in Different Cases.** Complete each sentence by writing in the blank an appropriate pronoun in the case given in parentheses.

EXAMPLE: We said goodbye to ___her___ at the airport. (objective)

1. _____ have been hoping to receive a letter from him. (nominative)
2. Singing is easy for you, but not for _____. (objective)
3. It has always been _____ ambition to study at that ballet school. (possessive)
4. _____ aggressive manner made him a natural for football. (possessive)
5. _____ has always been an amateur figure skater. (nominative)
6. These blueprints were drawn by _____. (objective)
7. _____ cannot guarantee the accuracy of these numbers. (nominative)
8. It is not up to _____ to tell you what to do. (objective)
9. If it hadn't been for _____ advice, Sonja never would have taken that job.
   (possessive)
10. These books are mine, and those books are _____. (possessive)

22.1 Case (The Nominative Case, The Objective Case)
• Practice 1

The Nominative Case   Use the nominative case for the subject of a verb, for a predicate nominative, and for the pronoun at the beginning of a nominative absolute.

USES OF NOMINATIVE PRONOUNS	
Present	*She* ordered a pizza with anchovies.
Predicate Nominative	The man to the right of the microphone is *he*.
Nominative Absolute	*We* knowing the answer, Donna looked to us for help.

The Objective Case   Use the objective case for the object of any verb, preposition, or verbal or for the subject of an infinitive.

USES OF OBJECTIVE PRONOUNS	
Direct Object	Lou told Ann and *me* about the party.
	Finding *us* at home, the Holts stayed for a visit.
Indirect Object	Pam found Mom and *me* a place to stay.
Object of a Preposition	The house seems empty without *them*.
Subject of an Infinitive	Did you ask *her* to make a centerpiece?

▶ **Exercise 1**   **Identifying Pronouns in the Nominative Case.**   Circle the pronoun in the nominative case to complete each sentence. Then indicate the use of the pronoun by writing *S* (subject), *PN* (predicate nominative), or *NA* (pronoun in nominative absolute).

EXAMPLE: The old woman carrying the basket of flowers is ((she), her). ____*PN*____

1. It was (she, her) whom the boss promoted. _____

2. Is the town's oldest couple (they, them) or the Halberts? _____

3. My father and (he, him) have been friends since high school. _____

4. (He, Him) being short of funds, Lenny was eager for any job at all. _____

5. Both her sister and (she, her) have often sat for the Newtons. _____

▶ **Exercise 2**   **Identifying Pronouns in the Objective Case.**   Circle the pronoun in the objective case to complete each sentence. Then indicate the pronoun's use as *DO* (direct object), *IO* (indirect object), *OP* (object of a preposition, or *SI* (subject of an infinitive).

EXAMPLE: Grandma asked (I, (me)) to set the table. ____*SI*____

1. Please tell (we, us) about the game. _____

2. My friends left for the game without (I, me). _____

3. Pa ordered (he, him) to feed the horses. _____

4. The committee asked Tom and (she, her) to give their reports. _____

5. We brought Grandpa and (she, her) a gift from our trip. _____

6. Looking at all the pies, I had trouble choosing among (they, them). _____

7. Their parents did everything to encourage Anna and (she, her). _____

8. Will their parents allow (they, them) to come with us? _____

9. Please ask (she, her) to join us for dinner. _____

10. The coach gave (I, me) another chance to try out. _____

22.1 Case (The Nominative Case, The Objective Case)
• Practice 2

▶ **Exercise 1**   **Identifying Pronouns in the Nominative Case.**   Underline the pronoun in the nominative case to complete each sentence. Then write the use of the pronoun.

EXAMPLE: The driver of the car was (he, him). _____predicate nominative_____

1. Reggie and (she, her) will pay the bill. _____

2. I think (he, him) will be the best judge. _____

3. Her complexion shone with good health, (she, her) having thrived in the cold climate. _____

4. Cautiously, Grace and (them, they) crossed the street. _____

5. History will prove that the best president was (him, he). _____

6. (We, Us) taxpayers will have to pay for this project. _____

7. Never was there a better gymnast than (him, he). _____

8. The teacher said that he and (I, me) will count the votes. _____

9. Kevin and (I, me) are going to Maine this weekend. _____

10. (We, Us) entrepreneurs appreciate the risks in the venture. _____

▶ **Exercise 2**   **Using Pronouns in the Nominative Case.**   Write a nominative pronoun in the blank to complete each sentence. Then, in the blank following the sentence, write the use of the pronoun.

1. Pat and _____ shoveled the snow from the sidewalk. _____

2. Did Francisco and _____ organize the block party? _____

3. The oldest members of the family are grandfather and _____. _____

4. People knew J. P. Morgan was a philanthropist, _____ having endowed the Pierpont Morgan Library. _____

5. _____ are the leading publishers of children's literature. _____

6. Before signing, _____ read the small print carefully. _____

7. The worst archers at the field trials were Gary and _____. _____

8. Late for a meeting, _____ quickly hailed a taxi. _____

9. The most diligent students are Edith and _____. _____

10. Jacques serves braised veal that _____ gourmets appreciate. _____

▶ **Exercise 3**   **Identifying Pronouns in the Objective Case.**   Underline the pronoun in the objective case to complete each sentence. Then write the use of the pronoun.

1. Asking (him, he) for a raise will not be easy. _____

2. Africa's diamond mines provide for (they, them). _____

3. They make (us, we) waiters wear uniforms. _____

4. The guilt haunting (him, he) was unrelenting. _____

5. The librarian gave (us, we) boys invaluable help. _____

6. I forgot to inform (her, she) of her legal rights. _____

7. The landscape challenged (we, us) backpackers. _____

8. A low flying bat gave Lynn and (I, me) a moment of panic. _____

9. Our sister always wanted (us, we) to take her with us. _____

10. The fear paralyzing Marion and (I, me) was irrational. _____

22.1 Case (Errors to Avoid with Possessive Pronouns)
• Practice 1

Errors to Avoid with Possessive Pronouns   Use a possessive pronoun before a gerund.

POSSESSIVE PRONOUNS
The committee authorized *her* buying the equipment. She appreciated *their* responding so quickly.

Do not use an apostrophe with a possessive pronoun since it already indicates ownership. Do not confuse a possessive pronoun with a contraction.

Possessive Pronoun	Contraction
The dog was pacing up and down in front of *its* dog house.	I wonder when *it's* going to stop raining.

Exercise 1   **Using Pronouns in the Possessive Case.**   Write the correct word from the parentheses to complete each sentence.

EXAMPLE: Dad complains about ___*my*___ playing the stereo so loud. (me, my)

1. The coach encouraged _____ entering the competition. (him, his)
2. The best proposal of all was _____. (theirs, their's)
3. The cause of _____ feeling so awful was simply motion sickness. (him, his)
4. Each of the tables has _____ own centerpiece. (its, it's)
5. My brother was nervous about _____ teaching him to drive. (me, my)
6. The first house on the left is _____. (hers, her's)
7. Surely the hostess appreciated _____ bringing the dessert. (you, your)
8. Dad agreed to _____ painting the house. (them, their)
9. No one objected to _____ inviting a friend along. (us, our)
10. Please take the rolls out of the oven when _____ done. (their, they're)

Exercise 2   **Using All Three Cases of Pronouns.**   Write the correct pronoun from the parentheses to complete each sentence.

EXAMPLE: My family approves of ___*my*___ going away to school. (me, my)

1. My brother and _____ have shared a room for years. (I, me)
2. _____ teaching Andy how to play baseball pleased us. (Him, His)
3. Dad wanted Heather and _____ to wait for the delivery. (she, her)
4. A barred owl can hunt in total darkness using only _____ hearing. (it's, its)
5. Jack never would have finished without help from Ann and _____. (I, me)
6. Which of the collages is _____? (your's, yours)
7. If anyone deserves to win, it is _____. (she, her)
8. It was _____ speaking during the report that angered the teacher. (him, his)
9. _____ deciding to move came as a surprise to us. (They're, Their)
10. Neither Janice nor _____ heard anything unusual. (she, her)

22.1 Case (Errors to Avoid with Possessive Pronouns)
• Practice 2

▶ **Exercise 1** **Using Pronouns in the Possessive Case.** Write the correct word from the parentheses to complete each sentence.

1. The car's noise made _____ approach easy to detect. (its, it's)

2. _____ experience makes them valuable employees. (Their, They're)

3. _____ light tap on the door wasn't heard by us. (Your, You're)

4. This house has been well maintained, and _____ in a desirable location. (its, it's)

5. Steep losses precipitated _____ selling the business. (me, my)

6. The winning ticket is _____. (yours, your's)

7. Frightened by _____ raving, I edged toward the door. (him, his)

8. _____ is a radically new approach. (Hers, Her's)

9. They dislike _____ meddling in these matters. (your, you)

10. _____ invited to attend the premier. (Your, You're)

11. _____ going to have a wonderful time this weekend. (Your, You're)

12. The crocodile had just _____ eyes poking out of the water. (its, it's)

13. It was _____ confidence that made him so attractive. (him, his)

14. The most valuable contributions to this project were _____. (hers, her's)

15. Because of _____ foolishness, we all have to pay. (they're, their)

▶ **Writing Application** **Writing Sentences with Nominative, Objective, and Possessive Pronouns.** Use the following instructions to write sentences of your own.

1. Use *us* as the subject of an infinitive.

_____

2. Use *my* before a gerund.

_____

3. Use *yours* and *ours* as a compound predicate nominative.

_____

4. Use *she* as the subject of a nominative absolute construction.

_____

5. Use *he and I* as a compound predicate nominative.

_____

6. Use *I* as the subject of a nominative absolute.

_____

7. Use *her* as an indirect object.

_____

8. Use *him and me* as the compound subject of an infinitive.

_____

9. Use *you and I* as a compound predicate nominative.

_____

10. Use *our* before a gerund.

_____

22.2 Special Problems with Pronouns • Practice 1

Using *Who* and *Whom* Correctly   Learn to recognize the various cases of *who* and *whom* and to use them correctly in sentences. *Who* and *whoever* are in the nominative case and are used as subjects and predicate nominatives. *Whom* and *whomever* are in the objective case and are used as direct objects and objects of prepositions. For the possessive case, use *whose*, not *who's*.

THE CASES OF *WHO* AND *WHOM*	
Nominative	*Who* gave you that information?
	Leave the package with *whoever* is at home.
	Everyone wondered *who* the winner would be.
Objective	*Whom* will you ask?
	Have you apologized to *whomever* you offended?
	Whom have you shown the pictures to?
Possessive	*Whose* house is big enough for the party?

Pronouns in Elliptical Clauses   In elliptical clauses beginning with *than* or *as*, use the form of the pronoun that you would use if the clause were fully stated.

Elliptical Clauses	Completed Clauses
Henry studied harder than _____?_____	Henry studied harder than *I* [did].
The game meant more to Sue than _____?_____ .	The game meant more to Sue than [it meant to] *me*.

▶ **Exercise 1**   **Using *Who* and *Whom* Correctly.**   Complete each sentence by writing *who, whom, whoever,* or *whomever*.

EXAMPLE: _____*Whoever*_____ is on duty will accept the delivery.

1. We will accept help from _____ offers it.

2. The student _____ you reported has been suspended.

3. From _____ did you get your information?

4. Phil is a player _____ always does his best.

5. _____ told you that story has the facts mixed up.

6. I wonder _____ the mayor will support.

7. Did Jack say _____ was having the party?

8. _____ will the board nominate as treasurer?

9. Everyone _____ met Angela admired her.

10. Are there any applicants _____ we haven't seen yet?

▶ **Exercise 2**   **Using Pronouns in Elliptical Clauses.**   Complete each sentence with an appropriate pronoun from the parentheses.

EXAMPLE: My sister is a better musician than _____*I*_____ . (I, me)

1. The test was harder for Carol than _____ . (I, me)

2. Can you make better brownies than _____ ? (she, her)

3. Success means more to some people than _____ . (we, us)

4. Jenny worked as hard as _____ . (they, them)

5. Lou has a newer bike than _____ . (he, him)

22.2 Special Problems with Pronouns • Practice 2

▶ **Exercise 1**   Using *Who* and *Whom* Correctly in Questions.   Underline the correct pronoun to complete each sentence.

1. (Who, Whom) volunteered to take the children to the park?
2. (Who, Whom) did Elizabeth Bennett ultimately marry?
3. (Who, whom) did they blame?
4. (Who, Whom) did she expect to find at home?
5. To (who, whom) should I direct my question?
6. (Who, whom) was the last to leave the classroom?
7. (Who, Whom) are you asking to the dance Saturday?
8. From (who, whom) are you expecting a call?
9. (Who, Whom) is the manager of this store?
10. (Who, Whom) did the President appoint as the ambassador?

▶ **Exercise 2**   Using *Who* and *Whom* Correctly in Clauses.   Underline the subordinate clause in each sentence. Then indicate how the form of *who* or *whom* is used.

EXAMPLE: She wants to know who will be coming.   *subject*

1. I don't know who won the election yesterday. _____
2. You should always respond to whoever challenges your honesty. _____
3. His pranks are played only on people whom he likes. _____
4. Anyone who likes tennis will also like this game. _____
5. Mercury was the god who, I think, carried messages. _____
6. I would like to thank whoever sent the anonymous gift. _____
7. Your brusque manner annoys whomever you approach. _____
8. That young man is a talented gymnast whom I admire. _____
9. It is Matthew who plays lead guitar in the band. _____
10. We will help whoever applies for financial aid. _____

▶ **Exercise 3**   Identifying the Correct Pronoun in Elliptical Clauses.   Rewrite each sentence, choosing one of the pronouns in parentheses and completing the elliptical clause.

EXAMPLE: They have a larger house than (we, us).
        They have a larger house than we do.

1. You are less skilled in gymnastics than (she, her).

_____

2. Carla works as hard as (we, us).

_____

3. My friend enjoyed your company more than (I, me).

_____

4. These chores are more of a bother to me than to (he, him).

_____

5. Henry was friendlier to her than (I, me).

_____

23.1 Subject and Verb Agreement (The Number of Nouns, Pronouns, and Verbs; Singular and Plural Subjects)

• Practice 1

The Number of Nouns, Pronouns and Verbs Number refers to the two forms of a word: singular and plural. Singular words indicate one; plural words indicate more than one.

NUMBER OF WORDS			
Part of Speech	Singular	Plural	Singular or Plural
Nouns	analogy mouse	analogies mice	trout, reindeer, sheep
Pronouns	I, he, she, it	we, they	you
Verbs	am, is, was has, does, eats		(you) are, were (we, you, they) are, were (I, you) have, do, eat (we, you, they) have, do, eat

Singular and Plural Subject A singular subject must have a singular verb. A plural subject must have a plural verb. A phrase or clause that interrupts a subject and its verb does not affect its subject-verb agreement.

SUBJECT-VERB AGREEMENT	
Singular	Plural
He plays basketball.	We play touch football.
The girl setting up the chairs is Ann.	The people helping her are ushers.

The antecedent of a relative pronoun determines its agreement with a verb.

Plural Antecedent	Singular Antecedent
He is one of those *people* who never rest.	He is the only *one* of those people who never rests.

▶ **Exercise 1**   **Determining the Number of Words.**   Write *S* (singular), *P* (plural), or *both*.

EXAMPLE: you ____both____

1. she _____
2. deer _____
3. has found _____
4. island _____
5. geese _____

6. open _____
7. moose _____
8. departs _____
9. learn _____
10. became _____

▶ **Exercise 2**   **Making Subjects and Verbs Agree.**   Complete each sentence by writing the verb form from parentheses that agrees with the subject.

EXAMPLE: The message from Grandma and Grandpa ____is____ on the desk. (is, are)

1. Recent heavy frosts _____ ruined the citrus crops. (has, have)
2. Mary is the only one of the swimmers who _____ a chance to make the all-state team. (has, have)
3. Our teacher, along with several others, _____ judging the essays. (is, are)
4. Which of the scouts is the one who _____ the map? (has, have)
5. The windows on the north side _____ thermal glass. (has, have)

23.1 Subject and Verb Agreement (The Number of Nouns, Pronouns, and Verbs; Singular and Plural Subjects) • Practice 2

▶ Exercise 1 **Determining the Number of Nouns, Pronouns, and Verbs.** Identify each item as *singular, plural,* or *both.*

EXAMPLE: explodes ___*singular*___

1. volcano _____
2. speaks _____
3. am _____
4. puddles _____
5. you _____
6. bakes _____
7. is _____

8. they _____
9. behave _____
10. memories _____
11. ivy _____
12. are _____
13. vitamins _____
14. will be _____

15. tells _____
16. meteorite _____
17. has fallen _____
18. was skating _____
19. have _____
20. tried _____

▶ Exercise 2 **Making Subjects Agree with Their Verbs.** Underline the verb in parentheses that agrees with the subject of each sentence.

1. Her powerful grip (results, result) from much exercising.
2. A gravel driveway (provides, provide) better traction.
3. Dark blue (goes, go) well with most other colors.
4. Seen through a microscope, the snowflake's lacy pattern (fills, fill) us with wonder.
5. They sometimes (provokes, provoke) me to anger.

▶ Exercise 3 **Making Separated Subjects and Verbs Agree.** Underline the verb in parentheses that agrees with the subject of each sentence.

1. In the park a crumbling pavilion used for concerts (evokes, evoke) memories of the past.
2. Turpentine, derived from coniferous trees, (is, are) used to clean messy paint spills.
3. This casserole, which is made with beef and various vegetables, (serves, serve) six people.
4. Her only piece of jewelry, an unusual pendant made with tiny seashells, (is, are) hanging from her neck.
5. These easy exercises, along with the one described in that book, (is, are) designed to relax you.

▶ Exercise 4 **Making Relative Pronouns Agree with Their Verbs.** Underline the verb in parentheses that agrees with the subject of each subordinate clause.

1. These games of chance, which often (costs, cost) players a fortune, will be investigated by the district attorney.
2. Brandy is the only one out of the twenty dogs in the obedience class that (ignores, ignore) every command.
3. The orchestra will play a new medley of songs that (appeals, appeal) to most audiences.
4. Jeanette is the strongest of the survivors who (was, were) trapped in the cave.
5. The collection of poems, which (was, were) not favorably reviewed, won two awards nevertheless.

23.1 Subject and Verb Agreement (Compound Subjects) • Practice 1

Compound Subjects   Two or more singular subjects joined by *or* or *nor* must have a singular verb. Two or more plural subjects joined by *or* or *nor* must have a plural verb. If one or more singular subjects are joined to one or more plural subjects by *or* or *nor*, the subject closest to the verb determines agreement. A compound subject joined by *and* is generally plural. Exceptions occur when the parts of a compound subject equal one thing or when the word *each* or *every* comes before the compound subject.

AGREEMENT WITH COMPOUND SUBJECTS	
Joined by *or* or *nor*	The ambassador or another diplomat gladly *receives* visitors. Neither the President nor his staff members *are* attending. Neither cookies nor a candy bar *is* a healthful snack. Either fruit or vegetables *are* preferable.
Joined by *and*	Hemingway and Fitzgerald *were* friends in Paris. Chicken, meat, and fish *spoil* quickly if not refrigerated. Pancakes and sausage *is* the breakfast special. Each junior and senior *was* given a chance to try out.

▶ **Exercise 1**   **Compound Subjects Joined by *Or* or *Nor*.**   Write the verb form from parentheses that agrees with the subject in each sentence.

EXAMPLE: A bed roll or a sleeping bag ____*is*____ essential. (is, are)

1. Brioche or Beef Wellington _____ patience to make. (takes, take)
2. Neither they nor she _____ any intention of going. (has, have)
3. A plant or a flower arrangement _____ a touch of color. (adds, add)
4. Pasta, potato, or a salad _____ each entree. (accompanies, accompany)
5. Neither sheets nor a blanket _____ on the guest-room bed. (was, were)
6. Kevin, Tina, or Len _____ a copy of the article. (has, have)
7. Air conditioning or power steering _____ extra. (costs, cost)
8. Either custard or fruit _____ a nutritious dessert. (makes, make)
9. Neither Paula nor her children _____ to the neighbors. (speaks, speak)
10. Candles or a flashlight _____ with this job. (helps, help)

▶ **Exercise 2**   **Compound Subjects Joined by *And*.**   Write the verb form from parentheses that agrees with the subject in each sentence.

EXAMPLE: Cream cheese and lox ____*is*____ a popular deli item. (is, are)

1. Coral reefs and sudden squalls _____ serious hazards to small craft. (is, are)
2. Socks and sweaters _____ in that drawer. (goes, go)
3. Each boy and girl _____ given a favor to take home. (was, were)
4. Both Uncle Ben and Aunt Ella _____ on selling the house. (agrees, agree)
5. The hotel and some shops _____ at the end of the summer. (closes, close)
6. The park and the shopping mall _____ assets to the town. (is, are)
7. Fish and chips _____ a popular meal in British pubs. (is, are)
8. Scissors and paper _____ all that you need to make this. (is, are)
9. Every parent and child on the block _____ helped with the project. (has, have)
10. Both my sister and I _____ cooking. (enjoys, enjoy)

23.1 Subject and Verb Agreement (Compound Subjects) • Practice 2

Exercise 1 **Making Compound Subjects Agree with Their Verbs.** Underline the verb in parentheses that agrees with the subject of each sentence.

1. Each crack and crevice (was, were) filled with cement.

2. The many days of waiting and weeks of uncertainty (has, have) kept Marian in an anxious state.

3. Several dented helmets and a few shattered swords (was, were) found strewn across the ancient battlefield.

4. Glass, wood, tile, or other materials (is, are) used to create beautiful mosaics.

5. Coal or wood (is, are) burned in this stove.

6. Probably neither Jupiter nor the other outer planets (is, are) capable of sustaining life.

7. A hammer and a screwdriver (is, are) all you will need.

8. Thrilling rides and an exciting midway (draws, draw) people to the annual fair.

9. Neither threats nor coaxing (causes, cause) Art to be swayed from a decision.

10. Ham and eggs (is, are) my favorite breakfast.

11. Several household utensils and a bronze cauldron (has, have) been recovered from the burial mound.

12. Neither redwoods nor giant sequoias (grows, grow) in this part of the country.

13. The cost of the eye examination and the price of new glasses (was, were) paid for by my parents.

14. Leather coats or down jackets (is, are) being worn this year.

15. Every table and chair in this house (was, were) built by my great-grandfather.

16. A book or a magazine (helps, help) to pass the time spent on the bus.

17. Both the children and their nanny (was, were) exhausted.

18. Either expertly applied paint or varnish (has, have) given a professional look to these wooden dressers.

19. Either the elevator or the escalators (takes, take) you there.

20. Beside the fireplace two calico cats and a spotted dog (was, were) waiting for our return.

Exercise 2 **Making Compound Subjects Agree with Their Verbs.** Complete each sentence by writing the form of the verb in parentheses that agrees with the subject.

EXAMPLE: Either rain showers or cloudy weather is forecast for tomorrow. (is, are)

1. Alligators and crocodiles _____ alike in many ways. (is, are)

2. Wes and Wally _____ the cooking at the barbecue. (was doing, were doing)

3. Each rubber band and paper clip _____ by the office manager. (was counted, were counted)

4. Tenth-graders, eleventh-graders, and twelfth-graders _____ in attendance at the assembly. (was, were)

5. The athletes and the coach _____ your kind donations. (appreciate, appreciates)

6. Neither the dancers nor the director _____ how to operate the lights. (know, knows)

7. Either board games or dancing _____ the children entertained during rainy weather. (keep, keeps)

8. Beads or buttons _____ the design very nicely. (complete, completes)

9. A single rose or a box of candy _____ a suitable gift. (make, makes)

10. Both the boy and his dog _____ their afternoon run. (enjoy, enjoys)

Name _____ Date _____

 23.1 # Subject and Verb Agreement (Confusing Subjects) • Practice 1

Confusing Subjects Always check certain kinds of subjects carefully to make sure they agree with their verbs.

AGREEMENT WITH CONFUSING SUBJECTS	
Subject After Verb	There *is* only one direct *flight* daily.
	Beyond my personal objections *is* the *question* of the candidate's qualifications.
Subject Versus Predicate Nominative	My first *choice* is checkers.
	Tortilla *chips are* a good snack.
Collective Nouns	The *jury looks* sympathetic.
	The *jury have* rooms on the top floor of the hotel.
Plural Form with Singular Meaning	*Scabies* is caused by a mite.
	Mathematics is my favorite subject.
Amounts and Measurements	Three *days is* not enough time to finish our job.
	Eight *ounces equals* one cup.
Titles	*Green Eggs and Ham* is a popular children's book.
Indefinite Pronouns	*Either* of the houses *is* expensive. (always singular)
	Many in the group *were* disgruntled. (always plural)
	Most of the cheese *has* mold on it.
	Most of the apples *are* ripe now.

▶ **Exercise 1** **Deciding on the Number of Subjects.** Assume that each item below is to be the subject of a sentence. Label each one *S* if it needs a singular verb or *P* if it needs a plural verb.

EXAMPLE: *Little Women* _____S_____

1. Some of the cookies _____
2. Gymnastics _____
3. *Of Mice and Men* _____
4. Half of the crackers _____
5. Mumps _____

6. All of the money _____
7. *All the King's Men* _____
8. Physics _____
9. Neither of the speakers _____
10. Any of the fabric _____

▶ **Exercise 2** **Choosing Verbs to Agree with Difficult Subjects.** Write the correct verb form from parentheses to complete each sentence.

EXAMPLE: There _____is_____ no one home at the moment. (is, are)

1. The series of six lectures _____ next week. (begin, begins)
2. The panel _____ disagreeing on the rules. (is, are)
3. Among the old clothes _____ several usable sweaters. (is, are)
4. Three fourths of the records _____ scratched. (is, are)
5. The executive council _____ to make its decision tonight. (meets, meet)
6. All of the members of the family _____ present at the reunion. (was, were)
7. The least of the problems _____ where to have the party. (is, are)
8. Among the students, there _____ been little interest. (has, have)
9. *Romeo and Juliet* _____ a popular Shakespearean play. (remains, remain)
10. The orchestra _____ tuning their instruments. (is, are)

23.1 Subject and Verb Agreement (Confusing Subjects) • Practice 2

▶ **Exercise 1** **Making Confusing Subjects Agree with Their Verbs.** Complete each sentence by writing the form of the verb in parentheses that agrees with the subject.

1. Here _____ the options for your consideration. (is, are)

2. Our swimming team _____ likely to win the competition. (is, are)

3. *The Virginians* _____ a novel by William Thackeray. (is, are)

4. His tactics at first _____ to be self-serving. (seems, seem)

5. His mumbled apology and its obvious insincerity _____ my reason for disliking him. (was, were)

6. Two gallons of whitewash _____ all that we need. (is, are)

7. Economics _____ my sister's major in college. (is, are)

8. Her broken eyeglasses _____ lying on the ground. (is, are)

9. A swarm of killer bees _____ advancing northward. (is, are)

10. A good idea for raising money _____ having everyone demonstrate a craft and having people sign up for lessons. (is, are)

▶ **Writing Application** **Applying the Rules of Subject and Verb Agreement.** Use each item at the beginning of a sentence, followed by the verb *is* or the verb *are*.

1. Neither of the boys

_____

2. The audience

_____

3. Two dollars

_____

4. Genetics

_____

5. Next to the desk

_____

6. Each of the club members

_____

7. Most of the cement

_____

8. Spaghetti and meatballs

_____

9. Either she or her parents

_____

10. Some of the children

_____

23.2

Pronoun and Antecedent Agreement
(Agreement Between Personal Pronouns and Antecedents)
• Practice 1

Agreement Between Personal Pronouns and Antecedents A personal pronoun must agree with its antecedent in number, person, and gender. Use a singular personal pronoun with two or more singular antecedents joined by *or* or *nor*. Use a plural personal pronoun with two or more antecedents joined by *and*. Use a plural personal pronoun if any part of a compound antecedent joined by *or* or *nor* is plural. When dealing with pronoun-antecedent agreement, take care not to shift either person or gender. When gender is not specified, use a combination (*he or she, his or her*) or rewrite the sentence.

```
          PRONOUN-ANTECEDENT AGREEMENT

Ben has misplaced his notecards.

This basketball has a leak in it.

Pam or Janice will have the party at her house.

The letter and the envelope will have coffee stains on them.

Neither the guide nor the tourists could believe their eyes.

Every player must do his or her best.

All players must do their best.
```

▶ **Exercise 1** **Choosing Personal Pronouns to Agree with Antecedents.** Assume that each item below is an antecedent for a personal pronoun. After each, write *his, her, its,* or *their* to show which pronoun you would use to refer to it.

EXAMPLE: My father or my uncle _____his_____

1. most public speakers _____

2. the tape recorder _____

3. either Kevin or Marc _____

4. Grace, Maria, or Anna _____

5. only one waitress _____

▶ **Exercise 2** **Pronoun-Antecedent Agreement in Sentences.** Write an appropriate personal pronoun to complete each sentence.

EXAMPLE: My brothers and I are planning a surprise for _____our_____ parents.

1. Al is someone who uses _____ time wisely.

2. The food was so spicy that _____ burned my mouth.

3. Neither Sue nor Kathy had any trouble choosing _____ topic.

4. The doctor and her assistant have published _____ findings.

5. Harold hopes _____ application will get to the admissions office in time.

6. Ken is coaching _____ sister's softball team.

7. Several members are giving _____ time to work with senior citizens.

8. Mr. Simpson, _____ order is ready now.

9. Marcia has gotten a part-time job to help with _____ college expenses.

10. Either Hugh or Brian will volunteer _____ time for the food pick-up.

23.2 Pronoun and Antecedent Agreement
(Agreement Between Personal Pronouns and Antecedents)
• Practice 2

> **Exercise 1** **Making Personal Pronouns Agree with Their Antecedents.** Write an appropriate personal pronoun to complete each sentence.

1. Boris and Leo improved _____ act by constant practice.
2. If the dark blue paint or the pale yellow is not oil-based, don't use _____.
3. Neither the bed nor the rugs retained _____ new look.
4. All the participants showed _____ appreciation.
5. Neither Mark nor Sam brought _____ radio to the game.
6. Lincoln is Nebraska's capital, and Omaha is _____ largest city.
7. My parents gave me _____ permission to go on the trip.
8. Andy and Lois sold several acres of _____ joint property.
9. Either Wanda or Wendy left _____ scarf in the car.
10. Ms. Stone and _____ secretary attended the convention.

> **Exercise 2** **Avoiding Shifts in Person and Gender.** Rewrite each sentence, correcting the unnecessary shift in person or gender.

EXAMPLE: With mischief in his eyes, the baby hid its rattle.
_____ With mischief in his eyes, the baby hid his rattle. _____

1. Each girl must submit their report before leaving.

2. Those hikers will soon realize that you cannot walk for miles in shoes meant for dress wear.

3. The welders wear goggles so that your eyes will be shielded from the sparks.

4. Trying to protect its calf, the cow disregarded her own safety as the coyotes approached.

5. We learned in chemistry that you should often try again.

6. The students want to know what you should bring to class on Monday.

7. As hurricane Donna swept along the predicted path, it left destruction in her wake.

8. All the team members learned that you have to practice hard to win.

9. Each athlete was accompanied by their manager.

10. Anyone can use their tickets for this ride.

23.2 # Pronoun and Antecedent Agreement
(Agreement with Indefinite and Reflexive Pronouns)
• Practice 1

Agreement with Indefinite Pronouns Use a singular personal pronoun when the antecedent is a singular indefinite pronoun. Use a plural personal pronoun when the antecedent is a plural indefinite pronoun. With an indefinite pronoun that can be either singular or plural, agreement depends on the antecedent of the indefinite pronoun.

AGREEMENT WITH INDEFINITE PRONOUNS

Each of the woman brought *her* own specialty to the party.

Few of the neighbors have raked *their* leaves yet.

Some of the cupcakes on *them.*

Some of the lawn has dandelions in *it.*

Agreement with Reflexive Pronoun A reflexive pronoun must agree with an antecedent that is clearly stated.

REFLEXIVE PRONOUN AGREEMENT	
Incorrect	**Correct**
Jason and *myself* enjoy the same kind of music.	Jason and *I* enjoy the same kind of music.

▶ **Exercise 1**   **Making Personal Pronouns Agree with Indefinite Pronouns.**   Write an appropriate personal pronoun to complete each sentence.

EXAMPLE: Each of the Brownies has sold ____her____ quota of Girl Scout cookies.

1. Most of the fans brought blankets with _____.

2. Most of our furniture has scratches on _____.

3. Several of my classmates handed in _____ essays early.

4. No one on the girls' swim team wears _____ goggles in a meet.

5. Everyone in the Women's Club brings _____ own expertise to the project.

6. Few of the voters changed _____ minds after the debate.

7. Much of the glass has smudges on _____.

8. Has anyone in Dan's Cub Scout pack decided on _____ project yet?

9. All of the musicians are tuning _____ instruments.

10. I think some of the tourists brought cameras with _____.

▶ **Exercise 2**   **Using Reflexive Pronouns Correctly.**   Underline the misused reflexive pronoun in each sentence. Write the correct pronoun on the line.

EXAMPLE: Please leave a message with Carlo or <u>himself</u>. ____him____

1. Gina or herself may be able to help you. _____

2. Don't forget to bring two sharpened pencils with yourself. _____

3. Kara and myself are on the decorations committee. _____

4. Pete will wear a jester's costume if ourselves can find one. _____

5. I loved the stories Grandma told yourself and me when we were little. _____

Name _____ Date _____

23.2 Pronoun and Antecedent Agreement
(Agreement with Indefinite and Reflexive Pronouns)
• Practice 2

▶ **Exercise 1** **Making Personal Pronouns Agree with Indefinite Pronouns.**   Underline the correct pronoun in each sentence.

1. Each of the men raised (his, their) arms to the crowd.

2. All of the paints will keep (its, their) color for years.

3. Both of the boys will complete (his, their) assignments.

4. Many who heard the thunder thought (he, they) would outwit the storm.

5. Either of the actresses will do (her, their) best.

6. Prior to living in the dormitory, each of the girls had tried living in (her, their) own apartment.

7. Several of the photographs had lost (its, their) finish.

8. Few of the items in the store seemed worth (its, their) price.

9. If everybody rushes toward you at once, avoid (him, them) by stepping aside.

10. Most of the girls like (her, their) new swimming coach.

11. While neither of the apples looked ripe, we had no choice but to eat (it, them).

12. All of those who spoke seemed unwilling to state (his, their) honest opinions.

13. Each of the boys looked out for (his, their) buddy.

14. Only one of the girls had (her, their) hair cut.

15. Each of the patrons wanted (his or her, their) money back when the play was canceled.

▶ **Exercise 2** **Using Reflexive Pronouns Correctly.**   Rewrite each sentence, correcting the misused reflexive pronoun.

1. Scott and myself were the first ones to arrive.

   _____

2. To whom other than herself should the award be given?

   _____

3. Mary and Jean forgot to invite John and myself.

   _____

4. Andrea and himself were the most popular couple there.

   _____

5. The only person who can convince them is yourself.

   _____

6. Carmen looked at themselves in the photograph.

   _____

7. May Jerry and myself have a piece of your pizza?

   _____

8. Who besides yourself can stay late today?

   _____

9. The person who has the best batting average is himself.

   _____

10. The teacher and herself will hand out the books.

   _____

23.3 Special Problems with Pronoun Agreement (Vague Pronoun References) • Practice 1

Vague Pronoun References   A pronoun requires an antecedent that is either clearly stated or clearly understood. The pronouns *which*, *this*, *that*, and *these* should not be used to refer to a vague or overly general idea. The personal pronouns *it*, *they*, and *you* should not be used with vague antecedents. Note that the use of *it* as a subject in such expressions as *it is raining* and *it is true* is acceptable and need not be avoided.

Vague Reference	Correct
Jake had good grades and was an outstanding athlete. He hoped *this* would help him get a scholarship.	Jake had good grades and was an outstanding athlete. He hoped *these factors* would help him get a scholarship.
In the paper, *it* says we had six inches of snow.	*The paper* reports that we had six inches of snow.
When visiting Paris, *you* can see the Eiffel Tower.	*Visitors to Paris* can see the Eiffel Tower.

▶ **Exercise 1**   **Correcting Vague Pronoun References.**   Rewrite each sentence below to correct a vague reference involving *which*, *this*, *that*, or *these*.

EXAMPLE: We lost the game and it rained, which made us unhappy.

_____ *We lost the game and it rained. Both events made us unhappy.* _____

1. Jeff needs to improve his average and pass the final. This seems unlikely.

   _____

2. The boys promptly wrote thank-you notes, which shocked their mother.

   _____

3. Missy's boutique is the most successful shop in town. She deserves that.

   _____

4. Occasionally, we have a power failure or a bad storm. This frightens the children.

   _____

5. Many valuables were broken and some were lost, which makes me angry.

   _____

▶ **Exercise 2**   **Solving More Problems with Pronouns References.**   Rewrite each sentence below that is faulty because of vague pronoun reference. If a sentence is correct as written, write *correct* in the space.

EXAMPLE: It was past midnight when the snow stopped. _____ *correct* _____

1. At the annual picnic, they always feature barbecued chicken.

   _____

2. In that game, you can only reach "home" with an exact roll of the dice.

   _____

3. In Boston, they often drop their *r*'s.

   _____

4. It is just beginning to snow.

   _____

5. It suggests in the article that Perkins is guilty.

   _____

23.3 Special Problems with Pronoun Agreement (Vague Pronoun References) • Practice 2

▶ **Exercise 1** **Correcting Vague Pronoun References.** Rewrite the sentences below, correcting the vague pronouns.

EXAMPLE: She heard that they had discovered a new fuel.

_____She heard that scientists had discovered a new fuel._____

1. To stake a claim on the frontier, you had to live there.

_____

2. We grumbled about the work done on the house because they left the roof open and the floor warped.

_____

3. I quickly shifted to a more neutral topic, and this prevented the inevitable argument over politics.

_____

4. She wore a sweater over her blouse and a vest over the sweater. That was too bulky.

_____

5. Valery is self-disciplined and energetic. These will be useful throughout life.

_____

6. We are adding to our small ranch, and it should help everyone feel less cramped.

_____

7. After waxing his new car, Jack polished the chrome and cleaned the interior. This became a monthly project.

_____

8. When my father spoke angrily, you listened.

_____

9. Near the East River in New York City you can see the United Nations Headquarters.

_____

10. George was too busy and involved with his own work, which was his way of ignoring people.

_____

▶ **Exercise 2** **Correcting Vague Pronoun References.** Rewrite each sentence below that is faulty because of vague pronoun reference. If a sentence is correct as written, write *correct* in the space.

EXAMPLE: Dina hoped that they would be able to find out why her tooth ached.

_____Dina hoped that the dentist would be able to find out why her tooth ached._____

1. Sam worked in a music store last summer and enjoyed it very much.

_____

2. Managers sometimes have to discipline or even fire employees, which might make you uncomfortable.

_____

3. We found spilled milk on the counters and broken dishes on the floor. This was our first clue.

_____

4. I could never figure out why they took my favorite program off the air.

_____

5. I sprinkled parts of maps, postcards, and ticket stubs throughout my memory book. These details make the book more interesting.

_____

23.3 # Special Problems with Pronoun
Agreement • Practice 1

Ambiguous Pronoun References   A personal pronoun should never refer to more than one antecedent. A personal pronoun should always be tied to a single, obvious antecedent.

Ambiguous Reference	Clear Reference
Angie told Faye that *she* had a flat tire.	Angie told Faye that *Faye* had a flat tire.

Do not repeat a personal pronoun if it can refer each time to a different antecedent.

Ambiguous Repetition	Correct
Phil told Jack that he would wait until after *his* football practice.	Phil told Jack that he would wait until after *Jack's* football practice.

Avoiding Distant Pronoun Reference   A personal pronoun should always be close enough to its antecedent to prevent confusion.

Distant Reference	Corrected
Teachers and counselors will be available in the senior lounge every Friday afternoon. All students are welcome to stop by. *They* will answer questions about schedules and curriculum.	Teachers and counselors will be available in the senior lounge every Friday afternoon. All students are welcome to stop by to ask questions about schedules and curriculum.

▶ **Exercise 1**   **Recognizing Problems of Pronoun Reference.**   In the space at the right, write the antecedent of each underlined pronoun. If the pronoun has no single antecedent to which it clearly refers, write *FR* (for faulty reference) in the space.

EXAMPLE: Bill and Gary shared his lunch.   ___*FR*___

1. After Nancy had spoken to Laura, she felt much calmer. _____

2. Mr. Pardi asked Tom to repeat the experiment he had just completed. _____

3. The still life was a masterpiece. The wine seemed to sparkle in the goblet, and the fruit looked real enough to eat. It made me gasp. _____

4. The approaches to the bridge were clogged, as they often were at rush hour. _____

5. The coach told Hankins that he would not renew his contract. _____

▶ **Exercise 2**   **Correcting Problems of Pronoun Reference.**   Rewrite three of the items you marked *FR* in Exercise A, correcting the faulty reference.

EXAMPLE: _Bill and Gary shared Gary's lunch._

1. _____
   _____

2. _____
   _____

3. _____
   _____

23.3 Special Problems with Pronoun Agreement • Practice 2

Exercise 1 **Correcting Ambiguous Pronoun References.**   Rewrite the following sentences, correcting the ambiguous pronoun references.

1. The flight attendant told the woman that she would ask someone to help her find the missing luggage.

   _____

2. This bonsai is growing in a container that discourages root growth, but it still seems too large.

   _____

3. Stephanie asked Betty Jane if she could help with the cooking.

   _____

4. While Barney wheeled his small son around the park, he was very contented.

   _____

5. Craig informed Harry that he would have to leave soon.

   _____

Exercise 2 **Correcting Distant Pronoun References.**   Rewrite the following sentences, correcting the distant pronoun references.

1. In many stories by Ray Bradbury, the Martians are described as gentle, highly intelligent creatures who are destroyed by people from earth. They are written so skillfully that readers truly feel they have entered another world.

   _____

   _____

   _____

2. Not far from the shore, a small sailboat seemed motionless, its mast like a needle. Red and white buoys dotted the horizon. There was no one on it to unfurl the sail.

   _____

   _____

   _____

3. We plunged our hands into the huge mound of popcorn. Before us on the screen were the faces of the men, women, and children starving in Africa. Once it was gone, we guiltily put the box under the seat.

   _____

   _____

   _____

4. Muffins fresh from the oven lay in wicker baskets. Jars of homemade jam, the fruit glistening along the glass sides, made our mouths water. Their smell filled the room.

   _____

   _____

   _____

5. The meeting had gone badly, Mr. Snelling reflected, as he loosened his tie. He had forgotten to bring his notes, and he felt that he was not dressed appropriately. It had been given to him by his daughter and was a conservative brown.

   _____

   _____

   _____

24.1 Degrees of Comparison (Recognizing Degrees of Comparison, Regular Forms) • Practice 1

Recognizing Degrees of Comparison   Most adjectives and adverbs have three different forms to show degrees of comparison.

DEGREES OF COMPARISON			
	Positive	**Comparative**	**Superlative**
Adjectives	ugly	uglier	ugliest
	beautiful	more beautiful	most beautiful
	bad	worse	worst
Adverbs	fast	faster	fastest
	slowly	more slowly	most slowly
	badly	worse	worst

Regular Forms   Use *-er* or *more* to form the comparative degree and *-est* or *most* to form the superlative degree of most one- and two-syllable modifiers. Use *more* and *most* to form the comparative and superlative degrees of all modifiers with three or more syllables.

REGULAR FORMS OF COMPARISON			
One- and two-syllable modifiers	sad	sadder	saddest
	happy	happier	happiest
	tranquil	more tranquil	most tranquil
Three or more syllables	sorrowful	more sorrowful	most sorrowful
	carefully	more carefully	most carefully

▶ **Exercise 1**   **Recognizing Degrees of Comparison.**   Identify the degree of comparison of the underlined word in each sentence by writing *pos.* (positive), *comp.* (comparative), or *sup.* (superlative).

EXAMPLE: They have been waiting <u>longer</u> than we have. _____*comp.*_____

1. The room will look <u>brighter</u> with a fresh coat of paint. _____

2. We congratulated the <u>proud</u> parents. _____

3. That was the <u>heaviest</u> rainfall on record. _____

4. Gretchen was voted <u>most likely</u> to succeed. _____

5. If I had been <u>more careful</u>, I wouldn't have made that mistake. _____

6. Casa Iguana serves the <u>spiciest</u> food in town. _____

7. The burglar moved <u>stealthily</u> along the balcony. _____

8. Surely the koala bear is one of the <u>laziest</u> animals. _____

9. An ice pack may make you feel <u>more comfortable</u>. _____

10. The stubborn child shook his head <u>vigorously</u>. _____

▶ **Exercise 2**   **Comparing Adjectives and Adverbs.**   Write the missing forms of each modifier.

EXAMPLE: broad _____*broader*_____ _____*broadest*_____

1. clever _____ _____

2. _____ _____ softest

3. _____ more unusual _____

4. friendly _____ _____

5. awkwardly _____ _____

24.1 Degrees of Comparison (Recognizing Degrees of Comparison, Regular Forms) • Practice 2

▶ **Exercise 1** **Recognizing Positive, Comparative, and Superlative Degrees.** Identify the degree of each underlined modifier.

EXAMPLE: My uncle was <u>more generous</u> than I expected. _comparative_

1. This chair is <u>more</u> comfortable than that one. _____
2. Andrew wore his <u>good</u> suit to the celebration. _____
3. His was the <u>most concerned</u> voice she had heard. _____
4. Jan <u>deftly</u> flipped the pancake in the air. _____
5. Your <u>best</u> decision should be made after you rest. _____
6. Max is <u>more determined</u> when the odds are against him. _____
7. These pears will ripen <u>more quickly</u> if the sun hits them. _____
8. The cat's claws were <u>swiftly</u> unsheathed. _____
9. Please let me try on the <u>smallest</u> size. _____
10. I was <u>more disappointed</u> by his attitude than by his failure. _____

▶ **Exercise 2** **Forming Regular Comparative and Superlative Degrees.** Write the comparative and superlative form of each modifier.

EXAMPLE: wise _____wiser_____ _____wisest_____

1. lucky
2. pleasing
3. soon
4. strange
5. thick
6. pretentious
7. heavily
8. fond
9. clever
10. curly
11. rapid
12. rapidly
13. tasty
14. wide
15. green
16. safely
17. cold
18. hopeful
19. hard
20. proudly
21. shocking
22. delightful
23. stunning
24. carefully
25. short

© Prentice-Hall, Inc.

24.1 Degrees of Comparison (Irregular Forms)

• Practice 1

Irregular Forms The irregular comparative and superlative forms of certain adjectives and adverbs must be memorized.

IRREGULAR MODIFIERS		
Positive	Comparative	Superlative
bad	worse	worst
badly	worse	worst
far (distance)	farther	farthest
far (extent)	further	furthest
good	better	best
ill	worse	worst
late	later	last *or* latest
little (amount)	less	least
many	more	most
much	more	most
well	better	best

▶ **Exercise 1**   **Forming Irregular Comparative and Superlative Degrees.**   Write the appropriate form of the modifier in parentheses to complete each sentence.

EXAMPLE: The hikers felt _____*better*_____ after a short rest period. (good)

1. Students seldom do their _____ on tests when they are overtired. (well)

2. Max swam out _____ than he should have. (far)

3. That plant looks even _____ today than it did yesterday. (bad)

4. Of all the tourist attractions, we were _____ interested in seeing the White House. (little)

5. Her gown was in the _____ style. (late)

6. Only the second paragraph needs to be developed _____. (far)

7. Everyone agreed about who was the _____ player on the football team. (good)

8. People often feel even _____ on the second day of a cold than on the first. (ill)

9. Beginning musicians never play very well, but beginning violinists often play _____ of all. (badly)

10. We should have ordered _____ sandwiches for the party. (many)

▶ **Exercise 2**   **Using Adjectives and Adverbs to Make Comparisons.**   Use each modifier in a sentence of your own to show a clear comparison. Use three comparative forms and two superlatives.

EXAMPLE: (much)   _____*This project is going to be more work than I thought.*_____

1. (bad) _____

2. (badly) _____

3. (good) _____

4. (many) _____

5. (well) _____

24.1 Degrees of Comparison (Irregular Forms)
• Practice 2

▷ **Exercise 1** Forming Irregular Comparative and Superlative Degrees. Write the appropriate form of the underlined modifier to complete each sentence.

EXAMPLE: The film is good, but the book is _____better_____ .

1. The old line of cars is selling well, but we hope the new line will sell even _____.
2. We drove far to reach a gas station and even _____ to reach a restaurant.
3. Jan looks better in blue than in red, but she looks _____ in green.
4. Joe has little patience for board games and even _____ for word games.
5. Connie has much interest in physics and even _____ in chemistry.
6. The scientist pursued her research quite far last year, but she intends to pursue it even _____ this year.
7. There were many guests at Sam's party, but there were _____ at Roxanne's.
8. I still feel ill this morning, but I felt _____ last night after dinner.
9. George arrived late, but Walter arrived even _____.
10. Sandra did badly on the written test and even _____ on the driving test.

▷ **Writing Application** Using Adjectives and Adverbs to Make Comparisons. Write a sentence with each word in the degree indicated.

EXAMPLE: nervous—comparative

_____Penelope was more nervous after the test than she was before the test._____

1. clear—superlative

_____

2. trustworthy—comparative

_____

3. alert—positive

_____

4. good—superlative

_____

5. bad—positive

_____

6. badly—superlative

_____

7. far—positive

_____

8. malicious—comparative

_____

9. windy—comparative

_____

10. secretive—superlative

_____

24.2 # Clear Comparisons (Using Comparative and
Superlative Degrees) • Practice 1

Using Comparative and Superlative Degrees   Use the comparative degree to compare two persons, places, or things. Use the superlative degree to compare three or more persons, places, or things.

Comparative (comparing two)	Superlative (comparing three or more)
Jerry studies *harder* than his brother. The child moved *closer* to the horse.	Jerry studies *hardest* of the four children in the family. That was the *closest* he had ever been to a large animal.

▶ **Exercise 1**   **Using the Comparative and Superlative Degrees Correctly.**   Underline the correct form in each sentence.

EXAMPLE: If we had played (more, most) aggressively, we might have won.

1. Of all these movies, I have the (less, least) interest in seeing this one.
2. That watch is the (older, oldest) piece of jewelry in the collection.
3. Al should have proofread his essay (more, most) thoroughly.
4. Be sure to store the chicken in the (colder, coldest) part of the freezer.
5. The researchers will have to examine the specimen (more, most) closely.
6. That is the (more, most) delicate piece of needlework I have ever seen.
7. A speech for that audience should have a (more, most) formal tone.
8. Latin IV has the (fewer, fewest) students of any course.
9. The cheetah is the (faster, fastest) animal in the world.
10. This is the area of town I am (more, most) familiar with.

▶ **Exercise 2**   **Recognizing Inappropriate Comparisons.**   In the sentences below, underline any problems that exist in comparisons. On the line below, rewrite each sentence correctly. If a sentence contains no errors, write *correct* on the line.

EXAMPLE: This is the lovelier party I have ever been to.

This is the loveliest party I have ever been to.

1. Ben is happiest on his boat than on ours or the Petermans'.

_____

2. Miguel seems to be the brightest of the twins.

_____

3. The Jacobsons are the friendlier people on this block.

_____

4. This is the lengthiest novel I have ever read.

_____

5. I would be happier if you had chosen a safest route.

_____

24.2 Clear Comparisons (Using Comparative and Superlative Degrees) • Practice 2

Exercise 1 **Using the Comparative and Superlative Forms Correctly.** Underline the correct comparative or superlative form in each sentence.

1. Abe is (nicer, nicest) than his friend Hal.

2. Which of your parents is (more likely, most likely) to drive us to school tomorrow?

3. The movie was much (worse, worst) than we were told.

4. Carolyn is the (younger, youngest) of the four daughters.

5. Which of the two campsites is (farther, farthest)?

6. Jim's plan is (more viable, most viable) than Kay's plan.

7. Suzie is (better, best) at chess than Robert.

8. Edgar is the (better, best) player on the basketball team.

9. The noise in our classroom was (louder, loudest) than the noise in the classroom next to us.

10. Carla is clearly the (brighter, brightest) of the twins.

11. Jocelyn is the (more talented, most talented) of the three sisters.

12. That movie was the (most violent, more violent) one I've seen all year.

13. Sean arrived at the store (later, more later) than Sid.

14. Of the two, Denise seems (more bewildered, most bewildered).

15. The moon is the (most brilliant, more brilliant) object in the night sky.

Exercise 2 **Supplying the Comparative and Superlative Degrees.** Write the appropriate comparative or superlative degree of the modifier in parentheses.

EXAMPLE: Winston is the _____*funniest*_____ student in our class. (funny)

1. This road will be _____ after the snow melts. (muddy)

2. He has the _____ record on the team. (good)

3. Your reasoning would be _____ if you would think through the problem slowly. (clear)

4. Wear a _____ coat and leave the other in the closet. (warm)

5. My grades in art history were _____ this semester than last semester. (good)

6. Randy is the _____ of the three boys. (old)

7. Brad is _____ eager to participate than I am. (much)

8. Snow is _____ than usual after a rainfall. (heavy)

9. Josh is _____ to colds than his brother is. (susceptible)

10. The problem is _____ serious than you thought. (much)

11. That bully is the _____ child I have ever met. (rude)

12. Your first plan seems _____ than your second plan. (beneficial)

13. This is the _____ outfit I own. (casual)

14. Of the two students, Harry is the one who is _____ with Poe. (familiar)

15. The _____ entry in the contest was the one submitted by Alan. (impressive)

24.2 Clear Comparisons (Logical Comparisons)
• Practice 1

Logical Comparisons   Make sure that your sentences compare only items of a similar kind.

Unbalanced Comparisons	Correct
Andre's car is newer than his mother.	Andre's car is newer than his mother's.
The damage from yesterday's rainstorm is greater than last month.	The damage from yesterday's rainstorm is greater than that from last month's.

When comparing one of a group with the rest of the group, make sure that your sentence contains the word *other* or the word *else*.

Illogical Comparisons	Correct
My grandmother is older than anyone in the family.	My grandmother is older than anyone else in the family.
Vincent's typing skills are greater than any student's in his class.	Vincent's typing skills are greater than any other student's in his class.

▶ **Exercise 1**   **Making Balanced Comparisons.**   Rewrite each sentence, correcting the comparison.

EXAMPLE: Sue's dress is prettier than Jane.

Sue's dress is prettier than Jane's.

1. Your bonsai plant looks better than my mother.

    _____

2. Ted's bowl of spaghetti was bigger than his father.

    _____

3. The directions for putting together this model are more complicated than that model.

    _____

4. The test Frank took is harder than Judy.

    _____

5. At that store, dresses are less expensive than this store.

    _____

▶ **Exercise 2**   **Using *Other* and *Else* in Comparisons.**   Rewrite each sentence, correcting the comparison.

EXAMPLE: Mr. McMurty lived longer than anyone in his family.

Mr. McMurty lived longer than anyone else in his family.

1. Tom can throw farther than anyone on his team.

    _____

2. Brenda's report was more interesting than anyone's.

    _____

3. The boy who sits next to me speaks Spanish more fluently than anyone.

    _____

4. The flowers in this yard are prettier than any flowers on this street.

    _____

5. The wildcats are better than any football team.

    _____

24.2 Clear Comparisons (Logical Comparisons)
• Practice 2

▷ **Exercise 1** **Making Balanced Comparisons.** Rewrite each sentence, correcting the unbalanced sentence.

EXAMPLE: Shelly's voice is better than Ted.

_____Shelly's voice is better than Ted's._____

1. Duane's work on the blackboard is more legible than Linda.

_____

2. The conditions in the eye of a hurricane are calmer than the perimeter.

_____

3. Feeding the seals is more fun than the alligators.

_____

4. A moose's antlers are bigger than a deer.

_____

5. The spots on a serval are similar to a bobcat.

_____

6. Contact with poison ivy can hurt as much as poison oak.

_____

7. Jonathan's term paper is longer than Richard.

_____

8. The floats in this year's parade are fewer than last year.

_____

9. Listening to music is more relaxing than a television show.

_____

10. The flowers in Ms. Devick's garden are healthier than Ms. Patterson.

_____

▷ **Exercise 2** **Using *Other* and *Else* in Comparisons.** Rewrite each sentence, correcting the illogical comparison.

1. Arnold's report on the history of humanism was more fascinating than anyone's.

_____

2. The village parson was more respected than any person who lived there.

_____

3. Dora steered her canoe through the rapids with a skill greater than that of any of the contestants.

_____

4. Ask Marge to check the records because she is more thorough than anyone.

_____

5. Rosalie, the winner of five consecutive magic contests, could perform more tricks than anyone we ever saw.

_____

24.2 **Clear Comparisons** (Absolute Modifiers)

   • **Practice 1**

Absolute Modifiers   Avoid using absolute modifiers illogically in comparisons.

Illogical	Correct
My glass is *fuller* than yours.	My glass is *more nearly full* than yours. My glass has *more in it* than yours.
I have never seen a *more spotless* house.	That is the only *spotless* house I have ever seen.

▶ **Exercise 1**   **Correcting Illogical Comparisons.**   Rewrite each sentence, correcting any illogical comparisons.

EXAMPLE: Joan's opinions are the most opposite of mine.

   Joan's opinions are the opposite of mine.

1. This model comes in a more infinite number of colors than that one.

   _____

2. Be sure the two posts are most perpendicular.

   _____

3. That snake has the most poisonous venom.

   _____

4. Mom should treat us more equally.

   _____

5. Try to make these two lines more parallel.

   _____

▶ **Exercise 2**   **Writing Clear Comparisons.**   For each of the following items, write an effective comparison in one sentence.

EXAMPLE: Compare two of your favorite sports.

   I think basketball is more strenuous than baseball.

1. Compare two brands of cereal.

   _____

2. Compare the difference in weight between two of your friends.

   _____

3. Compare three of your favorite television programs.

   _____

4. Compare two animals found in a circus.

   _____

5. Compare what you had for dinner with what your friend had for dinner.

   _____

24.2 Clear Comparisons (Absolute Modifiers)
• Practice 2

▶ **Exercise 1** **Avoiding Absolute Modifiers in Comparisons.** Rewrite each sentence, correcting the illogical comparison.

1. His report was more complete than mine.

   _____

2. My Aunt Jane's solution was more perfect than my Uncle Walter's.

   _____

3. This step is more irrevocable than the last one.

   _____

4. Julie was more overwhelmed with math homework than Keith was.

   _____

5. We wanted a painting that was less unique than Aunt Mary's.

   _____

6. They finally found a route that led straighter to their destination.

   _____

7. These two white kittens are more identical than those two gray ones.

   _____

8. Her decision was more opposite mine than his was.

   _____

9. A coral snake's venom is more fatal than a rattlesnake's.

   _____

10. The flowers I picked are less dead than the ones you picked.

   _____

▶ **Writing Application** **Writing Effective Comparisons.** Use the following instructions to write five sentences of your own.

1. Compare three units of measurement.

   _____

2. Compare one profession with another.

   _____

3. Compare three actors or actresses.

   _____

4. Compare one musical instrument with another.

   _____

5. Compare two movies.

   _____

Negative Sentences (Recognizing Double Negatives, Forming Negative Sentences Correctly)

• **Practice 1**

Recognizing Double Negatives   Do not write sentences with double negatives.

CORRECTING DOUBLE NEGATIVES	
Double Negatives	**Corrections**
I *won't never* tell.	I *won't* ever tell. I will *never* tell.
Luis wouldn*'t* let *no one* help him.	Luis wouldn*'t* let anyone help him. Luis would let *no one* help him.
Michelle did*n't* know *nothing* about feeding chickens.	Michelle knew *nothing* about feeding chickens. Michelle did*n't* know anything about feeding chickens.

Forming Negative Sentences Correctly   Do not use two negative words in the same clause. Do not use *but* in its negative sense with another negative. Do not use *barely*, *hardly*, or *scarcely* with another negative word.

▶ **Exercise 1**   **Recognizing Double Negatives.**   Label each sentence below as *DN* (containing a double negative) or *C* (correct).

EXAMPLE: Zach hadn't had no special training in scuba diving. _____*DN*_____

1. Miss Conklin had not heard anything about a special program. _____

2. The guard hadn't seen nothing suspicious. _____

3. You can't find any better pet than a turtle. _____

4. The Number 4 bus no longer goes up Maple Avenue. _____

5. At first we couldn't see nothing in the darkness. _____

6. They don't have no more morning papers at the candy store. _____

7. The burglar didn't think of looking in the wastebasket. _____

8. The baby can't eat no more of those apples. _____

9. Neither of those boys has done nothing wrong. _____

10. Ms. Martinez won't accept no late papers. _____

▶ **Exercise 2**   **Correcting Double Negatives.**   Correctly rewrite five of the sentences you labeled *DN* in Exercise 1.

EXAMPLE: _____*Zach hadn't had any special training in scuba diving.*_____

1. _____

2. _____

3. _____

4. _____

5. _____

25.1 Negative Sentences (Recognizing Double Negatives, Forming Negative Sentences Correctly) • Practice 2

▶ **Exercise 1**   **Avoiding Double Negatives.**   Underline the word in parentheses that makes each sentence negative without forming a double negative.

1. We don't have (no, any) tickets for tonight's concert.

2. Carlos won't (ever, never) make that mistake again.

3. Don't hide the keys (nowhere, anywhere) obvious.

4. The witness had seen (no one, anyone) suspicious.

5. The professor wouldn't accept (no, any) late papers.

▶ **Exercise 2**   **Avoiding Problems with Negatives.**   Rewrite each of the sentences to eliminate the double negatives.

1. Phil never did nothing to antagonize the crew members.

_____

2. You should not drive that car nowhere without snow tires.

_____

3. Hardly no one knew the answers on the exam.

_____

4. I can't find my address book nowhere.

_____

5. No one never saw the bear tracking us.

_____

▶ **Exercise 3**   **Correcting Double Negatives.**   Eliminate the error in each of the following phrases and expand the corrected phrase into a sentence of your own.

1. wouldn't hardly try

_____

2. wasn't nobody there

_____

3. couldn't scarcely walk

_____

4. weren't but a few

_____

5. didn't want no pity

_____

25.1 Negative Sentences (Understatement) • Practice 1

Understatement   Understatement can be achieved by using a negative word and a word with a negative prefix.

UNDERSTATEMENTS
The special investigator found that the mayor's conduct was *not improper*. Owen was *not unimpressed* with her command of Mongolian.

▶ **Exercise 1**   **Using Understatement.**   Rewrite each sentence using understatement.

EXAMPLE: Dinner was expensive.   *Dinner was not inexpensive.*

1. The new crop of rookies was promising.

_____

2. The climb is difficult, but possible.

_____

3. The judge was sympathetic, but firm in his decision.

_____

4. The extra cost of air conditioning is significant.

_____

5. The reviews of the critics were enthusiastic.

_____

▶ **Exercise 2**   **Writing Negative Sentences.**   None of the following sentences contain negative words. Rewrite each sentence to express a negative idea.

EXAMPLE: Mr. Killerlane was pleased with my report.

   Mr. Killerlane was displeased with my report.

1. It is easy for me to read the small print on the bottle.

_____

2. Some of these pictures are mine.

_____

3. Will was finished with his project.

_____

4. Everybody came to the Millers' surprise party.

_____

5. All the students bought the book.

_____

25.1 Negative Sentences (Understatement) • Practice 2

Exercise 1 Using Understatement. Rewrite each sentence, using understatement.

1. Interruptions from inquisitive children were frequent.

    _____

2. This dime store trinket is expensive.

    _____

3. I am impressed by your fluency in Russian.

    _____

4. The sentimental value of the ring is important.

    _____

5. Taking some time for yourself is essential.

    _____

6. Her opinion is relevant.

    _____

7. Tad is certainly a conformist.

    _____

8. His prose style was pleasing.

    _____

9. Considering the barbaric manners of his guests, I think Bob's conduct was honorable.

    _____

10. The findings from the study were significant.

    _____

Writing Application Writing Negative Sentences. Use each item in a negative sentence.

1. not appreciated

    _____

2. can see nothing

    _____

3. never bothered

    _____

4. not unintelligent

    _____

5. barely recognizable

    _____

6. has hardly begun

    _____

7. but two possibilities

    _____

8. scarcely noticed

    _____

Name _____   Date _____

 25.2 # Common Usage Problems • Practice 1

Solving Usage Problems   Study the items in the usage glossary in your textbook, paying particular attention to similar meanings and spellings, words that should never be used, pairs that are often misused, and problems with verb forms.

TYPES OF PROBLEMS		
Similar Spellings	beside, besides	all ready, already
Wrong Words	irregardless	nowheres
Misused Pairs	learn, teach	bring, take
Verb Forms	burst	have done

▶ **Exercise 1**   **Avoiding Common Usage Problems.**   Underline the word(s) in parentheses that correctly complete each sentence.

EXAMPLE: Mr. Salvin (<u>burst</u>, busted) out laughing when he read my paper.

1. Who (beside, besides) you is planning to be absent?

2. The game was postponed (due to, because of) rain.

3. Boris's grandfather (learned, taught) him to play chess.

4. How is a dromedary different (from, than) a camel?

5. Chris was (eager, anxious) to begin working at her new job.

6. The rescue team was determined to go (irregardless, regardless) of the risks.

7. Years of smoking will likely have a bad (affect, effect) on your lungs.

8. (Leave, Let) that poor cat alone!

9. Small animals (adapt, adopt) quickly to changes in their environment.

10. Buoyancy is an important (principal, principle) of physics.

▶ **Exercise 2**   **Correcting Common Usage Problems.**   Underline the word or expression that creates a usage problem in each sentence below. Then correctly rewrite the sentence, using formal English.

EXAMPLE: The President <u>excepted</u> the challenge to debate.

The President accepted the challenge to debate.

1. Nancy became real discouraged when the tenth publisher rejected her novel.

_____

2. I done my homework already.

_____

3. A slice of pizza is more healthy than a candy bar.

_____

4. This here watch belonged to my great-grandfather.

_____

5. The owner of this shop prides herself on her very unique selection of gifts.

_____

25.2 Common Usage Problems • Practice 2

▶ **Exercise 1**　**Avoiding Usage Problems.**　Underline the correct expression to complete each sentence.

1. What (affect, effect) did her speech have on you?
2. They should have (all ready, already) left by now.
3. Jim (ain't, isn't) capable of doing that stunt.
4. Everyone (accept, except) me was dressed in black.
5. You can do (alot, much) to improve yourself.
6. My keys must be (somewhere, somewheres) here.
7. We should shout the cheer (all together, altogether).
8. One black orchid grew (among, between) many white ones.
9. You look (all right, alright) without any mascara.
10. She feels (anxious, eager) about the colt's injured leg.
11. She is (awfully, very) frightened in crowded elevators.
12. As a child, my father was (blond, blonde).
13. Listen to this piece of music for (a while, awhile).
14. Do you know where the children (are, are at)?
15. The reason the cat ran is (because, that) a dog came.
16. My new computer (can, may) do more than my old one.
17. We (can't help but admire, can't help admiring) her grace.
18. The soap bubbles will (burst, bust) upon contact.
19. I take umbrage at your offensive (ad, advertisement) in yesterday's paper.
20. The (continual, continuous) noise of trains rumbling past his house every half hour kept him awake.
21. I was nervous when I (dived, dove) into the pool.
22. Thousands of Cubans have (emigrated, immigrated) to this country.
23. She was very (enthused, enthusiastic) about the race.
24. (Due to, Because of) an unavoidable delay, the results of the poll can't be given until next week.
25. We visited New York and Boston. The (former, latter) is the home of the United Nations and the Statue of Liberty.

▶ **Exercise 2**　**Avoiding Usage Problems.**　Underline the correct expression to complete each sentence.

1. Eugene is a (nice, friendly) person.
2. Colorful lanterns were (hanged, hung) from the beams.
3. Sandra (got, earned) the respect of the class.
4. (Irregardless, Regardless) of the choppy water, Matt guided the boat beyond the buoys.
5. (Lie, Lay) the baby on the scales.
6. There (may be, maybe) a hidden clause in the contract.
7. The sun looks (kind of, somewhat) reddish as it sets.
8. A (lose, loose) knot was tied around his wrists.
9. There (had ought, ought) to be a law against this.
10. (Only admit, Admit only) those who have a ticket.

26 Capitalization (First Words, Proper Nouns, Proper Adjectives) • Practice 1

Capitals for First Words   Use capital letters to begin words in each situation shown in the chart below.

Sentences	He is asleep. Who called?
Interjection and Question	He took a terrible fall. Ghastly!
Fragment	Of course, I'll meet you. But where?
Sentence in Quote	Didn't the sign say, "Trespassers will be prosecuted"?
Sentence After Colon	The storm has halted traffic: Most roads are blocked.
Lines of Most Poetry	Mary, Mary, quite contrary, / How does your garden grow?
Formal Resolutions	Resolved: That dues be increased by $1.00 per year.
The Words *I* and *O*	Remember, O ye of little faith, I will return.

Capitals for Proper Nouns   Capitalize each important word in all proper nouns, as shown below.

People/Animals: E. B. White, Rover	*Place Names:* Oak Place, Eiffel Tower
Specific Events: the Iron Age, May Day	*Specific Groups:* Girl Scouts, Republicans
Religious Terms: Bible, Koran	*Awards:* Grammy, Gold Glove
Specific Craft: Model T, Concorde	*Brand Names:* Sunbest, Rickel

Capitals for Proper Adjectives   Capitalize most proper adjectives.

Proper Adjectives with Capitals	Adjectives Without Capitals
Proper Nouns Used as Adjectives: French painter	*Common Terms:* french fries
Brand Names: Curall bandages	*Most Prefixes:* anti-American
Combinations: Anglo-Saxon poem	*Parts of Compounds:* German-made automobile

▷ **Exercise 1**   **Using Capitals for First Words.**   Underline the word or words that should be capitalized in each of the following items.

EXAMPLE: afterward i remembered someone having said, "watch your step."

1. the first two lines of the poem are "tell me where is fancy bred, / in the heart or in the head?"

2. we must find a way to help. but how?

3. what a silly thing that was to say! golly!

4. resolved: that students with straight *A*'s be exempt from taking mid-terms.

5. the driver exclaimed, "wow! that was a close call!"

▷ **Exercise 2**   **Capitalizing Proper Nouns and Proper Adjectives.**   Underline each word or word part that should be capitalized in the sentences below.

EXAMPLE: The city of montreal has many french-speaking residents.

1. The halbert clinic accepts both blue cross and medicare patients.

2. The alhambra in granada is a famous example of moorish architecture.

3. Both the republican and the democratic candidates are hoping for a big win in new york.

4. This metroliner does not stop in metro park, new jersey.

5. Our neighbor, ellen blair, has just replaced her surephoto brand camera with a unilens.

26 Capitalization (First Words, Proper Nouns, Proper Adjectives) • Practice 2

Exercise 1 **Capitalizing First Words.**   Underline the word or words that should be capitalized in each item.

EXAMPLE: <u>drive</u> carefully.

1. "your explanation," said the teacher, "is difficult to accept."

2. i lived with visions from my company.
   instead of men and women, years ago,
   and found then gentle mates, nor thought to know
   a sweeter music than they played on me.
   —Elizabeth Barrett Browning

3. resolved: that the state legislature increase the school year by three days.

4. the candidate expressed his anger: he could not believe the allegations of the opposing party.

5. oh! this is dreadful!

Exercise 2 **Using Capitals for Proper Nouns.**   Underline the word or words that should be capitalized in each sentence. Some sentences might not need further capitalization.

EXAMPLE: The most powerful god of the early <u>greeks</u> was <u>zeus</u>.

1. The army of the cumberland operated mainly in the states of georgia, tennessee, and kentucky during the civil war.

2. He speaks three languages: spanish, french, and italian.

3. In the class on comparative religions, we read the old testament, the new testament, and the koran.

4. This term we will read the declaration of independence, the constitution, and the bill of rights.

5. Bolivia, located in the central part of south america, is separated from the pacific ocean by chile and peru.

6. My sister received a new york state regents scholarship and a westinghouse science award.

7. Of all the methods of travel, I prefer flying in a skyliner tristar airplane.

8. For science I prepared a chart illustrating the different positions of the big dipper.

9. Now that we have learned so much about the moon, I wonder how long it will take to get new information about the sun.

10. If you have a complaint about your nash rambler automobile, I suggest you write to the customer relations department of unity motor company in dearborn, michigan.

Exercise 3 **Using Capitals for Proper Adjectives.**   Rewrite each item that is capitalized incorrectly, making the necessary changes. If an item is already capitalized properly, write *correct*.

EXAMPLE: a brazilian diplomat ____*a Brazilian diplomat*____

1. french fries _____

2. bible study _____

3. First and Second Avenues _____

4. Japanese people _____

5. Spanish-speaking delegate _____

6. lake Erie _____

7. pasteurized milk _____

8. himalayan village _____

9. Boice Automobile _____

10. a herculean task _____

26 Capitalization (Titles, Letters) • Practice 1

Capitals for Titles Capitalize titles of people and titles of works.

People	Works
Social: Lady Astor	*Book: All the King's Men*
Business: Chairman Iacocca	*Periodical: Reader's Digest*
Military: General Westmoreland	*Poem:* "Birches"
Government: Senator Watkins	*Story:* "Shredni Vashtar"
Religious: Archbishop Sheen	*Sculpture: the Piet*
Compound: Lieutenant Governor Hall	*Composition: The Seasons*
Abbreviations: Mrs., Jr., Ph.D.	*Course:* Creative Writing II

Capitals in Letters Capitalize the first word and all nouns in letter salutations and the first word in letter closings.

Salutations	Closings
My dear Friend,	With much love,
Dear Ambassador Parker:	Very truly yours,

▶ **Exercise 1** **Using Capitals in Titles.** Underline the words that should be capitalized in each sentence.

EXAMPLE: Although it is somewhat dated, *It's a Wonderful Life* still has its charm.

1. The young recruits dreaded sergeant Kerwin's temper.
2. The poem "the dry salvages" is the third of T. S. Eliot's *four quartets.*
3. The guest speaker will be senator Gerald Markham.
4. The course will be taught by Janet Saybrook, m.f.a.
5. I'm sure aunt Marnie would enjoy reading that book about general MacArthur.
6. Leonardo da Vinci painted both the *mona lisa* and *the last supper.*
7. On the feast of saint Francis, pastor Manners will bless the animals.
8. The publishers of *consumer reports* also publish *penny power* for young people.
9. One of the most popular songs from *annie* is "tomorrow."
10. Next semester, mr. Polari will teach poetry II.

▶ **Exercise 2** **Using Capitals for Salutations and Closings.** Rewrite each of the following letter parts, adding the missing capitals.

EXAMPLE: dear uncle harry, _____*Dear Uncle Harry,*_____

1. dear rabbi hartman, _____
2. your grateful neighbor, _____
3. with deep regret, _____
4. my dear ethel, _____
5. sincerely yours, _____
6. dear chairman gott: _____
7. your friend always, _____
8. dear sir or madam: _____
9. dearest cousin, _____
10. with warm regards, _____

26 **Capitalization** (Titles, Letters) • **Practice 2**

▶ **Exercise 1** **Using Capitals in a Business Letter.** Underline the words that should be capitalized in the following letter.

43 berry hill lane
cornwall, new york 12518
november 5, 2001

director of admissions
fairleigh dickinson university
1000 river road
teaneck, new jersey 07666

dear director:

   after speaking with my college adviser, i may be interested in enrolling in the college of business administration at fairleigh dickinson university in september of next year.
   would you please send me your catalog for the college of business administration? i am also interested in your admission requirements and details of the financial aid package provided by the university.
   since i live some distance from teaneck, i would also like information about on-campus housing or housing in the area.
   thank you very much for your assistance.

           yours truly,

           elizabeth green

▶ **Writing Application** **Using Capitalization Rules in Original Sentences.** Use the following directions to write sentences of your own, using capitals wherever necessary.

1. Write a sentence in which you name the title of a book and its author. Underline the title.

   _____

2. Write a sentence in which you mention the name of the governor of your state.

   _____

3. Write a sentence in which you give someone directions. Use words such as *east, northwest, south,* and so on.

   _____

4. Write a sentence about your favorite professional athletic team.

   _____

5. Write a sentence about a person who speaks two or more languages. Name the languages.

   _____

6. Write a sentence about a famous historic site that you have visited or would like to visit.

   _____

7. Write a sentence about two oceans that border the United States.

   _____

8. Write a sentence naming your three favorite courses.

   _____

9. Write a sentence in which you mention both your junior and senior high school by name.

   _____

10. Write a sentence that includes a direct quotation.

   _____

27.1 End Marks • Practice 1

Basic Uses of End Marks   Use a period to end a declarative sentence, a mild imperative, or an indirect question. Use a question mark to end an interrogative sentence, an incomplete sentence, or a statement intended as a question. Use an exclamation mark to end an exclamatory sentence, a forceful imperative, or an interjection expressing strong emotion.

Periods	Question Marks	Exclamation Marks
No one answered the door.	Is anyone home?	How long we have waited!
Ring the bell again.	Why not?	Keep knocking!
I wonder where Ed could be.	It doesn't work?	Whew! There's someone coming.

Other Uses of End Marks   Use a period to end most abbreviations and after numbers and letters in outlines. Use a question mark in parentheses after a fact or statistic to show its uncertainty.

Periods	Question Marks
Roger Marple, D.D.S.	The owner offered a $50 (?) reward.
I. The era of live TV	April 15 (?) is Easter this year.
A. The variety show	

▷ **Exercise 1**   **Using End Marks for Sentences and Phrases.**   Write the proper end mark at the end of each item.

EXAMPLE: I must have misunderstood. You didn't mean that ___?___

1. What a beautiful town that was _____

2. What time does the second feature begin _____

3. The child asked how long his parents would be gone _____

4. That was a first down. Super _____

5. Duck _____

6. I have misplaced my notecards _____

7. How pleased Grandma was to see us _____

8. I wondered how long the test would take _____

9. Check over your work before you hand in your paper _____

10. When did Andy call _____

▷ **Exercise 2**   **Using End Marks in Your Own Sentences.**   Follow the directions to write your own sentences.

EXAMPLE: Write a sentence that suggests uncertainty about a date.

Lincoln was assassinated on April 14, 1865 (?).

1. Write a sentence that contains an abbreviation for a title.

   _____

2. Write a sentence that begins with a strong interjection.

   _____

3. Write a sentence that expresses uncertainty about a price.

   _____

4. Write a sentence that includes an indirect question.

   _____

5. Write a forceful imperative.

   _____

27.1 End Marks • Practice 2

▶ **Exercise 1**   **Using End Marks.**   Rewrite each item, punctuating it correctly.

1. Whew What a scare that was

_____

2. How many times have you tried to win a race

_____

3. Fowler's book on English usage is a very helpful reference book

_____

4. Watch out for that car

_____

5. She asked if I had achieved my goal

_____

▶ **Exercise 2**   **Using End Marks in Other Situations.**   Rewrite each sentence, adding the necessary end marks to each item. If an item does not need any additional end marks, write *correct*.

EXAMPLE: Did Mrs Jackson offer to bake cookies for the party

       Did Mrs. Jackson offer to bake cookies for the party?

1. Confucius, who died in 470 BC, was a philosopher.

_____

2. Are more space flights being planned by NASA?

_____

3. The tiny toad was 15 mm long.

_____

4. The calendar page gave the following date: Oct 26.

_____

5. The package was addressed to Mr Luis Ramirez, 23 Grove St, St Paul, Minn.

_____

6. At 10:30 PM the baby finally fell asleep.

_____

7. I   Vitamin A
       A.   Sources
              1   Milk, butter, eggs
              2   Green and yellow vegetables
       B   Value
              1   Preserves health of skin
              2   Preserves health of mucous membranes

_____

8. His train is due to arrive on Sat, Apr 17, at 8 AM.

_____

9. Jeannette Rankin was the first woman elected to the US Congress.

_____

10. The book was written by historian Arthur Schlesinger, Jr.

_____

Commas (That Separate Basic Elements) • Practice 1

Commas That Separate Basic Elements   Use a comma before the conjunction to separate two independent clauses in a compound sentence. Use commas to separate three or more words, phrases, or clauses in a series. Use commas to separate coordinate adjectives.

COMMAS THAT SEPARATE BASIC ELEMENTS	
Independent Clauses	Everyone played well, but we still lost the game.
	Several people were ill, so we postponed the party.
Elements in a Series	Billy, Joe, and Ed tried out for the team. (3 people)
	Billy Joe and Ed tried out for the team. (2 people)
Adjectives	That ring contains a rare, exotic gem. (coordinate)
	My grandmother just got a new fur coat. (cumulative)

▶ **Exercise 1**   **Using Commas Correctly.**   Add commas where they are needed; not all sentences need commas.

EXAMPLE: The first four batters were Kyle Marc Pete and Jason.
The first four batters were Kyle, Marc, Pete, and Jason.

1. The dessert had a fluffy cream topping.

2. We requested the book weeks ago yet it hasn't come back so far.

3. The cookies should be cooled drizzled with melted chocolate and sprinkled with chopped nuts.

4. The fish was served with a rich tangy sauce.

5. The marshmallows melted in the steaming hot chocolate.

6. Paula tried to reach Jack all day but she had no luck.

7. Potted palms Easter lilies and pink azaleas banked the stage.

8. My first job was a happy rewarding experience.

9. We had hoped to see that new musical but no tickets were available.

10. Mr. Hawkins has a large collection of rare valuable coins.

▶ **Exercise 2**   **Recognizing Rules for Commas.**   Describe the comma rule for each sentence in Exercise 1 by writing *compound sentence*, *series*, *coordinate adjectives*, or *cumulative adjectives*.

EXAMPLE: _____series_____

1. _____

2. _____

3. _____

4. _____

5. _____

6. _____

7. _____

8. _____

9. _____

10. _____

27.2 **Commas** (That Separate Basic Elements) • **Practice 2**

▶ **Exercise 1** **Punctuating Simple and Compound Sentences.** Add the necessary commas to compound sentences only. If a sentence is not compound, write *correct.*

EXAMPLE: I shoveled snow all morning and now I am tired.
I shoveled snow all morning, and now I am tired.

1. My mother and father arrived on time but we had to wait for the other relatives. _____

2. Our family traveled to Canada last summer and hopes to visit parts of Europe next
year. _____

3. Leslie will graduate from high school this June and several of her other friends will graduate with her
but her best friend will not graduate until next year. _____

4. These customers want their merchandise delivered today or they plan to cancel their
orders. _____

5. We want to do some shopping and then go to a movie. _____

6. Our car needs a complete tune up for it has been over six months since it has had
one. _____

7. We neither wanted their assistance now nor would we accept it at some future
time. _____

8. Mother baked three peach pies and froze them for the picnic. _____

9. Join us at the meeting this evening for it promises to be dramatic and exciting. _____

10. The sun rose early and shone until the afternoon shower. _____

▶ **Exercise 2** **Punctuating Items in a Series and Coordinate Adjectives.** Add commas where
they are needed in each of the following sentences. For any sentences that do not need commas, write
correct.

EXAMPLE: I cleaned my closet my desk and my room.
I cleaned my closet, my desk, and my room.

1. The leader of the rock group was a friendly attractive youth. _____

2. Fresh fruit green vegetables lean meat and grain products were part of her diet. _____

3. She wore her new blue jeans. _____

4. Our advisor planned the trip chartered the bus and arranged the hotel reservations. _____

5. A well-planned thoughtful speech followed the introduction. _____

6. Battles were fought in New Jersey New York Pennsylvania Delaware and Virginia during the
Revolutionary War. _____

7. These hardy plants grow equally well in window boxes in home gardens and in open
fields. _____

8. The survey of the city showed that many buildings were abandoned that many small businesses had
closed and that the streets needed repair. _____

9. For Christmas I bought Father a pair of soft pigskin gloves. _____

10. The vessel slipped into port on a rainy moonless night. _____

Name _____ Date _____

 27.2 # Commas (That Set Off Added Elements) • **Practice 1**

Commas That Set Off Added Elements   Use a comma after an introductory word, phrase, or clause. Also use commas to set off a variety of parenthetical expressions and all nonessential expressions.

COMMAS WITH ADDED ELEMENTS	
Introductory Words	*Frankly,* I doubt we will win.
Introductory Phrases	*Not having studied,* I was nervous about the test.
Introductory Clauses	*As soon as the curtain fell,* the audience applauded.
Direct Address	There is no question, *Pam,* that you are right.
Certain Adverbs	We should note, *however,* that membership is rising.
Common Expressions	That watch, *as a matter of fact,* is a family heirloom.
Contrasting Expressions	Please give this note to Ben, *not to his brother.*
Nonessential Expressions	Bonnie, *who is new in town,* comes from San Diego.

▶ **Exercise 1**   **Using Commas with Added Elements.**   Add commas where they are needed in these sentences.

EXAMPLE: Luckily the train had not pulled out yet.
Luckily, the train had not pulled out yet.

1. What time is dinner Mom?

2. Before I knew what was happening I was at the bottom of the stairs.

3. I think that in addition we should get a small gift for Mr. Bailey.

4. Without thinking of his own safety the firefighter rushed into the burning building.

5. The principal not the class advisor will make the final decision.

6. Several teachers moreover have given us their support.

7. The previous owner I assure you took excellent care of this car.

8. Don't you think Ellen that we need more punch?

9. Once the movie was over I wondered why I had sat through the whole thing.

10. Tanya is without a doubt a stronger candidate than Mandy.

▶ **Exercise 2**   **Distinguishing Between Essential and Nonessential Elements.**   Decide whether the underlined words in each sentence are essential or nonessential. If they are nonessential, add commas where they are needed. If they are essential, make no changes.

EXAMPLE: Their new house a restored New England farmhouse is charming.
Their new house, a restored New England farmhouse, is charming.

1. Yul Brynner created the role of the king in the musical *The King and I.*

2. The song "Shall We Dance?" comes from *The King and I* which was written by Rodgers and Hammerstein.

3. The woman approaching the podium is the governor-elect.

4. The gloves that I gave Mom were the wrong color.

5. This sweater which was a gift from my aunt was handmade in Scotland.

6. Emily Dickinson who seldom left her home in Amherst became famous only later.

7. The reporter who wrote that story was a classmate of my father's.

8. The President speaking unofficially to reporters deplored the act.

9. Jeremy a somewhat retiring person surprised us all by winning the debate.

10. The famous soprano Beverly Sills will host the benefit.

27.2 **Commas** (That Set Off Added Elements) • **Practice 2**

▶ **Exercise 1**   **Setting Off Introductory Material.**   Add commas where they are needed in each of the following sentences. If a sentence needs no commas, write *correct*.

1. To practice my speech I rehearsed it in front of a mirror. _____
2. Cautioned by her mother and warned by her friends Betsy drove slowly through the busy intersection. _____
3. At the supermarket checkout counters always seem to have long lines. _____
4. In the kitchen we packed provisions for our camping trip. _____
5. If the weather is pleasant we hope to attend a concert in the park tonight. _____
6. George will you help at the bazaar on Saturday? _____
7. Of course the judge will punish the offenders. _____
8. Weakened by the storm the battered merchant ship limped into port two weeks late. _____
9. Delightedly Steve opened the door and greeted his cousins. _____
10. No I never thought I would have a chance to win first prize. _____

▶ **Exercise 2**   **Setting Off Parenthetical Expressions.**   In each of the following sentences, insert any commas needed to set off parenthetical expressions.

1. There are five houses on that street now not the two you remember.
2. You must nevertheless do the assignments.
3. Professor Watkins is I believe one of the top economic experts in the country.
4. The results we hope will be beneficial to everyone.
5. You know Mrs. Grey we will do whatever we can to help.

▶ **Exercise 3**   **Distinguishing Between Essential and Nonessential Material.**   Add commas where they are necessary in each sentence that contains nonessential material. If a sentence contains essential material, write *correct*.

1. The surf cresting against the sea wall damaged a number of summer cottages. _____
2. O'Hare Airport which is one of the busiest airports in the world handles many daily arrivals and departures. _____
3. The building chosen for rehabilitation was on our block. _____
4. Dr. Stevenson whom you heard lecture last week will speak again today. _____
5. Heinrich Schliemann who unearthed the ruins of Troy and Mycenae wanted to excavate the Minoan ruins on Crete. _____
6. I recognized the road that you described in your letter. _____
7. The three little boys playing near the fence all live on the next street. _____
8. The Interstate Commerce Commission which was authorized by Congress in 1887 has the power to regulate commerce among the states. _____
9. The original Fort Laramie built by fur traders William Sublette and Robert Campbell was established in 1834 near the junction of the North Platte and Laramie rivers in what is now the state of Wyoming. _____
10. The two books recommended by our science teacher are available in the library. _____

27.2 Commas (Other Uses) • Practice 1

Other Uses of the Comma   When a date, a geographical name, or an address is made up of two or more parts, use a comma after each part. Also use commas in the other situations shown in the chart below.

Date	On Friday, July 8, 1983, Grandma retired.
Geographical Name	We visited Phoenix, Arizona, on our vacation.
Address	The building at 597 Fifth Avenue, New York, New York, may be declared a National Historic Site.
Name with Title	Carol Hartman, LL.D., will give the second speech.
Salutation and Closing	Dear Uncle Jed, Very truly yours,
Large Numbers	2,687 3,489,620
Elliptical Sentence	Pam is going to Purdue next year; John, to Brown.
Direct Quotation	"Our next contestant," said the emcee, "is a banker."
To Avoid Confusion	With Betty, Jean planned the entire party.

▶ **Exercise 1**   **Adding Commas to Sentences.**   Insert commas where they are needed.

EXAMPLE: The Hermitage near Nashville Tennessee was Andrew Jackson's home.
The Hermitage near Nashville, Tennessee, was Andrew Jackson's home.

1. An article by Janet Coburn M.D. appeared in the Sunday magazine supplement.

2. My favorite breakfast is ham and eggs; Dad's pancakes and sausage.

3. In one week the station attracted 1238 new subscribers.

4. "I wonder" Joyce said "if anyone gave Tim my message."

5. Phil's new address is 17026 Parker Court Dover Delaware 19901.

6. To Peggy Anne confided her deepest fears.

7. On June 20, 1986 my sister will graduate from law school.

8. Entry-level salaries at that factory are $14000 a year.

9. "In the south wing" the guide continued "were the family's private living quarters."

10. Besides coffee cake is needed to feed this hungry crew.

▶ **Exercise 2**   **Punctuating a Letter.**   Add commas wherever necessary in the following letter.

> 672 Pondfield Road
> Bronxville New York 10708
> October 25 2001

Dear Gerri
   Well it looks as if I will see you this fall after all. My family and I will be coming to Bronxville next Saturday November 2 to visit Sarah Lawrence College. It has been a busy fall with all this college shopping going on. My current favorite is Rutgers in New Brunswick New Jersey. In addition we have visited Drew St. Johns and Seton Hall. I am applying to all of them but I haven't made any firm decision yet.
   My parents would like to take us out to lunch when we are in town next Saturday so think of some likely places. It will be good to see you again.

> Your old friend
> Sal

27.2 # Commas (Other Uses) • Practice 2

▶ **Exercise 1** **Using Commas in Other Situations.** Insert commas where necessary in each of the following sentences.

1. Mail entries by May 30 2000 to Box 5 Troy Iowa 52537.

2. Harold Andre Sr. lives in Santa Barbara California.

3. In 1978 the United States imported 8230000 barrels of oil.

4. In one day 5675 people called the toll-free phone number (800) 555-0220 to pledge money for the charity drive.

5. Jim spent his savings on a new bicycle; Pat on a CD player.

6. "We'll be late" Virginia worried "unless we hurry."

7. In the dark stairways can prove hazardous.

8. Karen Wilson D.D.S. will open an office in this building.

9. Paul said "On Saturday I will mow the lawn."

10. In what encyclopedia did you read that Montreal Quebec Canada has about 1214300 people?

▶ **Exercise 2** **Using Commas in a Social Letter.** In the following friendly letter, insert the necessary commas.

> 736 Williams Avenue
> Dayton Ohio 45402
> August 5, 1999

Dear Margaret
    Well after almost six weeks of travel my family and I have returned from our exciting trip to Egypt. Returning to the United States we were struck by the difference in cultures. It felt I think like going from an old world to a new.
    Naturally we saw all the famous sights: the Pyramids and Sphinx at Giza the temples of Karnak and Luxor the Aswan Dam and of course Cairo. Much to my surprise I was fascinated by Cairo the capital city of Egypt. I visited the Egyptian Museum the Cairo Tower Mohammed Ali Mosque and other places.
    My mother bought an old expensive bracelet. As if that weren't enough she also invested in a caftan called a galabias and two brass trays.
    I'm looking forward to your visit next week and I'll tell you about the rest of my experiences then.

> Affectionately
> Brad

▶ **Writing Application** **Using Commas Correctly in Your Own Writing.** Write five original sentences according to the following directions.

1. Write a compound sentence joined by the conjunction *but.*

_____

2. Write a sentence beginning with a participial phrase.

_____

3. Write a sentence containing a parenthetical expression.

_____

4. Write a sentence containing a nonessential appositive.

_____

5. Write a sentence that includes a direct quotation.

_____

27.3 **Semicolons and Colons • Practice 1**

The Semicolon Use semicolons in situations such as those illustrated in this chart.

USES OF THE SEMICOLON	
Independent Clauses Without Coordinating Conjunctions	The walls had been gray; we painted them yellow.
With Conjunctive Adverbs	Jim's chances were poor; nevertheless, he won the marathon.
With Transitional Expressions	Singles tennis games require energy; at the same time, they are fun.
With Elements Already Containing Commas	Our summer house, a ramshackle bungalow, is far from elegant; but the views from the porch are spectacular.

The Colon Use a colon after an independent clause to introduce the following elements: list of items, a formal quotation, a summarizing or explanatory sentence, and a formal appositive. Also use colons in the other situations shown in the chart.

USES OF THE COLON	
Lists	These students are competing: Ed Barker, Janet Arms, and Phil Mason.
Formal Quotations	The doctor turned to the woman: "There is no hope."
Explanatory Sentences	Our neighbor is wealthy: Her grandmother left her a million dollars.
Formal Appositives	We were lucky to get such a good advisor: Ms. Ward.
Numerals Giving Time	3:15 A.M. 9:27 P.M.
Periodical References	*Historical Review* 37:285 (volume: page)
Biblical References	Exodus 12:43 (chapter: verse)
Subtitles	*Write If You Get Work: The Best of Bob and Ray*
Labels Signaling Important Ideas	Caution: Contents are under pressure; do not use near fire, sparks, or flames.

▶ **Exercise 1** **Using Semicolons Correctly.** In each sentence below a comma is used in place of a semicolon. Circle the comma to show that a semicolon could or should be used there instead.

EXAMPLE: The weight-reduction program does not use scare tactics(,) it relies on behavior modification.

1. The yearbook, which should be published by mid-May, is still accepting ads from local merchants, however, we have enough ads to cover expenses.

2. Jed overslept, as a result, he wasn't ready when we called for him.

3. I am considering photography, film making, or figure drawing as an elective, but typing, driving, or career planning seem more practical.

4. Greg plans to follow in his father's footsteps, he is studying law.

▶ **Exercise 2** **Using Colons Correctly.** Add colons where they are needed.

EXAMPLE: The agent nodded "The 7 55 is boarding on Track 2."
   The agent nodded: "The 7:55 is boarding on Track 2."

1. These holiday plants are poisonous holly, mistletoe, and poinsettias.

2. The senator pounded the table "I refuse to concede."

3. The article was in *The New England Journal of Medicine* 11 215.

4. The solution seems plain We must attract more sponsors.

5. Our textbook is entitled *World History Connections to Today.*

27.3 Semicolons and Colons • Practice 2

▶ **Exercise 1**   **Using Semicolons.**   Insert one or more semicolons in each of the following sentences.

EXAMPLE: She skis well in fact, she is the state champion.
She skis well; in fact, she is the state champion.

1. The committee was unhappy with the decision nevertheless, they understood why it had been made.

2. Ben struggled up the steep, rocky hill and when he reached the top, Ben collapsed in a heap on the ground.

3. The clipper ship, battered by the vicious storm, fought a losing battle the main mast, weakened by the winds, broke.

4. We have invited cousin Hank, who is an attorney in Atlanta my friend Betty, who lives next door and Betty's brother, who is home from college for the weekend.

5. The storm washed out the road therefore, it took us an additional hour to reach the cabin.

▶ **Exercise 2**   **Using Colons.**   Add the necessary colons to each of the following sentences.
Underline any words in italics.

EXAMPLE: The article is in *Explorer* 5 11.
The article is in Explorer 5:11.

1. The office manager gave us a list of needed supplies paper clips, correction fluid, rubber bands, and brass fasteners.

2. Warning This product is for external use only.

3. The coach's explanation was simple and direct The team had decided to try to rebuild by using the younger players.

4. His historical research took him to a number of countries England, Belgium, France, Austria, and Germany.

5. The book you need is called *The Revolution Remembered Eyewitness Accounts of the War for Independence.*

▶ **Exercise 3**   **Using Semicolons and Colons Correctly.**   Add necessary semicolons or colons to each of the following sentences.

EXAMPLE: I have just reread my favorite children's book *Bambi.*
I have just reread my favorite children's book: Bambi.

1. Joanne purchased all the picnic supplies soda, potato chips, frankfurters, rolls, and fresh fruit.

2. The family agreed with the doctor's prognosis nevertheless, they decided to get another opinion.

3. The United States Postal Service issued an unusually attractive commemorative stamp It depicts General Bernardo de Galvez at the Battle of Mobile in 1780.

4. The first CD contains selections from the group's concert the second CD is a compilation of old hits.

5. The host was a well-known scientist and author Carl Sagan.

6. The President welcomed the foreign dignitary "The people of the United States welcome you and hope that your visit will be a pleasant and productive one."

7. This is her plan She wants to visit Milan and then Rome.

8. Mary Ellen invited Bill, who enjoyed playing cards Sue, who loved to dance and Glen, who didn't enjoy parties at all.

9. The flight to Ireland left at 11 30 P.M.

10. Six pupils took the state scholarship examination today the rest decided to wait for the next test.

27.4 Quotation Marks and Underlining (Quotation Marks for Direct Quotations) • Practice 1

Quotation Marks for Direct Quotations   A direct quotation represents a person's exact speech or thoughts and is enclosed in quotation marks (" "). An indirect quotation reports only the general meaning of what a person said or thought and does not require quotation marks. In writing direct quotations, use a comma or colon after an introductory expression and a comma, question mark, or exclamation mark after a quotation followed by a concluding expression. If there is an interrupting expression in the middle of a quoted sentence, set it off with commas. If an interrupting expression falls between two quoted sentences, treat it as a concluding expression.

Direct Quotations	Indirect Quotations
Sue asked, "What can I do to help?"	Sue asked what she could do to help.
"What can I do to help?" Susan asked.	
"I have a feeling," said Joe, "that a storm is brewing."	Joe had a feeling that a storm was brewing.
"Hurry!" shouted Ben. "The train is about to leave."	Ben shouted that we should hurry because the train was about to leave.

▶ **Exercise 1**   **Distinguishing Between Direct and Indirect Quotations.**   Label each sentence below *D* (for direct quotation) or *I* (for indirect quotation).

EXAMPLE: Mr. Dillon suggested, Spend no more than twenty minutes on the short answers so that you will have a half hour left for the essay. _____D_____

1. Louise suggested that I try out for the part. _____

2. Frank's parents told him that he would be grounded for a month if his grades didn't get better. _____

3. What time shall I pick you up? Andrew inquired. _____

4. Don is sure that Mr. Hawkins will give him a good reference. _____

5. Get off the bus at Dowling Street, Bill explained, and then walk two blocks south to Market. _____

6. That certainly is an odd color for a house, Pete observed. _____

7. Warren remarked that the harpist had been exceptionally good. _____

8. I asked Jill if I could borrow her notes on Chapter 15. _____

9. Oh, my gosh! Phil exclaimed. That jump was incredible! _____

10. Without a doubt, the owner stated, we will surpass last year's sales. _____

▶ **Exercise 2**   **Using Quotation Marks Correctly.**   In each sentence labeled *D* above, add quotation marks where they are needed. Rewrite below each sentence labeled *I* so that it contains a direct quotation.

EXAMPLE: _Mr. Dillon suggested, "Spend no more than twenty minutes on the short answers so that you will have a half hour left for the essay."_

1. _____

2. _____

3. _____

4. _____

5. _____

27.4 Quotation Marks and Underlining (Quotation Marks for Direct Quotations) • Practice 2

▶ **Exercise 1** **Enclosing Direct Quotations in Quotation Marks.** Add quotation marks where they are needed. The quoted fragment has been underlined to indicate where it begins and ends. If no quotation marks are needed, write *correct.*

EXAMPLE: I had pancakes for breakfast, announced Kathleen.

"I had pancakes for breakfast," announced Kathleen.

1. I am going to take my driver's test today, said Gloria. _____

2. My father replied, I will be happy to help you. _____

3. Tell me what happened, I pleaded. I can't bear to be in suspense any longer. _____

4. The principal asked us if we were on our way to the concert. _____

5. The bus driver sighed, Don't you have the correct change? _____

6. The salesclerk told us the price of the piano. _____

7. I know, she answered, I just heard the news on the radio. _____

8. My little brother says I am the world's bossiest sister. _____

9. The judge rapped the gavel: I want order in the courtroom. _____

10. I am so pleased you can visit us, wrote Joyce. We have all missed you since you moved away. _____

11. How many times have I told you, sighed Margaret, that you must not track mud into the house? _____

12. This is the hardest thing I have ever had to do, said my boss ominously. _____

13. Danielle wondered whether or not she should buy tickets for the concert. _____

14. Katherine announced, I have registered to vote in the next election. _____

15. Please leave the house right now, said Paulette. I need some peace and quiet. _____

▶ **Exercise 2** **More Work With Direct and Indirect Quotations.** Add quotation marks where necessary in each of the following sentences. Then label each sentence *D* (for direct quotation) or *I* (for indirect quotation).

EXAMPLE: "I'm going hiking right now," said Dan. ____D____

1. Karen thinks we should go on a picnic, announced Rick. _____

2. Dorian warned, Mr. Dombrowski frowns on tardiness. _____

3. Skip told us that he had just learned three new songs. _____

4. The movie was excellent, said Angelo. You really should go see it. _____

5. The woman at the ticket counter said, That will be forty-five dollars, please. _____

6. The acrobat told us that he practiced for several hours each day. _____

7. You are wrong, said Marco. I have been there, and I can tell you the sand is really white. _____

8. Margaret says that you were mean to her, Jason. _____

9. Darlene stood straight and tall: I passed my driving test. _____

10. We are looking forward to meeting you in person, wrote Allan. Letters and photographs are not really enough. _____

27.4 Quotation Marks and Underlining (Other Punctuation Marks with Quotation Marks, Quotation Marks in Special Situations) • Practice 1

Other Punctuation Marks with Quotation Marks   Always place a comma or a period inside the final quotation mark. Always place a semicolon or colon outside the final quotation mark. Place a question mark or exclamation mark inside the final quotation mark if the end mark is part of the quotation. If the end mark is not part of the quotation, place a question mark or exclamation mark outside the final quotation mark.

PLACING OTHER PUNCTUATION MARKS	
Commas and Periods **Colons and Semicolons**	"It seems evident," Dad said, "that we need a new roof." Ted observed, "What we really need around here is some organization"; then he proceeded to take charge.
Question Marks and Exclamation Marks	Pam asked, "Will the test cover only the first chapter?" Didn't Ms. Yu say, "The test will cover only the first chapter"?

Quotation Marks in Special Situations   Use single quotation marks for a quotation within a quotation. Use three ellipsis marks in a quotation to show that words have been omitted. When writing dialogue, begin a new paragraph with each change of speaker. For quotations longer than a paragraph, put quotation marks at the beginning of each paragraph and at the end of the final paragraph.

SPECIAL SITUATIONS IN QUOTATIONS	
Quotation Within a Quotation **Omitted Words**	Janice asked, "Wasn't it Patrick Henry who said, 'Give me liberty or give me death'? Kennedy's famous line "Ask not what you can do . . ." is from his inaugural address.
Dialogue	"Have you always been interested in gourmet food?" asked the interviewer. "Hardly," the famous chef answered. "Until I was sixteen, I subsisted on the typical American junk food diet. I lived for burgers, fries, and shakes and totally rejected anything green or anything that had lived in the ocean. "The summer I was sixteen, I went to Europe with my father, and my life was changed forever!"

▶ **Exercise 1**   **Punctuating Direct Quotations.**   Add the missing punctuation marks in each sentence.

EXAMPLE: The teacher asked, Who can tell me who said, Et tu, Brute?
           The teacher asked, "Who can tell me who said, 'Et tu, Brute'?"

1. Are you sure you told them, Take Exit 7, not 7A? Jane asked.

2. Max reminded me, The book is due on Thursday; but I still forgot.

3. We all hope, Sally wrote, that you will be back in school soon.

4. Have you seen Sharon since she got her hair cut? Donna asked.

5. Joyce exclaimed, What a glorious sunset that is!

6. Ann said, I am submitting my resignation effective immediately; then she left the meeting.

7. Can't you see, Josh pleaded, that we must act quickly?

8. Agnes asked, Who wrote the poem that begins, Whose woods these are . . . ?

9. Mike announced his plan: I will do the yard work and then use their swimming pool.

10. Wow! Harvey said. We can forget about beating this team.

▶ **Exercise 2**   **Paragraphing Dialogue.**   On the back of this sheet, write a short dialogue between two characters. Include at least one quotation that is over a paragraph long.

27.4 Quotation Marks and Underlining (Other Punctuation Marks with Quotation Marks, Quotation Marks in Special Situations) • Practice 2

▶ **Exercise 1** **Using Other Punctuation Marks Correctly with Quotations.**   In the following sentences, add quotation marks where necessary. Quoted fragments are underlined to show where they begin and end.

EXAMPLE: I am so angry with you! Randy shouted.
　　　　　"I am so angry with you!" Randy shouted.

1. According to H. L. Mencken, William Jennings Bryan was the national tear duct.
2. Did they ask, What can we do to help?
3. I think you can be whatever you want to be, Father said.
4. Emma Lazarus described the poor people of the world as huddled masses yearning to breathe free.
5. She agreed to work day and night; we never believed her.
6. When she saw the new car, she screamed, Hooray!
7. Oscar Wilde commented about a famous contemporary: Mr. Henry James writes fiction as if it were a painful duty.
8. Is that clear? she asked.
9. In the bottle were his secret ingredients: frog legs, talcum powder, and an old arrowhead.
10. Gertrude Stein gave the following advice to Ernest Hemingway: Remarks are not literature.

▶ **Exercise 2** **Punctuating with Ellipsis Marks and Single Quotation Marks.**   In each of the following sentences, insert double or single quotation marks as required.

EXAMPLE: Eudora Welty described a woman as moving . . . with the balanced heaviness and lightness of a pendulum in a grandfather clock.
　　　　　Eudora Welty described a woman as moving ". . . with the balanced heaviness and lightness of a pendulum in a grandfather clock."

1. "Then the president turned to us and said, I'm afraid I must decline, and walked from the room."
2. Robert Benchley once jested, I haven't been abroad in so long that I almost speak English without an accent.
3. A quotation from Katherine Mansfield begins, I want, by understanding myself, to understand others . . . .
4. "Later they studied Hamlet's famous soliloquy, which begins, To be, or not to be, that is the question."
5. Catherine Drinker Bowen has written: All artists quiver under the lash of adverse criticism. . . . When Beethoven heard that a certain conductor refused to perform one of his symphonies, he went to bed . . . until the symphony was performed.
6. "She asked, How did it happen? and burst into tears."
7. Mark Twain ends his criticism of Scott with these words: . . . He did measureless harm; more real and lasting harm, perhaps, than any other individual that ever wrote.
8. My mother said, I always wanted to sing professionally.
9. About Bernhard Shaw, Oscar Wilde said that he . . . hasn't an enemy in the world, and none of his friends like him.
10. "What did he mean when he said, You'll be sorry?"

27.4 # Quotation Marks and Underlining
(Underlining and Quotation Marks) • Practice 1

Underlining and Quotation Marks   Underline the titles of books, full-length plays, movies, series, periodicals, long musical compositions, albums, and works of art. In addition, underline the names of individual land, air, sea, and space craft; foreign words not yet accepted into English; numbers, symbols, letters, and words used to name themselves; and words that you want to stress.

USES OF UNDERLINING	
Titles	**Other Uses**
<u>David Copperfield</u> (novel)	The <u>Orient Express</u> (train)
<u>Our Town</u> (play)	The <u>Oceanic</u> (ship)
<u>Casablanca</u> (movie)	Our guide waved <u>au revoir</u>. (foreign word)
<u>The Waltons</u> (TV series)	A schwa looks like an upside down <u>e</u>.
<u>Aldonville Gazette</u> (newspaper)	What does <u>rococo</u> mean? (word as word)
<u>American Gothic</u> (painting)	Leave your boots <u>outside</u>. (emphasis)

Use quotation marks around the titles of short written works, episodes in a series, songs, and parts of long musical compositions or collections.

USES OF QUOTATION MARKS	
"Winter Dreams" (short story)	"Sounds of Silence" (song)
"The Raven" (poem)	"The Glorious Whitewasher" (chapter)
"Before Breakfast" (one-act play)	

The names of sacred writings and their parts and the titles of government charters, alliances, treaties, acts, statutes, and reports require no marking.

TITLES THAT REQUIRE NO MARKING	
the Koran	the Treaty of Paris
the Pentateuch	the Taft-Hartley Act

▶ **Exercise 1**   **Using Underlining and Quotation Marks.**   Add underlining and quotation marks where they are needed in these sentences. Not all sentences will require marking.

EXAMPLE: The Financial Journal ran an article entitled Adam's Fall.
The <u>Financial Journal</u> ran an article entitled "Adam's Fall."

1.   The song Moon River was the theme from the movie Breakfast at Tiffany's.

2.   The first book of the Old Testament is Genesis.

3.   Many of Amy's a's look like o's.

4.   O'Neil's Long Day's Journey into Night is a theatrical tour de force.

5.   I must learn to stop misusing the word imply.

▶ **Exercise 2**   **More Work with Underlining and Quotation Marks.**   Follow the directions for Exercise 1.

1.   Lindbergh made his famous trans-Atlantic flight in The Spirit of St. Louis.

2.   The Fox and the Grapes may be the most famous fable that Aesop wrote.

3.   Many consider the painting Guernica Picasso's chef-d'oeuvre.

4.   There are some excellent recipes in the chapter Soups and Stews.

5.   The title of the novel The Sound and the Fury is taken from a line in Shakespeare's Macbeth.

27.4 Quotation Marks and Underlining
(Underlining and Quotation Marks) • Practice 2

▶ Exercise 1 **Using Underlining and Quotation Marks.** Add underlining or quotation marks to each of the following sentences that require them. For items requiring neither, write *correct*.

EXAMPLE: In 1610 at the age of 17, Artemisia Gentileschi created the painting Susanna and the Elders.
In 1610 at the age of 17, Artemisia Gentileschi created the painting <u>Susanna and the Elders</u>.

1. The French expression le style c'est l'homme was one of her favorite sayings. _____

2. The train called the Twentieth Century Limited traveled between New York and
   Chicago. _____

3. Wilkommen, the opening song in the musical Cabaret, is considered a most effective opening
   number. _____

4. I just read the poem Wild Swans by Edna St. Vincent Millay. _____

5. The Daily Times has great political influence. _____

▶ Exercise 2 **Applying the Rules Governing the Use of Quotation Marks and Underlining.** To each of the following sentences, add quotation marks or underlining as necessary.

EXAMPLE: In her poem Spring, Edna St. Vincent Millay asked, To what purpose, April, do you return again?
In her poem "spring," Edna St. Vincent Millay asked, "To what purpose, April, do you return again?"

1. Two of romantic painter John Constable's works are Salisbury Cathedral and Haystacks.
2. Chaucer's Canterbury Tales begins with the following words: When in April the sweet showers fall . . .
3. She had bought, Flannery O'Connor wrote, a new dress for the occasion.
4. In his essay Dunkirk, Winston Churchill describes the most famous retreat in history.
5. What factors led you to that conclusion? she asked.
6. I enjoyed Emily Brontë's novel, Wuthering Heights.
7. Bill continued, Then my sister said, I am going to enlist! and my mother began to cry.
8. In Shakespeare's Romeo and Juliet, Romeo sighs, . . . O! that I were a glove upon that hand . . .
9. That's my final offer, he blurted. Take it or leave it.
10. Remember to cross your t's and dot your i's.

▶ Writing Application **Using Quotation Marks and Underlining Correctly in Your Own Writing.** Write original sentences according to the following directions.

1. Write a sentence that contains the name of a movie.

   _____

2. Write as a direct quotation advice from a grandparent to grandchildren. Include a conversational tag.

   _____

3. Write a sentence containing the name of a song or a poem.

   _____

4. Write a sentence naming a local newspaper.

   _____

5. Write a sentence containing a word as a name for itself.

   _____

27.5 # Dashes, Parentheses, Brackets, and Hyphens (Dashes, Parentheses) • Practice 1

Dashes, Parentheses, Brackets, and Hyphens Use dashes to indicate an abrupt change of thought, a dramatic interrupting idea, or a summary statement. Dashes can also be used to set off a nonessential appositive, modifier, or parenthetical expression when it is long, when it is already punctuated, or when you want to be dramatic.

USES OF THE DASH	
Change of Thought	I'd like to finish—oh, well, I can do that later.
Dramatic Interruption	They arrived—can you believe it?—at exactly the same time.
Summary Statement	Speeches, debates, polls—all are part of election tradition.
Nonessential Element	Dolley Madison's gown—the one she wore at her husband's inauguration—is on display at the Smithsonian.

Parentheses Use parentheses to set off asides and explanations only when the material is not essential or when it consists of one or more sentences. Also use parentheses to set off numerical explanations such as the dates of a person's birth and death and around numbers and letters marking a series.

USES OF PARENTHESES	
Phrases	Fenwick's first novel (probably his best) has never been reprinted.
Sentences	If we go (Have you received the tickets?), we plan to leave early.
Letters, Numbers, and Dates	The job involves (a) preparing budgets, (b) keeping financial reports, and (c) issuing checks.
	Edgar Allan Poe (1809–1849) achieved fame as a short-story writer, poet, and journalist.

▶ **Exercise 1** **Using the Dash.** Add dashes where they are needed in the following sentences.

EXAMPLE: I told him he drove me to it that his behavior was inexcusable.
I told him—he drove me to it—that his behavior was inexcusable.

1. Dolls, toy soldiers, trucks all kinds of toys were heaped under the tree.

2. The key is right now, where did I put that key?

3. Fame, fortune, critical acclaim all these were suddenly hers.

4. She told me this is just between us, of course that she regrets her decision.

5. The new stadium it boasts a retractable dome seats fifty thousand.

▶ **Exercise 2** **Using Parentheses.** Add parentheses wherever they are appropriate.

EXAMPLE: One of the twins I don't remember which wanted to join the circus.
One of the twins (I don't remember which) wanted to join the circus.

1. The first word of the *Odyssey andra*, meaning "man" suggests the theme of the epic.

2. Elizabeth Cady Stanton 1815–1902 was an early champion.

3. The bactrian camel has two humps, while the Arabian camel also called a *dromedary* has only one.

4. Anything used for money must perform three functions: a it must serve as a freely accepted means of exchange; b it must have value in itself; and c it must permit the accumulation of wealth.

5. Pendleton bought ten shares of General Widget the price was the lowest in years and began to regard himself a capitalist.

27.5 Dashes, Parentheses, Brackets, and Hyphens (Dashes, Parentheses) • Practice 2

▶ **Exercise 1**   **Using the Dash.**   Add one or two dashes to each of the following sentences.

EXAMPLE: A balanced diet contains all the nutrients proteins, carbohydrates, fats, vitamins, and minerals.
A balanced diet contains all the nutrients—proteins, carbohydrates, fats, vitamins, and minerals.

1. Athletics that is, winning athletics can inspire college alumni to contribute large sums of money to their universities.

2. Once a year no more than that I like to visit my aunt in her house by the beach.

3. What would you do if someone like Albert Einstein that genius wanted to have a talk with you?

4. The delayed I should say, three hours overdue train will arrive soon.

5. The flowers in the vases roses carnations and lilies certainly do cheer up this room.

6. Boots, jeans, cowboy hats, and belts Jake had all the trappings of the urban cowboy.

7. Alex the one who had given her the locket would be arriving in twenty minutes.

8. To dance, to sing, to laugh these were Sally's only ambitions.

9. In her entire life all ninety-two years my great-grandmother never traveled out of New York.

10. Her house or should I say cottage? was decorated in a very unusual manner.

▶ **Exercise 2**   **Enclosing Material in Parentheses.**   Rewrite the following items, adding parentheses and capitals where needed.

EXAMPLE: Mosquitoes how I hate their buzzing! bit us.

_____ _Mosquitoes (How I hate their buzzing!) bit us._ _____

1. Florence Nightingale 1820–1910 is regarded as the founder of modern nursing.

   _____

2. She served as a nurse during the Crimean War 1854–1856.

   _____

3. For dinner we had steak, baked potatoes, and broccoli. I have always disliked broccoli. A homemade apple pie was served for dessert.

   _____

4. Built in 1826, the stone barn a Hancock Shaker Village landmark housed fifty-two cows.

   _____

5. Estoril we drove there from Lisbon is a popular tourist resort in Portugal.

   _____

6. Mystic Village in Connecticut and Sturbridge Village in Massachusetts have you ever visited either of them? recreate life of an earlier period.

   _____

7. Her plan is to create a garden of 1 lilacs, 2 roses, 3 tulips, and 4 daffodils.

   _____

8. The firm's New Jersey phone number is 201 555-4678.

   _____

9. Because of the storm what a blizzard!, school was canceled.

   _____

10. When you apply to a college, be sure you send a the completed application, b your high school transcript, c your SAT scores, d several references, and e the registration fee.

   _____

27.5 Dashes, Parentheses, Brackets, and Hyphens (Brackets) • Practice 1

Brackets Use brackets to enclose a word or words inserted in a quotation by a writer who is quoting someone else. Brackets are also used sometimes with *sic* (thus) to show that the author of the quoted material misspelled or mispronounced a word or phrase.

USES OF BRACKETS	
Inserted	The mayor declared, "They [the reporters] have quoted me out of context."
With *sic*	The closing on the letter was "Yours respectively [sic]."

▶ **Exercise 1**   **Using Brackets Correctly.**   Add brackets where they are needed in each of the following sentences.

EXAMPLE: The epigram about weather usually attributed to him Mark Twain was actually written by a newspaper editor in Connecticut.
The epigram about weather usually attributed to him [Mark Twain] was actually written by a newspaper editor in Connecticut.

1. An American who won the world chess championship Bobby Fischer eventually forfeited the title.

2. As Oscar Wilde observed, "It experience is the name everyone gives to their mistakes."

3. One fact in the paper was footnoted as follows: "Found somewhere in *Encyclopaedia Brittanico* sic."

4. In this novel *Pudd'nhead Wilson*, the main character takes up fingerprinting as a hobby.

5. The actor misquoted slightly: "We are such stuff as dreams are made of sic."

▶ **Exercise 2**   **Using Dashes, Parentheses, and Brackets.**   Rewrite the sentences below, inserting the proper punctuation in each sentence.

EXAMPLE: The bar graph see page 146 shows the relation between imports and exports in 1985.
The bar graph (see page 146) shows the relation between imports and exports in 1985.

1. The legislature is likely to choose one of the following plans for tax reduction: a a cut of 1 percent in the sales tax; b a cut in income taxes; c a reduction of corporate taxes.

_____

_____

2. Mrs. Malaprop accuses Lydia of being "as headstrong as an allegory sic on the banks of the Nile."

_____

_____

3. The smell of greasepaint, the roar of the crowd Tompkins was turning his back on all that.

_____

_____

4. Mr. Wilkes Wasn't he the man that carved birds? is now working on a replica of a California condor.

_____

_____

5. We will need to oh, here comes my bus, finally.

_____

_____

27.5 Dashes, Parentheses, Brackets, and Hyphens (Brackets) • Practice 2

▶ **Exercise 1** **Enclosing Material in Brackets.** In the following items, insert brackets where necessary.

EXAMPLE: "The shoulders sic marched down the street," reported the little girl.
"The shoulders [sic] marched down the street," reported the little girl.

1. "Fourscore and seven years ago 87 years, our fathers brought forth on this continent a new nation . . ."

2. "We the people of the United States, in order to form a more perfect Union of the thirteen former colonies, establish justice, insure domestic tranquility, provide for the common defense . . ."

3. "No perking sic" was written on the sign at the corner.

4. "The figures sculptures made of ice melted in the heat."

5. "Who won it the World Series?" asked the little boy.

6. "It is well-known fact according to whom? that our team will win," boasted Scott.

7. "That restaurant Susanne's has live jazz every Friday and Saturday, during dinner," said Stan.

8. According to Alma, "You could have knocked her over with a fender sic."

9. The reporter wrote, "They the family of the victim are not going to forget this sight for as long as they live!"

10. Darlene wrote, "I am too ill to go to Helen's her friend's birthday party."

▶ **Writing Application** **Using Dashes, Parentheses, and Brackets in Your Own Writing.** Write ten sentences. Each one should illustrate a rule governing the use of dashes, parentheses, and brackets. Remember to follow the rules governing the use of other punctuation marks with parentheses.

1. _____

_____

2. _____

_____

3. _____

_____

4. _____

_____

5. _____

_____

6. _____

_____

7. _____

_____

8. _____

_____

9. _____

_____

10. _____

_____

27.5 # Dashes, Parentheses, Brackets, and
Hyphens (Hyphens) • Practice 1

Hyphens   Use a hyphen when writing out numbers from *twenty-one* through *ninety-nine* and with fractions used as adjectives. Also use hyphens with certain prefixes and compound nouns, with compound modifiers (unless they are proper adjectives or contain an adverb ending in *-ly*), and to avoid confusion.

USING HYPHENS		
With Numbers	fifty-two cards	one-third cup
With Prefixes	non-Germanic	ex-governor
With Compound Nouns	son-in-law	good-for-nothing
With Compound Modifiers	an ill-timed comment	North American bird
	a first-rate player	highly recommended movie

At the end of a line, divide words only between syllables. Most words with prefixes and suffixes can be divided between the prefix and root or root and suffix. However, never leave a single letter standing alone. In addition, do not divide proper nouns and proper adjectives, divide hyphenated words only after the hyphen, and do not divide a word that falls at the end of a page.

HYPHENS AT THE ENDS OF LINES				
Correct	con-cern	post-pone	re-mark	ex-husband
Incorrect	conc-ern	e-nough	Den-mark	self-de-feat

▶ **Exercise 1**   **Using Hyphens.**   Place hyphens where they are needed. (Not all sentences need hyphens.)

EXAMPLE: At the beginning of the story, Scrooge is a tight fisted employer.
At the beginning of the story, Scrooge is a tight-fisted employer.

1. His great grandfather had been Lincoln's best friend.

2. His round head resembled a jack o'lantern.

3. Out of a possible hundred, Alice got ninety six answers right.

4. The route traced on the map is self explanatory.

5. Mark had always wanted to visit New Orleans for the Mardi Gras festivities.

6. The new law requires children's clothing to be made of fire resistant materials.

7. The driver swerved sharply to avoid a head on collision.

8. I did not remember that this was such a totally impossible task.

9. The five story building will be replaced by a much taller one.

10. Senator elect Robinson personally thanked all of her campaign workers.

▶ **Exercise 2**   **Hyphenating Words.**   Rewrite each word below, using a hyphen at any place where the word could be divided at the end of a line of writing.

EXAMPLES: carefully ____*care-fully*____   among ____*among*____

1. misspell _____   6. length _____

2. elbow _____   7. Belgium _____

3. erase _____   8. disagree _____

4. interfere _____   9. around _____

5. all-important _____   10. circumspect _____

27.5 Dashes, Parentheses, Brackets, and Hyphens (Hyphens) • Practice 2

▶ **Exercise 1** **Using Hyphens to Join Words.** If an item does not need hyphens, write *correct*. If it does, add them.

EXAMPLE: up to date report
up-to-date report

1. thirty first floor _____
2. semiinvalid _____
3. ex Senator _____
4. self adjusting _____
5. pro American _____
6. well intentioned advice _____
7. South American history _____
8. greatly exaggerated story _____
9. two thirds cup _____
10. all around athlete _____
11. twenty six students _____
12. two thirds of the marbles _____
13. wildly enthusiastic crowd _____

14. much sought after painting _____
15. pre Columbian art _____
16. a comic strip character _____
17. out of date styles _____
18. three fourths cup _____
19. a well decorated room _____
20. reexamination _____
21. ex roommate _____
22. deemphasize _____
23. president elect _____
24. a five year old girl _____
25. thirty seven new homes _____

▶ **Exercise 2** **Using Hyphens at the Ends of Lines.** If a word is broken correctly, write *correct*. If not, rewrite it.

EXAMPLE: cur-ed   *cured*

1. Span-ish _____
2. sis-ter-in-law _____
3. excitem-ent _____
4. un-usual _____
5. partici-pation _____
6. frisk-y _____
7. re-lease _____
8. Amer-ican _____
9. gentle-ness _____
10. self-inter-est _____
11. vibr-ant _____
12. great-grand-mother _____
13. tri-umph _____

14. dis-gusting _____
15. tourna-ment _____
16. a-bandon _____
17. classif-y _____
18. chip-munk _____
19. mott-o _____
20. gera-nium _____
21. noc-turnal _____
22. change-able _____
23. nin-th _____
24. news-paper _____
25. undec-ided _____

27.6 # Apostrophes • Practice 1

Apostrophes   The possessives of nouns are formed as shown in the first chart below. The possessives of some pronouns are formed with apostrophes, but the possessives of personal pronouns are not. Apostrophes are also used in contractions and a few special plurals.

POSSESSIVE FORMS OF NOUNS			
Singular Nouns	**Plural Nouns**	**Compound Nouns**	**Joint and Individual Ownership**
a day's work	two days' work	sister-in-law's idea	Ted and Paula's dog (joint)
an actress's role	two actresses' roles	Elizabeth I's crown	Ann's and Jim's answers (individuals)
a man's opinion	two men's opinions	runner-up's words	

POSSESSIVE FORMS OF PRONOUNS		
Indefinite		**Personal**
someone's	anyone else's	my, mine, our, ours, your, yours
anybody's	each other's	his, her, hers, its, their, theirs

OTHER USES OF APOSTROPHES			
Contractions			**Special Plurals**
aren't	we'd	o'clock	There are three *h*'s in *Khrushchev*.
won't	you'd	Class of '97	Your *3*'s look like *?*'s.

▶ **Exercise 1**   **Writing Possessive Forms.**   Write the possessive form of each noun or pronoun below.

EXAMPLES: goose ____*goose's*____   they ____*their*____

1. dress _____
2. children _____
3. anyone _____
4. boys _____
5. days _____
6. each other _____
7. players _____
8. Smiths _____
9. it _____
10. brother-in-law _____

11. women _____
12. geese _____
13. Andy and Steven (joint) _____
14. minutes _____
15. our _____
16. one another _____
17. Lois _____
18. mice _____
19. motorists _____
20. passer-by _____

▶ **Exercise 2**   **Using Apostrophes in Other Ways.**   Add apostrophes where they are needed.

EXAMPLE: Arent the members of the Class of 82 having a reunion?
       Aren't the members of the Class of '82 having a reunion?

1. Richie gets straight *As* in math.
2. Weve put more water in its tank, but the fish still looks unhappy.
3. You shouldnt use so many *and*s.
4. Heres the package that theyve been waiting for.
5. At five oclock, please stop and sort out whats yours and whats ours.

27.6 Apostrophes • Practice 2

▶ Exercise 1 Using Apostrophes. Rewrite each of the following items, following the instructions in parentheses.

EXAMPLE: *T* (Write the plural form.) _____ *T's*

1. the computer of the man (Put in the possessive case.) _____
2. two of the clock (Write the contracted form.) _____
3. the book of James (Put in the possessive case.) _____
4. 1995 (Write the contracted form.) _____
5. the house of the Joneses (Put in the possessive case.) _____
6. the cribs of the babies (Put in the possessive case.) _____
7. the sports of the women (Put in the possessive case.) _____
8. the stories of each other (Put in the possessive case.) _____
9. *12* (Write the plural form, underlining the number.) _____
10. who is (Write the contracted form.) _____
11. will not (Write the contracted form.) _____
12. The sandwich belongs to whom? (Reword, the question using a possessive pronoun.)

_____

13. the advice of the Department of Defense (Put in the possessive case.)

_____

14. the comedy act of Pat and Mike (joint.) _____
15. they are (Write the contracted form.) _____
16. the report of someone (Put in the possessive case.) _____
17. the son of Queen Elizabeth II (Put in the possessive case.) _____
18. a vacation of two weeks (Put in the possessive case.) _____
19. the bicycles of Jane and Mike (individual.) _____
20. the dog's tail (Use a possessive pronoun for *dog's*.) _____

▶ Writing Application Using the Rules for Apostrophes in Original Sentences. Write ten sentences of your own that include apostrophes. Be sure your sentences illustrate at least five different ways in which to use apostrophes.

1. _____
2. _____
3. _____
4. _____
5. _____
6. _____
7. _____
8. _____
9. _____
10. _____

Diagraming Basic Sentence Parts (Subjects, Verbs, and Modifiers)

Subjects, Verbs, and Modifiers In a sentence diagram, the subject and verb are written on a horizontal line with the subject on the left and the verb on the right. A vertical line separates the subject and verb. Adjectives and adverbs are placed on slanted lines directly below the words they modify.

SUBJECT AND VERB	ADDING ADJECTIVES AND ADVERBS
James has arrived.	*Gail's new blue* coat tore *very badly.*
James │ has arrived	coat │ tore *(Gail's, new, blue)* *(very, badly)*

Orders and directions are diagramed with the understood subject *you* in parentheses. *Here* and *there* are usually adverbs and diagramed accordingly. When *there* is an expletive, it is positioned on a short line above the subject. The expletive style is also used for interjections and nouns of direct address.

IMPERATIVE SENTENCE	*THERE* AND *HERE* AS ADVERBS	EXPLETIVE STYLE
Go away.	*Here* is my book.	*There* is an important holiday tomorrow.
(you) │ Go *(away)*	book │ is *(my)* *(Here)*	There / holiday │ is *(an, important)* *(tomorrow)*

▶ **Exercise 1** **Diagraming Subjects, Verbs, and Modifiers.** Correctly diagram each sentence in the space provided. Refer to the examples above if you need to.

1. Her mother drives very carefully.

2. My baby brother speaks quite well.

3. Fresh green vegetables are sold here.

▶ **Exercise 2** **More Work with Diagrams.** Correctly diagram each sentence.

1. Drive carefully

2. There is a funny movie playing nearby.

Diagraming Basic Sentence Parts (Subjects, Verbs, and Modifiers)

▶ **Exercise 1**   **Diagraming Subjects, Verbs, and Modifiers.**   Correctly diagram each sentence.

1. Nine graceful deer grazed peacefully

2. There are seven extremely important rules.

3. Joyce, please drive very carefully.

4. Oh, here comes the wonderfully amusing Raymond.

5. The graceful, hard-working dancers practiced daily.

6. The large blue bus turned slowly.

Diagraming Basic Sentence Parts (Adding Conjunctions)

Adding Conjunctions   Conjunctions are generally shown in a diagram on a dotted line between the words being connected. In sentences with compound subjects and/or verbs, the horizontal line of the diagram is split so each of the compound parts appears on a line of its own. If compound verbs share a helping verb, the helping verb is placed on the main line of the diagram. If each part of the compound verb has its own helping verb, each helping verb is placed on the line with its verb.

COMPOUND SUBJECT AND VERB	OTHER USES OF CONJUNCTIONS
My *homework* and my *project are written* and *typed.*	*Blue* and *white* floodlights shine *brightly* and *dramatically.*

▶ **Exercise 1**   **Diagraming Sentences with Conjunctions.**   Correctly diagram each sentence in the space provided.

1. This basketball player jumps well and rebounds effectively.

2. Young and old people participate eagerly and often.

3. The suspects were questioned and released.

▶ **Exercise 2**   **More Work with Conjunctions.**   Correctly diagram each sentence.

1. The sun was shining brightly and intensely.

2. My father and my mother are leaving.

Diagraming Basic Sentence Parts (Adding Conjunctions)

> **Exercise 1**   Diagraming Sentences with Conjunctions.   Correctly diagram each sentence.

1. The white swan and its mate floated along lazily.

2. The comfortable but expensive bike was displayed here and there.

3. Both Carla and Jane should study harder and sleep more.

4. The players and the coaches will relax today and work again tomorrow.

5. Neither Alberta nor Johnny can lose gracefully.

6. The exhausted traveler quietly sat and waited.

Diagraming Basic Sentence Parts (Complements)

Complements   Place a direct object on the main horizontal line after the verb; separate it from the verb with a short horizontal line. Place an indirect object under the verb on a short horizontal line extending from a slanted line. An objective complement is placed next to the direct object on the horizontal line and separated from it with a slanted line.

Predicate nominatives and predicate adjectives are diagramed the same way. Place them on the main line after the verb and separate them from the verb with a line slanting toward the subject.

▶ **Exercise 1**   **Diagraming Sentences with Complements.**   Correctly diagram each sentence in the space provided.

1. Her spring outfit is unusually attractive.

2. The principal gave Betsy the message.

▶ **Exercise 2**   **More Work with Complements.**   Correctly diagram each sentence.

1. My best friend was elected chairperson.

2. She colored the letters gray and gold.

Diagraming Basic Sentence Parts (Complements)

▶ **Exercise 1** **Diagraming Complements.** Correctly diagram each sentence.

1. Ethel read that interesting book.

2. Marcie handed us a large, heavy envelope.

3. The mayor called the situation a terrible dilemma.

4. Louis Armstrong was a jazz musician.

5. Kevin and Edward gave their parents a solemn promise.

6. The cardboard box contained old photographs and handwritten letters.

Diagraming Phrases and Clauses (Prepositional Phrases)

Prepositional Phrases A prepositional phrase is diagramed directly beneath the word it modifies. The preposition goes on a slanted line and the object sits on a horizontal line. If a prepositional phrase modifies the object of a preposition in another phrase, it is diagramed directly under the object of the preposition of the first phrase.

ADJECTIVE PHRASES	ADVERB PHRASES
A young couple *with children in tow* arrived late.	A package came *for you* early *in the morning.*

▶ **Exercise 1** **Diagraming Prepositional Phrases.** Diagram the following sentences in the spaces below.

1. The singers from Italy and Germany were wonderful.

2. The car in the garage was damaged in the accident.

▶ **Exercise 2** **More Work with Diagrams.** Correctly diagram each sentence.

1. These spices are bitter to the taste.

2. I will speak to the person in charge.

Diagraming Phrases and Clauses (Prepositional Phrases)

▶ **Exercise 1**   **Diagraming Prepositional Phrases.**   Correctly diagram each sentence.

1. With some trepidation, the messenger approached the man in the dark corner of the room.

2. She left Dallas in the morning and never returned.

3. I will do this with you or without you.

4. From the ceiling of the furniture store hung lights of various kinds.

5. I planted the flowers in the garden near the house.

6. During the night, lightning from a thunderstorm flashed in the window.

Diagraming Phrases and Clauses (Appositives and Appositive Phrases)

Appositives and Appositive Phrases Put an appositive in parentheses following the noun or pronoun it renames. Any modifiers go directly beneath it.

APPOSITIVE PHRASES

I spoke to Bob Wilson, *my baseball coach.*

His poster, *a colorful drawing of modern Jerusalem*, is not accurate.

▶ **Exercise 1** **Diagraming Appositives and Appositive Phrases.**   Diagram the following sentences in the spaces below.

1. My new car, a sleek Exeter, is quite expensive.

2. I bought a warm shirt, a flannel with bright stripes.

▶ **Exercise 2** **More Work with Diagrams.**   Correctly diagram each sentence.

1. Harry Houdini, the famous magician, died in 1926.

2. The dancer was born in Hopkins, a city in Minnesota.

Diagraming Phrases and Clauses (Appositives and Appositive Phrases)

▶ **Exercise 1**   **Diagraming Appositive Phrases.**   Correctly diagram each sentence.

1. Alicia Perez, our cousin from Mexico, sent us a big box of cookies.

2. Kurt, the contractor in charge of this job, will be here at noon.

3. For information on this topic, call Cynthia, an excellent reference librarian.

4. Mr. Collins, an excellent history teacher, is in the next room.

5. In the morning Frank, our neighbor, walks around the block.

6. The museum guide, a very knowledgeable person, described the paintings in the gallery.

Diagraming Phrases and Clauses (Participles and Participial Phrases)

Participles and Participial Phrases   A participle is placed directly beneath the noun or pronoun it modifies. Write it partly on a slanted line and partly on a horizontal line with any modifiers beneath it. A complement, such as a direct object, is placed on the horizontal line. A nominative absolute, formed from a noun and a participle, is positioned above the rest of the sentence as shown in the example on the right.

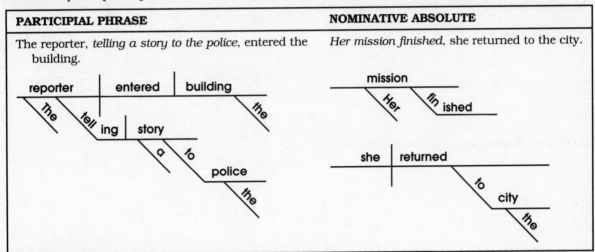

PARTICIPIAL PHRASE	NOMINATIVE ABSOLUTE
The reporter, *telling a story to the police*, entered the building.	*Her mission finished*, she returned to the city.

> **Exercise 1**   **Diagraming Participles and Participial Phrases.**   Diagram the following sentences using the spaces provided.

1. Reaching the window, the woman called for help.

2. His car destroyed, Tom notified the police.

> **Exercise 2**   **More Work with Diagrams.**   Correctly diagram each sentence.

1. The children, playing in the rain, ruined their shoes.

2. Unfrozen carefully, the turkey was ready for the oven.

Diagraming Phrases and Clauses (Participles and Participial Phrases)

> **Exercise 1** **Diagraming Participles and Participial Phrases.** Correctly diagram each sentence.

1. The man selling balloons at the circus is my uncle.

2. The jetliner, passing swiftly across the sky, disappeared.

3. The lady standing on the corner is waiting for the bus.

4. The girl working on the experiment is my friend.

5. Some of the people running in the park are on the track team.

6. The sun setting behind the mountains, we left the park.

Diagraming Phrases and Clauses (Gerunds and Gerund Phrases)

Gerunds and Gerund Phrases   Gerunds and gerund phrases used as subjects, direct objects, or predicate nominatives are placed on a stepped line atop a pedestal. Modifiers and complements are diagramed in the usual way. When a gerund or gerund phrase is used as an indirect object or object of a preposition, the stepped line extends from a slanted line.

GERUND PHRASES

Humming softly is a trademark of this conductor.

She was prevented from *eating dessert.*

▶ **Exercise 1**   **Diagraming Gerunds and Gerund Phrases.**   In the spaces provided below, diagram the following sentences.

1. Basking in the sun is her favorite activity.

2. I often remember waiting at his house.

▶ **Exercise 2**   **More Work with Diagrams.**   Correctly diagram each sentence.

1. My uncle relaxes by painting landscapes.

2. Preparing a schedule of activities is his major responsibility.

Diagraming Phrases and Clauses (Gerunds and Gerund Phrases)

Exercise 1 **Diagraming Gerund Phrases.** Correctly diagram each sentence.

1. Swimming in the lake was Glenda's favorite activity.

2. Jeremiah enjoys playing tunes on his harmonica.

3. Bob's greatest talent was making dollhouse furniture from paper.

4. Jack's job, landscaping for the county, could not be done in wet weather.

5. We need some new tools for making ceramic pots.

6. Serving meals at the diner was Pat's part-time job.

Diagraming Phrases and Clauses (Infinitives and Infinitive Phrases)

Infinitives and Infinitive Phrases   An infinitive used as a noun is diagramed on a pedestal. When an infinitive acts as an adjective or adverb, its diagram is similar to that of a prepositional phrase. The subject of an infinitive is placed on a line to the left. If *to* is understood, it is placed in parentheses.

▶ **Exercise 1**   **Diagraming Infinitives and Infinitive Phrases.**   Diagram the following sentences in the spaces provided.

1. We watched Terry swim the channel.

2. The reason to read newspapers is obvious.

▶ **Exercise 2**   **More Work with Diagrams.**   Correctly diagram each sentence.

1. To monitor the performance is Jean's role.

2. To fly to Denver is the best way.

Diagraming Phrases and Clauses (Infinitives and Infinitive Phrases)

▶ **Exercise 1**   **Diagraming Infinitives and Infinitive Phrases.**   Correctly diagram each sentence.

1. Tom took three hours to read his e-mail.

2. To be taken seriously was all Jesse ever wanted.

3. Michelle wanted to learn the names of all the plants along the hiking trail.

4. Hillary and Jane told Alice to pack her bags and move out.

5. To dance is to live.

6. The one-year-old clearly wanted to take her first step.

Diagraming Phrases and Clauses

Compound Sentences   Diagram each independent clause of a compound sentence as you would a separate sentence. Then join the verbs of the clauses with a dotted step line. On the step line, write either the coordinating conjunction or the semicolon that joins the two clauses.

COMPOUND SENTENCES

Phil brought the pizza, and Nell brought the soda.   I have no explanation; you must accept my word now.

▶ **Exercise 1**   **Diagraming Compound Sentences.**   In the spaces provided, diagram the sentences below.

1. The train arrived early, but we were waiting at the station.

2. I already know your answer; you will refuse my request.

▶ **Exercise 2**   **More Work with Diagrams.**   Correctly diagram each sentence.

1. Most of London was destroyed in the war, but every important building has been restored.

2. She read the recipe carefully; then she assembled the ingredients.

Diagraming Phrases and Clauses (Compound Sentences)

▶ **Exercise 1**   **Diagraming Compound Sentences.**   Correctly diagram each sentence.

1. A large family has moved into our neighborhood, so now each of my sisters has a new friend.

2. Jake likes to wear moccasins around the house, but Stacy prefers slippers or socks.

3. Hank phoned earlier, but you were at the shopping mall.

4. I removed the drawers, but I could not budge the heavy cabinet.

5. We must ship the gift today, or it will not reach my brother in time for his birthday.

6. Carol visited some friends during the day, but she did not have a good time.

Diagraming Phrases and Clauses (Complex Sentences)

Complex Sentences Both adjective and adverb clauses are diagramed on a line beneath the independent clause and connected to the independent clauses by a dotted line. With an adjective clause, the dotted line extends from the noun or pronoun the clause modifies to the relative pronoun or relative adverb in the clause. With an adverb clause, the dotted line extends from the word modified to the verb in the adverb clause. The subordinating conjunction is written along the dotted line.

A noun clause is placed on a pedestal extending upward from the position it fills in the independent clause. If the introductory word has no function in the noun clause, it is written along the pedestal.

▶ **Exercise 1** **Diagraming Complex Sentences.** Diagram the following complex sentences.

1. I know what she means.

2. We arrived after the party began.

▶ **Exercise 2** **More Work with Diagrams.** Correctly diagram each complex sentence. Use the back of this sheet, if neccessary.

1. The memo which he received explained the problem clearly.

2. Whichever hat she wants will be fine with us.

Diagraming Phrases and Clauses (Complex Sentences)

▶**Exercise 1** **Diagraming Complex Sentences.** Correctly diagram each complex sentence.

1. We had lunch after we finished our errands.

2. We celebrated on the day when the project was complete.

3. The couple sat inside the warm house while the snow fell.

4. When the rains finally ended, the fields and hills were green.

5. The traffic that passes by Andrea's house never stops.

6. Although the guest of honor arrived late, no one seemed to mind.

Diagraming Phrases and Clauses
(Compound-Complex Sentences)

Compound-Complex Sentences To diagram a compound-complex sentence, begin by diagraming each of the independent clauses. Then diagram the subordinate clause(s).

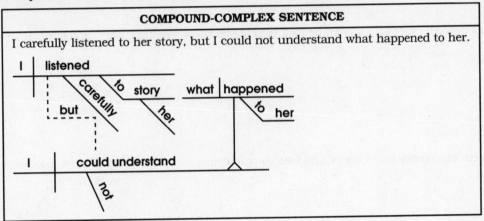

COMPOUND-COMPLEX SENTENCE

I carefully listened to her story, but I could not understand what happened to her.

▶ **Exercise 1** **Diagraming Compound-Complex Sentences.** Diagram the following sentences in the spaces provided.

1. Betty received the camera that she wanted, and she is eager to use it.

2. Since the plane was grounded, the passengers lost hope, and many left for home.

▶ **Exercise 2** **More Work with Diagrams.** Correctly diagram each sentence.

1. I read the book which my teacher recommended, and I liked it very to much.

2. The injured quarterback wanted to remain in the game, but he was come out because the pain was unbearable.

Diagraming Phrases and Clauses
(Compound-Complex Sentences)

▶ **Exercise 1**   Diagraming Compound-Complex Sentences.   Correctly diagram each sentence.

1. When he noticed the spot on his coat, he took it to the cleaners, but they were unable to remove the spot.

2. The bus that was scheduled to take us had engine problems, so the company sent us another.

3. After Jonas finished his homework, he walked the dog, and then he took out the trash.

4. Although other cars were passing his on the freeway, Paul was stopped by the police, and he was given a ticket for speeding.

5. We went to the amusement park that we had read about, and we were not disappointed.

6. I wanted to meet the author whose works I had enjoyed, so I called her publisher and asked for her phone number.

Answers

17.1 Nouns (Page 1)
Practice 1
Exercise 1   Recognizing Nouns
1. Elections, feelings, people
2. roof, barn, hurricane
3. Dubrovnik, resort, Yugoslavia, Adriatic
4. friends, success, long jump
5. walk, library
6. committee, persistence, determination
7. orchestra, strings, woodwinds, brass
8. morning, director, plan
9. Amy, explanation, failure
10. Mrs. Hope, Tom, cruise, West Indies, reward

Exercise 2   Recognizing Collective and Compound Nouns
1. compound
2. collective
3. compound
4. compound
5. collective
6. collective
7. collective
8. compound
9. compound
10. compound

17.1 Nouns (Page 2)
Practice 2
Exercise 1   Identifying the Types of Nouns
1. thing concrete singular compound common
2. thing concrete singular common
3. thing concrete plural common
4. place concrete singular compound proper
5. thing concrete plural compound common
6. person concrete singular compound proper
7. thing concrete singular or plural collective common
8. thing abstract plural common
9. thing abstract singular common
10. thing concrete singular compound proper
11. thing concrete plural common
12. thing concrete singular or plural collective common
13. place concrete singular compound proper
14. thing concrete singular common
15. thing abstract singular common
16. thing concrete plural compound common
17. thing concrete singular compound common
18. thing abstract singular common
19. place concrete singular compound proper
20. thing concrete singular compound common

Exercise 2   Recognizing Compound Nouns
1. compound; a form of postponement
2. an accumulation of rain
3. compound; a type of illness
4. a red glow
5. a red ribbon
6. an alert posted for a coming storm
7. compound; an extra window added for insulation
8. compound; hot weather
9. compound; an identification tag
10. compound; a bone given to a dog

17.1 Pronouns (Page 3)
Practice 1
Exercise 1   Recognizing Pronouns and Antecedents
1. Ruth, her
2. his, Ted
3. doctor, he
4. Jeff, you
5. her, Betty
6. Maimonides, his
7. bus, its
8. Allison, she
9. they, students
10. you, Lee Ann

Exercise 2   Recognizing Different Types of Pronouns
1. This, demonstrative
2. We, personal
3. Whom, interrogative
4. both, indefinite
5. Someone, indefinite

17.1 Pronouns (Page 4)
Practice 2
Exercise 1   Recognizing Antecedents
1. Jo/Jo
2. troops/troops
3. none/steak
4. seniors
5. pollution/schools
6. none/poems/Amy Lowell
7. none (or the person speaking)/people
8. students/listening
9. none (or the person speaking)/none/Marcia
10. actors/actors/actors

Exercise 2   Identifying the Different Types of Pronouns
1. personal
2. indefinite
3. demonstrative
4. indefinite
5. personal
6. indefinite
7. reflexive
8. demonstrative
9. relative
10. personal
11. demonstrative
12. relative
13. personal
14. interrogative
15. reflexive
16. indefinite
17. relative
18. personal
19. intensive
20. interrogative

17.2 Verbs (Action Verbs and Linking Verbs) (Page 5)
Practice 1
Exercise 1   Identifying Action and Linking Verbs
1. seems, linking
2. sailed, action
3. landed, action
4. is, linking
5. grew, linking

6. became, linking
7. reached, action
8. was, linking
9. looks, linking
10. slipped, action

Exercise 2   Using Linking Verbs
Linking verbs may vary; samples are given.
1. appears
2. is
3. became
4. tastes
5. feel
6. smells
7. turns
8. looked
9. looks
10. sounded

17.2   Verbs (Action Verbs and Linking Verbs) (Page 6)
Practice 2
Exercise 1   Identifying Action and Linking Verbs
1. action verb
2. linking verb
3. linking verb
4. linking verb
5. linking verb
6. action verb
7. action verb
8. linking verb
9. linking verb
10. linking verb
11. linking verb
12. action verb
13. linking verb
14. action verb
15. action verb
16. linking verb
17. action verb
18. action verb
19. action verb
20. linking verb

Exercise 2   Using Action Verbs in Sentences
1. quibble
2. injures
3. negotiated
4. translate
5. beckons
6. fascinate
7. vanquish
8. calculate
9. participates
10. hoards

17.2   Verbs (Transitive and Intransitive Verbs) (Page 7)
Practice 1
Exercise 1   Identifying Transitive and Intransitive Verbs
1. transitive
2. intransitive
3. intransitive
4. transitive
5. transitive
6. transitive
7. intransitive
8. transitive
9. intransitive

10. intransitive

Exercise 2   Writing Sentences with Transitive and Intransitive Verbs
Sample sentence completions are given.
1. wholeheartedly
2. Pam
3. village
4. to a halt
5. truth
6. loudly
7. on a large bus
8. diagnosis
9. into the mike
10. children

17.2   Verbs (Transitive and Intransitive Verbs) (Page 8)
Practice 2
Exercise 1   Identifying Transitive and Intransitive Verbs
1. transitive
2. transitive
3. intransitive
4. intransitive
5. transitive
6. transitive
7. intransitive
8. transitive
9. intransitive
10. intransitive
11. transitive
12. intransitive
13. transitive
14. intransitive
15. transitive
16. transitive
17. intransitive
18. transitive
19. intransitive
20. transitive

Exercise 2   Using Transitive and Intransitive Verbs
1. visualizes/transitive
2. gloat/intransitive
3. abbreviate/transitive
4. challenge/transitive
5. emphasized/transitive
6. banished/intransitive
7. deteriorate/intransitive
8. whimpers/intransitive
9. fractured/transitive
10. tolerate/transitive

17.2   Verbs (Verb Phrases) (Page 9)
Practice 1
Exercise 1   Identifying Verb Phrases
1. should have taken
2. will give
3. had been
4. Have opened
5. could have gotten
6. will appear
7. had grown
8. has been performed
9. could be selected
10. have made

Exercise 2   Using Verb Phrases
Sample verb phrases are given.
1. have been invited

2. is located
3. has received
4. must have been surprised
5. will fly
6. have agreed
7. was repaired
8. have been going
9. did buy
10. will give

17.2 Verbs (Verb Phrases) (Page 10)
Practice 2
Exercise 1   Using Verb Phrases
Sample verb phrases are given.
1. has classified
2. has been called
3. were donated
4. will participate
5. Should have been permitted
6. has attained
7. is presented
8. was known
9. will begin
10. has been manufacturing

Writing Application
Writing Sentences with Different Kinds of Verbs
Sample sentences are given.
1. We tasted her latest dish.
2. The potatoes tasted too salty.
3. They climbed the hill to see the mansion.
4. She climbed for twenty minutes.
5. This could have been prevented.

17.3 Adjectives (Page 11)
Practice 1
Exercise 1   Adding Pronouns Used as Adjectives
Sample adjectives are given.
1. Several
2. Which
3. my
4. many
5. their
6. My
7. Whose
8. that
9. another
10. these

Exercise 2   Using Proper Adjectives in Sentences
Sample sentences are given.
1. Dad bought French bread for dinner.
2. Anchorage is the largest Alaskan city.
3. Mexico is the Latin American country that is nearest to the United States.
4. They spent three weeks in a Himalayan village.
5. As a result of the war, the United States gained the former Spanish territory of Puerto Rico.
6. The Great Plains is a vast plain that stretches from southwestern Texas to the Canadian border.
7. Under Roman law, an accused person was considered innocent until proven guilty.
8. William Shakespeare, an Elizabethan dramatist, wrote *King Lear*.
9. During the Renaissance, European sailors ventured farther out into the Atlantic Ocean than they had ever done before.
10. His essays had an Emersonian tone.

17.3   Adjectives (Page 12)
Practice 2
Exercise 1   Identifying Adjectives
1. an East German
2. the greatest art
3. the sixteenth
4. the Saxon
5. the four
6. this
7. the Saxon/short-lived
8. most
9. the Allied
10. delicate Oriental
11. sensitive, moving
12. great
13. precious
14. the best European
15. shining diamond boot
16. jeweled shirt
17. the
18. these
19. priceless
20. eight Meissen china

Exercise 2   Putting Adjectives in Order
1. that small red British sports car
2. a narrow winding dirt road
3. this lovely hand-painted Japanese vase
4. many iridescent flying insects
5. the ancient bronze Roman coin
6. the tiny brown frightened field mouse
7. the green silk shirt
8. a little blue-eyed Siamese kitten
9. our new red brick library
10. several exciting mystery stories

17.3   Adverbs (Page 13)
Practice 1
Exercise 1   Recognizing Adverbs and the Words They Modify
1. still, adjective
2. there, verb
3. really, adverb; well, verb
4. yesterday, verb
5. gracefully, verb
6. already, verb
7. always, verb; carefully, verb
8. obviously, adjective
9. incessantly, verb
10. very, adjective

Exercise 2   Adding Adverbs to Sentences
Sample adverbs are given.
1. yesterday
2. promptly
3. sharply
4. nearly
5. quite
6. there
7. already
8. clearly
9. quickly
10. not

17.3   Adverbs (Page 14)
Practice 2
Exercise 1   Identifying Adverbs
1. Yesterday (explained), sketchily (explained)
2. quickly (approached), extremely (heavy)

3. Almost (apologetically), apologetically (presented)
4. crazily (raced), up (raced), down (raced), eventually (released)
5. involuntarily (jerked), violently (crashed)

Exercise 2   Adding Adverbs to Sentences
Sample adverbs are given.

   (1) Since the War of 1812, the symbol of Uncle Sam has <u>continuously</u> characterized the American government. (2) <u>Incredibly</u>, this famous symbol came from the initials that were stamped on barrels of salted meat by a United States Army meat inspector. (3) Citizens in New York and Vermont liked the nickname and began to use it <u>frequently</u>. (4) Uncle Sam achieved <u>more</u> fame in 1813 when he was pictured in a Troy, New York, newspaper. (5) By 1830, Uncle Sam had <u>already</u> donned his familiar, splashy costume of stars and stripes. (6) A clown dressed as Uncle Sam <u>greatly</u> delighted crowds during the 1800's and helped to popularize the costume. (7) In 1813, <u>most</u> newspaper cartoonists depicted Uncle Sam as a rather young man. (8) By 1917, he had grown much <u>older</u>. (9) On a poster that was used during the First World War, Uncle Sam pointed his wrinkled finger at the young men across the United States and <u>sternly</u> declared, "I want you." (10) Congress <u>finally</u> made Uncle Sam an official national symbol in <u>1961</u>.

17.4   Prepositions (Page 15)
Practice 1
Exercise 1   Identifying Prepositions
1. for, to
2. between
3. from, about, in
4. Over, with
5. for, about
6. of, below
7. through, into
8. With, across
9. from
10. under, near

Exercise 2   Identifying Prepositional Phrases
1. in the attic, with old furniture
2. from the park
3. at Lascaux, in 1940
4. Near the hotel, of craft shops
5. between Sally and me
6. through the town, in an hour and a half
7. For years, for a letter, from her son
8. of travelers, by air
9. in high school, with Mr. Poole
10. through the night, to the next town

17.4   Prepositions (Page 16)
Practice 2
Exercise 1   Identifying Prepositional Phrases

1. (of) cross-country skiing, (around) the globe

2. (across) the Atlantic Ocean, (in) the Scandinavian countries,
   (to) the United States, (by) Scandinavian settlers

3. (According to) recent figures

4. (for) prizes, (in) races, (around) the world

5. (to) safety, (amid) a civil war, (in) the early thirteenth century

6. (because of) the birch, (around) their legs, (for) warmth

7. (after) a mail carrier

8. (By means of) cross-country skiing, (through) the Sierras

9. (in) Sweden

10. (for) this competition

Exercise 2   Distinguishing Between Prepositions and Adverbs
1. preposition (flagpole)
2. adverb
3. adverb
4. adverb
5. adverb
6. adverb
7. adverb
8. preposition (sea)
9. preposition (condition)
10. adverb

Exercise 3   Using Prepositional Phrases
Sample prepositional phrases are given.
1. I longingly watched the sailing vessels <u>on the bay</u>.
2. We postponed the soccer match <u>because of the rain</u>.
3. <u>During the night</u>, the snow level topped three feet.
4. The pungent odor <u>of the fluid</u> assailed my senses.
5. <u>During the night</u>, the bats flew erratically <u>for hours</u>.

17.4   Conjunctions (Page 17)
Practice 1
Exercise 1   Identifying Conjunctions
1. even though, S
2. but, C
3. Not only, but also, CR
4. or, C
5. and, C
6. Whether, or, CR
7. As soon as, S
8. Both, and, CR
9. while, S
10. Neither, nor, CR

Exercise 2   Using Coordinating, Correlative, and Subordinating Conjunctions in Sentences
Sample sentence completions are given.
1. will go, will send my mother
2. my old one broke
3. Jane loves to act, joined the drama club
4. Diane, Walter
5. we didn't

17.4 Conjunctions (Page 18)
Practice 2
Exercise 1 Identifying Conjunctions in Sentences
1. but, coordinating
2. than, subordinating
3. since, subordinating
4. before, subordinating
5. Unless, subordinating
6. for, coordinating
7. Whenever, subordinating
8. Not only, but also, correlative
9. and, coordinating
10. Now that, subordinating
11. and, coordinating
12. not only, but also, correlative
13. Although, subordinating
14. but, coordinating
15. either, or, correlative

Exercise 2 Distinguishing Between Subordinating Conjunctions, Prepositions, and Adverbs
1. preposition
2. adverb
3. subordinating conjunction
4. adverb
5. subordinating conjunction
6. subordinating conjunction
7. preposition
8. subordinating conjunction
9. subordinating conjunction
10. preposition
11. subordinating conjunction
12. subordinating conjunction
13. adverb
14. preposition
15. adverb

17.4 Interjections (Page 19)
Practice 1
Exercise 1 Identifying Interjections
1. Ouch
2. Alas
3. Well
4. Wow
5. Psst
6. Tsk
7. Hurray
8. Oh
9. Whew
10. Goodness gracious

Exercise 2 Writing Sentences with Interjections
Sample sentences are given.
1. "Hurray," said our manager, "we won the championship!"
2. Wow! Look at that snowstorm.
3. "Ouch!" she cried. "That bee sting hurts."
4. Hey! Wait a minute. You're wearing my jacket.
5. My uncle said, "Tsk! You're going to be late."
6. Well, we tried our best.
7. Mary exclaimed, "Gee, I don't want to clean my room."
8. Aha, now I caught you.
9. "Tarnation," said Gramps. "Turn down your stereo."
10. It's all over. Alas, I wish the party were just beginning.

17.4 Interjections (Page 20)
Practice 2
Exercise 1 Identifying Interjections
1. Ah, this house is so warm and cozy.
2. Wow! That hair style looks terrific on you.
3. Aha! So that's where you've been hiding.
4. Whew! This must be the hottest day of the year.
5. Alas, these geraniums seem to be drooping.
6. Well, if you won't call me, I guess I'll have to call you.
7. Dear me! What were you thinking?
8. Goodness! What a wonderful surprise this is!
9. Hey, get away from there!
10. Oh, don't worry about it.

Exercise 2 Using Interjections
Sample sentences are given.
1. Well, I don't know what to do right now.
2. Alas, all is lost.
3. Hey, hurry up or we'll be late.
4. Whew, I can't go on.
5. Oh, what do you suppose will happen now?

Writing Application
Using Prepositions and Conjunctions in Sentences
Sample sentences are given.
1. Before the fourth inning of the baseball game was over, our team scored five runs.
2. We stepped up to the open door and we walked in, but no one was inside.
3. To reach the monument in the park, we can either walk up the path or drive to the parking lot.
4. After wandering aimlessly for hours, we wound up behind a huge factory near the highway.
5. When the sun had set, we knew we had to get home quickly and work on our homework.

17.5 Words as Different Parts of Speech (Page 21)
Practice 1
Exercise 1 Identifying Parts of Speech
1. adverb
2. noun
3. adjective
4. noun
5. adjective
6. verb
7. preposition
8. conjunction
9. noun
10. adjective

Exercise 2 Using Words as Different Parts of Speech
Sample sentences are given.
1. These trunks are very light.
2. Lamps light the streets.
3. We have a metal file cabinet.
4. File these letters alphabetically.
5. Put these letters in the file.
6. The soldiers marched one after the other.
7. They left the party after we did.
8. Bill received low marks in school.
9. Pitch the ball low.
10. The storm warnings made us nervous.

17.5 Words as Different Parts of Speech (Page 22)

Practice 2

Exercise 1   Identifying Parts of Speech
1. verb/adjective
2. adverb/adjective
3. pronoun/adjective
4. interjection/adverb
5. adverb/preposition
6. verb/adverb
7. interjection/noun
8. verb/noun
9. pronoun/conjunction
10. adjective/noun

Exercise 2   More Work with Parts of Speech
1. adverb
2. conjunction
3. verb
4. adjective
5. adverb
6. noun
7. interjection
8. adjective
9. conjunction
10. preposition
11. pronoun
12. verb
13. noun
14. adjective
15. pronoun
16. adjective
17. preposition
18. verb
19. adverb
20. noun

18.1   Subjects and Verbs (Complete Subjects and Predicates, Fragments) (Page 23)

Practice 1

Exercise 1   Recognizing Complete Subjects and Predicates
1. Waffles … cream; is … mine
2. The parishioners; reacted … appeal
3. Carrying … campers; departed
4. The … Inquiry; reached … decision
5. Beethoven's … *Prometheus:* has … times
6. My mother; uses … generations
7. My … Barcelona; has … postponed
8. The … man; entered the auditorium
9. Several … Dallas; are now available
10. This Thanksgiving; will … holiday

Exercise 2   Distinguishing Between Sentences and Fragments
1. F
2. F
3. F
4. S
5. S
6. F
7. F
8. S
9. F
10. F

18.1   Subjects and Verbs (Complete Subjects and Predicates, Fragments) (Page 24)

Practice 2

Exercise 1   Recognizing Complete Subjects and Predicates
1. Most of each year's thousands of earthquakes | are too small to be noticed.
2. The numbers on the Richter Scale | describe the strength of an earthquake.
3. The ancient Greeks | had the first public museums.
4. The Charleston Museum in South Carolina | is the oldest museum in the United States in continuous existence.
5. The Children's Museum in Boston | has a full-size Japanese house, a Latino market, and displays on Native Americans.
6. Millions of children around the world | work in factories and fields.
7. More than five million species of living things | inhabit our planet.
8. More than 1,000 of the more than 9,000 species of birds | are in danger of extinction.
9. The weight of ants on Earth | is almost half the weight of all the other insects combined.
10. The habitats of plants and animals | are often destroyed by deforestation.

Exercise 2   Recognizing Complete Subjects and Complete Predicates
(1) Morning | came quickly. (2) Long before sunrise, | the alarm clock | rang. (3) Sluggishly, | we | dragged ourselves from a restful sleep. (4) At five o'clock | we | left the dock. (5) We | were sailing out of the bay on a yacht equipped with every convenience. (6) From bow to stern, | the boat | measured forty feet. (7) During the night, | a fog | had crept in. (8) It | greatly limited visibility and made the air cold. (9) Sophisticated directional equipment | led us through the fog. (10) Inside the cabin | we | were warm, dry, and eager to begin deep-sea fishing.

Exercise 3   Locating and Correcting Sentence Fragments
Sample sentences are given.
1. His mother, a gentle, yet strong woman, taught him superb manners.
2. The Pilgrims stepped from the boat after a rugged trip across the Atlantic.
3. sentence
4. The plane roared into the sky filled with dark thunderclouds.
5. The car's hood, hot from the sun's rays, looked blistered.

18.1   Subjects and Verbs (Simple Subjects and Predicates) (Page 25)

Practice 1

Exercise 1   Recognizing Simple Subjects and Predicates
1. box, makes
2. envelope, had been opened
3. Beethoven, traveled
4. *Vertigo,* is
5. stamps, are
6. Groups, were stranded
7. Betty, met
8. house, contains
9. number, have been received

10. smudge, aroused

Exercise 2 Using Simple Subjects and Predicates to Write Sentences

Sample sentences are given.

1. Our principal | announced the fire drill.
2. The train | halted to a stop.
3. The report | indicated that prices would drop.
4. The recipe | uses two cups of sugar.
5. My uncle | trembled in the cold.
6. My birthday package | has arrived.
7. The football team | agreed to the new regulation.
8. Our new state senator | wrote his acceptance speech.
9. My grandmother | pickled beets.
10. The new swimmer | will attempt to win the race.

18.1 Subjects and Verbs (Simple Subjects and Predicates) (Page 26)

Practice 2

Exercise 1 Identifying Subjects and Verbs

1. Some apes | have been taught signs for words.
2. Rebecca Latimer Felton | was the first woman to serve as a United States Senator.
3. Many of the current television programs | are airing sensitive, controversial issues.
4. Members of the Coast Guard | rescued the passengers of the sinking ocean liner.
5. People in stressful situations | will often show symptoms of fatigue.
6. The pyramids in Egypt | have attracted tourists for thousands of years.
7. Two systems of weights and measures | coexist in the United States today.
8. The use of the metric system in the United States | has been increasingslowly and steadily.
9. The tides | are a natural phenomenon influenced by the pull of the moon and the sun.
10. Weather conditions | can influence the variations in the high and low tides.

Exercise 2 Locating Compound Subjects and Compound Verbs

1. We headed south for a mile and then turned east.
2. Shoppers and salespersons felt the tension of the holidays and snapped at one another.
3. Both Sara and Blythe liked the story "The Lie" by Kurt Vonnegut, Jr.
4. Both bees and hummingbirds gather nectar and pollinate flowers.
5. We built, sanded, and stained those tables.

Writing Application
Developing Sentences from Subjects and Verbs

Sample sentences are given.

1. The fields were plowed in the spring.
2. The sheep and goats were driven along.
3. The President-elect smiled and waved.
4. Dave and Gina surfed and swam all day.
5. My accountant and lawyer have arrived.

18.2 Subjects in Different Kinds of Sentences (Hard-to-Find Subjects) (Page 27)

Practice 1
Exercise 1 Finding Hard-to-Find Subjects

1. bushel, is
2. title, is
3. you, did buy
4. hotel, is
5. number, have been
6. restaurant, is
7. (You) tell
8. routes, are
9. operation, has been scheduled
10. pens, are

Exercise 2 Changing Sentences to Normal Word Order

1. A box of tissues is near the window.
2. The keys to the safe are here.
3. You have chosen a secretary.
4. Three strange men are at the door.
5. Pat did think what of his explanation?

18.2 Subjects in Different Kinds of Sentences (Hard-to-Find Subjects) (Page 28)

Practice 2
Exercise 1 Locating Hard-to-Find Subjects

Sample understood words are given in parentheses.

1. letter lay
2. you Are planning
3. sound came
4. thousands are
5. You do prefer
6. (We want)
7. you did buy
8. tips are
9. (You) remember
10. Henry Hudson Was
11. (You) Help
12. (You) Lead
13. check is
14. I could go
15. teenagers Are preparing
16. pioneers trudged
17. (you) finish
18. roundups are
19. (I need)
20. televisions did cost

Writing Application
Writing Different Kinds of Sentences with Hard-to-Find Subjects

Sample sentences are given.

1. There is my paper.
2. There were no more staples.
3. On the porch lay a hound.
4. Are you ready?
5. Look out!

18.3 Complements (Direct and Indirect Objects) (Page 29)
Practice 1
Exercise 1 Identifying Direct Objects
1. vegetables
2. dictionary, thesaurus
3. exit
4. him
5. newspaper
6. tea, coffee
7. sunset
8. hotel
9. him, her
10. graphic

Exercise 2 Finding Indirect Objects
1. class, award
2. Dad, speakers
3. them, news
4. Susan, game
5. Judy, him, binoculars

18.3 Complements (Direct and Indirect Objects) (Page 30)
Practice 2
Exercise 1 Recognizing Direct Objects
1. years
2. art
3. teachers
4. professors
5. Alfred Stieglitz
6. paintings
7. O'Keeffe
8. fame
9. rocks, bones, flowers
10. home

Exercise 2 Recognizing Indirect Objects
1. condominium, direct object / daughter, object of a preposition
2. freshman, indirect object / scholarship, direct object
3. owners, indirect object / additions, direct object
4. aria, direct object / ball, object of a preposition
5. piano, direct object / home, object of a preposition
6. campers, indirect object / tale, direct object
7. tree, direct object / me, object of a preposition
8. set, direct object / you, object of a preposition
9. ice cream, direct object / picnic, object of a preposition
10. you, indirect object / catalog, object of a preposition
11. her, indirect object / frame, direct object
12. earshot, object of a preposition / conspirators, object of a preposition
13. class, object of a preposition / expectations, direct object
14. teacher, indirect object / essay, direct object
15. me, indirect object / spine, object of a preposition

18.3 Complements (Objective and Subject Complements) (Page 31)
Practice 1
Exercise 1 Recognizing Objective Complements
1. open, adjective
2. president, noun
3. dangerous, adjective
4. executor, noun
5. captain, noun
6. ineligible, adjective
7. brown, adjective
8. spokesperson, noun
9. uninteresting, adjective
10. inappropriate, adjective

Exercise 2 Recognizing Predicate Nominatives and Predicate Adjectives
1. distracted, PA
2. captain, PN
3. job, PN
4. impressive, PA
5. valuable, PA

18.3 Complements (Objective and Subject Complements) (Page 32)
Practice 2
Exercise 1 Using Objective Complements
Sample objective complements are given.
1. Snoopy
2. hard-working
3. treasurer
4. sports editor
5. playground
6. secretary
7. dark / mysterious
8. Alex / Allison
9. fiasco
10. guilty
11. *Enterprise*
12. horrific
13. disaster
14. astonishing
15. competent

Exercise 2 Identifying Subject Complements
1. stargazer (predicate nominative)
2. distant (predicate adjective), forbidding (predicate adjective)
3. belligerent (predicate adjective), sullen (predicate adjective)
4. hybrid (predicate nominative)
5. silversmith (predicate nominative), maker (predicate nominative)
6. warm (predicate adjective), soft (predicate adjective)
7. sweet (predicate adjective)
8. doctor (predicate nominative), mother (predicate nominative)
9. bitter (predicate adjective), warm (predicate adjective)
10. green (predicate adjective)
11. unfair (predicate adjective)
12. surprising (predicate adjective)
13. aloof (predicate adjective)
14. treat (predicate nominative)
15. Helena Jameson (predicate nominative)

19.1 Prepositional Phrases and Appositives (Prepositional Phrases) (Page 33)
Practice 1
Exercise 1 Identifying Adjective and Adverb Phrases
1. with Jody's performance, unhappy, adverb
2. After lunch, visited, adverb
3. with two full baths, apartment, adjective
4. of traveling actors, group, adjective
5. In Ottawa, convened, adverb
6. after the game, was, adverb
7. on medieval customs, report, adjective

8. about her anniversary present, ecstatic, adverb
9. At a later time, will tell, adverb
10. to Boston, bus, adjective

Exercise 2 Writing Sentences with Adjective and Adverb Phrases
Sample phrases are given.
1. in eleventh grade, adverb
2. in the mall, adverb
3. for school, adverb
4. in town, adjective
5. to New Hampshire, adjective

19.1 Prepositional Phrases and Appositives (Prepositional Phrases) (Page 34)
Practice 2
Exercise 1 Identifying Adjective and Adverb Phrases
1. of the world (adjective), of physical beauty (adjective)
2. In China (adverb), at one time (adverb)
3. In some societies today (adverb), through the nose, lips, and ears (adverb)
4. In some Eskimo areas (adverb), of North America (adjective), through the lips (adverb)
5. of other cultures (adjective), with lace-like patterned bumps (adverb)
6. of Sudan (adjective), into small cuts (adverb), of scars (adjective)
7. In parts (adverb), of Burma (adjective), with long necks (adjective)
8. About their necks (adverb), of brass spirals (adjective)
9. In several Asian societies (adverb), with betel juice (adverb)
10. of unusual beauty habits (adjective)

Exercise 2 Identifying Adjective and Adverb Phrases
1. The cat and the dog (slept) soundly near the warm radiators. adverb
2. The frozen rain made the (branches) on the trees glisten. adjective
3. Happy children (rode) sleds down the snow-covered streets. adverb
4. The icy conditions (kept) the cars off the streets. adverb
5. Katie's mom prepared hot (drinks) for the chilly children. adjective
6. The (faucet) in the kitchen needs tightening. adjective
7. The latest (fashions) from Paris attracted Sharon's attention. adjective
8. Have you ever seen (pictures) of Norway's fiords? adjective
9. Jason (sat) near Maureen. adverb

10. The wedding (was held) in the hotel's picturesque garden area. adverb

19.1 Prepositional Phrases and Appositives (Appositives and Appositive Phrases) (Page 35)
Practice 1
Exercise 1 Identifying Appositives
1. *Lincoln*, book
2. a teacher, Miss Touvin
3. taxidermy, hobby
4. a Hessinger, camera
5. John Donne, poet
6. the viola, instrument
7. Phil, brother
8. the Spitfire, fighter
9. farmer, Rhonda Evans
10. guitar, instrument

Exercise 2 Identifying Appositive Phrases
1. ancient writings in Aramaic, Dead Sea Scrolls
2. a garment of cashmere and wool, coat
3. a dish of berries, bananas, and whipped cream, dessert
4. members of the Class of 1995, graduates
5. a record of gambling activities, files
6. a fast-paced, exciting game, Lacrosse
7. a group of co-eds, friends
8. a statue of Queen Victoria, thing
9. a brass hurricane model, lamp
10. two dismal rooms in an attic, apartment

19.1 Prepositional Phrases and Appositives (Appositives and Appositive Phrases) (Page 36)
Practice 2
Exercise 1 Using Appositives and Appositive Phrases to Combine Sentences
Sample combined sentences are given.
1. The city of Washington, D.C., was designed by Major Pierre Charles L'Enfant, a French architect and engineer.
2. Tourists flock to Washington, D.C., a beautiful city with historic significance.
3. The white marble Capitol, the building where Congress meets, has a large dome on top.
4. Many visit the White House, the President's residence.
5. The Washington Monument, an obelisk, is on the Mall.
6. The Jefferson Memorial, a replica of the Pantheon in Rome, overlooks the Potomac River.
7. The Library of Congress, possibly the world's largest library, has collections that anyone may use.
8. The National Gallery, one of the largest marble buildings in the world, houses many art treasures.
9. Many government officials have residences in Georgetown, a fashionable part of Washington, D.C.
10. Each September, the President's cup Regatta, an annual motorboat racing contest, is held on the Potomac River.

Writing Application
Using Prepositional and Appositive Phrases
Sample sentences are given.
1. The cars on the highway were moving fast.
2. Abraham Lincoln, the sixteenth President, was assassinated in 1865.

3. The pie with cherry filling is baking in the oven.
4. Whales, extremely large aquatic mammals, are very intelligent creatures.
5. Jesse was viewing Mars, the red planet, through a telescope.

19.2 Verbals and Verbal Phrases (Participles and Participial Phrases) (Page 37)
Practice 1
Exercise 1 Identifying Present, Past, and Perfect Participles
1. Having won, player, perfect
2. Smiling, sister, present
3. hesitating, man, present
4. Relieved, she, past
5. dedicated, woman, past
6. chosen, few, past
7. Irritated, speaker, past
8. Having been paroled, ex-convict, perfect
9. delighted, actress, past
10. Surprised, he, past

Exercise 2 Identifying Participial Phrases
1. Groping in the drawer, she
2. running at top speed, sailor
3. Told to report at once, I
4. Tired by her journey, she
5. broken in spirit, explorer
6. Jogging rapidly, cousin
7. computed with amazing speed, figures
8. dancing in the streets, victors
9. Dismayed at the news, man
10. swollen to new heights, river

19.2 Verbals and Verbal Phrases (Participles and Participial Phrases) (Page 38)
Practice 2
Exercise 1 Recognizing Participles and Participial Phrases
1. scathing (present)
2. swaying in the wind (present)
3. ruined by the fire (past)
4. billowing forth with hot air (present)
5. reserved (past)
6. representing the President (present)
7. Having interviewed several people (perfect)
8. cawing continuously in the fields (present)
9. Having been warned (perfect)
10. yellowed with age (past)
11. forged (past)
12. applauding loudly (present)
13. Having followed the guide for two hours (perfect)
14. bandaging the patient's arm (present)
15. divided against itself (past)
16. detached (past)
17. evaporating quickly (present)
18. having approached the judge boldly (perfect)
19. seldom seen (past)
20. quickly glimpsed from the street (past)

Exercise 2 Writing Participial Phrases
Sample sentences are given.
1. The flight, delayed by bad weather, arrived two hours late.
2. Celia, washing her car, didn't notice her pet dog sitting nearby.
3. Badgered by difficult questions, the witness took a sip of water.
4. Tired to the point of exhaustion, the marathon runner could hardly speak.

5. Money collected by the students was given to the chairperson of the charity.

19.2 Verbals and Verbal Phrases (Gerunds and Gerund Phrases, Infinitives and Infinitive Phrases) (Page 39)
Practice 1
Exercise 1 Identifying Gerunds and Gerund Phrases
1. driving too fast, direct object
2. teasing her sister, object of a preposition
3. dreaming, indirect object
4. Traveling, subject
5. growing old, appositive

Exercise 2 Identifying Infinitives and Infinitive Phrases
1. to eat properly every day, noun
2. to visit, adjective
3. To graduate from college, noun
4. to read to his grandchildren, noun
5. to study, adjective

19.2 Verbals and Verbal Phrases (Gerunds and Gerund Phrases, Infinitives and Infinitive Phrases) (Page 40)
Practice 2
Exercise 1 Identifying Gerunds and Gerund Phrases
1. Talking during a test (subject)
2. cataloging the newest books (direct object)
3. arranging flowers (appositive)
4. having an art degree (predicate nominative)
5. teaching (object of a preposition)

Exercise 2 Identifying Infinitives and Infinitive Phrases
1. To capture the scene on film (noun/subject)
2. to burn (adjective)
3. to use our dictionaries (noun/direct object)
4. to earn one million dollars by age thirty-two (noun/predicate nominative)
5. to see about your complaint (adjective)

Writing Application
Writing Sentences Using Verbals
Sample sentences are given.
1. The extremely confusing directions were puzzling.
2. To confuse good and evil is something no one should do.
3. The swiftly sailing ship entered the harbor.
4. Sailing on the ocean is a thrilling experience.
5. The actor achieving critical acclaim is from Canada.
6. To achieve fame can be quite difficult.
7. Undertaking a difficult mission worried the lieutenant.
8. To undertake a tough assignment takes courage.
9. Yearning to explore the wilderness was her goal.
10. The leader seemed to yearn for peace.

19.3 Adjective Clauses (Page 41)
Practice 1
Exercise 1 Identifying Adjective Clauses
1. which was described in the magazine/restaurant
2. that she told/story
3. whose invitation was lost/Judy
4. who has a large private income/governor
5. which portray different animals/stamps
6. that we have waited for/time
7. which doesn't improve/team
8. who wrote the appeal to the President/I
9. that she read/book

10. that we lost/tickets

Exercise 2 Identifying the Use of Relative Pronouns
1. subject
2. direct object
3. adjective
4. subject
5. subject
6. object of a preposition
7. subject
8. subject
9. direct object
10. direct object

19.3 Adjective Clauses (Page 42)
Practice 2
Exercise 1 Identifying Adjective Clauses

1. (which) have spectacular scenery (subject)

2. (that) I just made (direct object)

3. (whose) groceries I walked off with (adjective)

4. (who) sings at the Metropolitan Opera (subject)

5. (where) we want to stay (adverb)

6. (which) I will take (direct object)

7. (when) you arrived (adverb)

8. (that) I bought (direct object)

9. (that) a robin built (direct object)

10. on (which) she had built (object of a preposition)

Exercise 2 Punctuating Adjective Clauses
1. Model trains that can carry people have been built.
2. Arthur Ashe, who was a successful tennis star, was highly intelligent.
3. I devoured the fruit cake the day it arrived.
4. I joined an organization that raises money for charity.
5. People who work hard for their money appreciate its value.
6. I gave my baby sister, who was crying, some apple juice.
7. I must paint the front porch, which has started to peel.
8. The storm that was approaching us was a hurricane.
9. You would enjoy reading the book I just finished.
10. The telephone bill, which was very high this month, is a source of contention in the family.

19.3 Adverb Clauses (Page 43)
Practice 1
Exercise 1 Identifying Adverb Clauses
1. after he learned the truth, upset
2. than we expected, Sooner
3. Unless the weather changes rapidly, will postpone

4. before we did, arrived
5. since all the participants have arrived, can begin
6. until his mission is completed, will stay
7. Although we played brilliantly, lost
8. than we expected, faster
9. if everything goes according to schedule, happy
10. so that you will digest your food better, eat

Exercise 2 Writing Sentences with Adverb Clauses
Sample clauses are given.
1. than we expected
2. If you plan on attending
3. than I thought
4. as she entered the room
5. because I don't have my car
6. when the roads are icy
7. Unless I am ill
8. than I predicted
9. if the library was shut down
10. If you are willing

19.3 Adverb Clauses (Page 44)
Practice 2
Exercise 1 Identifying Adverb Clauses
1. whenever she caught a cold (verb)
2. while my foot heals (verbal)
3. than our competition did (adverb)
4. when the newspaper came (verb)
5. as they moved (verbal)
6. where the water table was high (verbal)
7. as butter is (adjective)
8. as it perked (verbal)
9. until a deadline approaches (verbal)
10. since I needed to do research (verb)
11. Whenever you want to visit (adjective)
12. while stirring the stew (verbal)
13. than a speeding locomotive was (adjective)
14. as new logs were added (verbal)
15. the majority does (adjective)

Exercise 2 Recognizing Elliptical Clauses
Sample understood words are given.
1. than the last one (did)
2. as Millicent Ramat (is)
3. than (he has) red
4. than (she helps) me
5. as gold (is)
6. than this one (did)
7. than (I did) criticism
8. than my old one (did)
9. as I (was)
10. than (it was) informative
11. Although (she was) tired
12. While (he was) getting a haircut
13. than those (pies are)
14. than a dog's (heart is)
15. than a human's (sense of smell is)

19.3 Noun Clauses (Page 45)
Practice 1
Exercise 1 Identifying Noun Clauses
1. what the results will be, direct object
2. How she appeared so suddenly, subject
3. whoever volunteered, indirect object
4. what she truly believes, object of a preposition
5. what we will discuss now, predicate nominative
6. Whichever trip she chooses, subject
7. that we remain firm, appositive
8. whoever wishes to do so, object of a preposition
9. whether she can go at all, predicate nominative

10. how they will react to this allegation, direct object

Exercise 2   Writing Sentences with Noun Clauses
Sample noun clauses are given.
1. that no one smile
2. How we will do it
3. that you will have a safe trip
4. that he did not feel well
5. what she planned to accomplish
6. whoever is still working
7. what they want
8. When the first snow will fall
9. what I did
10. what I want most

19.3   Noun Clauses (Page 46)
Practice 2
Exercise 1   Identifying Noun Clauses
1. whatever creativity I might have had (direct object)
2. whoever ate at our restaurant (indirect object)
3. that the group be expanded (appositive)
4. that her loquacity was difficult to bear (direct object)
5. Whoever signs this form (subject)
6. what time the bus was leaving (object of a preposition)
7. whoever had charge accounts (indirect object)
8. that she will be caught in an elevator (predicate nominative)
9. Whatever time the baby falls asleep (subject of a preposition)
10. whoever is at the desk (object of a preposition)

Exercise 2   Identifying Subordinate Clauses
1. noun
2. adjective
3. adjective
4. adverb
5. noun

Writing Application
Using Subordinate Clauses to Expand Sentences
Sample clauses are given.
1. If they raise enough money
2. which is excellent
3. that I told you about
4. Whatever time you arrive
5. what we remember most

19.4   Sentences Classified by Structure (Page 47)
Practice 1
Exercise 1   Identifying the Structure of Sentences
1. (2)
2. (1)
3. (3)
4. (1)
5. (4)
6. (2)
7. (3)
8. (1)
9. (3)
10. (4)

Exercise 2   Writing Different Types of Sentences
Sample sentences are given.
1. Highways will always be here, and automobiles will always create traffic jams whether we like it or not.
2. We can visit the museum, or we can go to the library.

3. There is a hummingbird in the garden.
4. The river, which flows through the valley, irrigates the farmers' crops.
5. Although he looked everywhere in the house, he could not find whatever he had lost.

19.4   Sentences Classified by Structure (Page 48)
Practice 2
Exercise 1   Identifying the Four Structures of Sentences
1. compound
2. simple
3. complex
4. complex
5. simple
6. complex
7. compound
8. compound-complex
9. simple
10. compound-complex
11. simple
12. simple
13. complex
14. complex
15. compound
16. compound-complex
17. compound-complex
18. simple
19. complex
20. compound

Writing Application
Writing Sentences with Different Structures
Sample sentences are given.
1. The sweet scent of gardenias fills the air.
2. Michelle and Andy had lunch in the kitchen.
3. Susan, the girl in the blue coat, is an excellent student.
4. One group enjoyed working in the garden, and the other group preferred fixing up the house.
5. Charles enjoyed working on what he was assigned.

20.1   The Four Functions of Sentences (Page 49)
Practice 1
Exercise 1   Identifying the Four Functions of Sentences
1. (?) Int.
2. (.) D
3. (.) Imp.
4. (!) E
5. (.) D
6. (?) Int.
7. (.) Imp.
8. (!) E
9. (?) Int.
10. (!) Imp.

Exercise 2   Writing Original Sentences
A sample of each type of sentence is given.
1. The night sky was filled with bright stars.
2. What time is it?
3. Please put your coat in the closet.
4. What an incredible sight!

20.1 The Four Functions of Sentences (Page 50)
Practice 2
Exercise 1   Identifying the Four Functions of Sentences
1. exclamatory (!)
2. imperative (.)
3. declarative (.)
4. interrogative (?)
5. declarative (.)
6. interrogative (?)
7. imperative (.)
8. declarative (.)
9. declarative (.)
10. exclamatory (!)
11. declarative (.)
12. declarative (.)
13. exclamatory (!)
14. interrogative (?)
15. declarative (.)

Writing Application
Writing Sentences with Different Functions
Sample sentences are given.
1. I watch history documentaries on television.
2. Do you watch very much television?
3. Tell me which candidate is ahead and what percentage of the ballots have been counted.
4. The mayor is winning in a landslide!
5. I know how many automobiles were in the United States in 1905.
6. That person set the world record for the longest finger nails!
7. Who won the basketball game?
8. Tell me the score of the basketball game.
9. The subway trains are always crowded during rush hour.
10. This subway goes really fast!

20.2 Improving Your Sentences (Sentence Combining) (Page 51)
Practice 1
Exercise 1   Sentence Combining
Sample sentences are given.
1. Elizabeth Cox, a former congresswoman, is now a district attorney.
2. Fred is a good student and a gifted athlete.
3. Sandy waited in line for eighthours to buy tickets for the concert, but all the tickets were sold before she reached the front of the line.
4. When Ron slipped and fell into a puddle, he ruined his best pair of pants.
5. The school's football team won easily, but the soccer team was defeated.

Exercise 2   More Work with Combining Sentences
Sample sentences are given.
1. Violet Snodgrass, who is an excellent actress, won the talent competition.
2. Trying to locate the gate that his parents would be coming through, Jimmy raced through the airport.
3. When Mr. and Mrs. Franklin returned from their vacation, they discovered that their house had been broken into, but nothing valuable had been stolen.
4. The wind whistled through the trees, the sound of thunder echoed through the air, and the rain steadily pounded the ground.
5. When school was canceled for the day because of

a major snowstorm the previous night, most of the students spent the day playing in the snow.

20.2 Improving Your Sentences (Sentence Combining) (Page 52)
Practice 2
Exercise 1   Sentence Combining
Sample sentences and methods are given.
1. Rust is a popular color often used in home decorating. (participial phrase)
2. She had trouble building the fire because a brisk breeze was blowing. (subordinate clause)
3. Our local newspapers, the *Kensington Chronicle* and the *Orinda Record* merged last year. (appositive)
4. The dog trotted down the main street, paused in front of the meat market, and sniffed eagerly. (compound verb)
5. Running to answer the phone, I slipped on a magazine and tripped over the coffee table. (subordinate clause)
6. As a canoe came around the bend of the shoreline, the weary campers shouted for help. (subordinate clause)
7. Especially cruel that year, February's frigid weather damaged fruit trees and evergreens. (modifying phrase)
8. As the homemade soup bubbled in the big pot, the boys remembered that they had not eaten since dawn. (subordinate clause)
9. When the customs officer opened the suitcase, he saw the toy animals and smiled. (subordinate clause and compound verb)
10. Since California and Florida both produce citrus, they vie to see who can grow the best oranges. (subordinate clause)

Exercise 2   Combining Sentences in a Passage
A sample rewritten passage is given.

(1) Since Rose Ann had always lived in the city, (2) street sounds, crowds, and motion were normal to her. (3) She thought she would never be content anywhere else until (4) one summer she drove across the country. (5) She stayed at small inns in little towns and (6) saw the many different ways Americans live. (7) Today, Rose Ann has a new career as (8) the innkeeper of (9) a ten-bedroom inn is on a wooded hill above a lazy river.

20.3 Vary Sentences (Expanding Short Sentences, Shortening Long Sentences) (Page 53)
Practice 1
Exercise 1   Expanding Sentences
Sample sentences are given.
1. Todd's research paper on the causes of pollution had many faults, including a total lack of footnotes.
2. The business district is congested with street peddlers, delivery trucks, sightseers, and other pedestrians.
3. Men from the State Highway Department are resurfacing and widening the main highway.
4. Fran drove slowly through the snowstorm on her way to Vermont.
5. Dave and Bridget held hands and watched the beautiful sunset.

Exercise 2   Shortening Sentences
Sample sentences are given.
1. Colorado, a state which produces sugar beets and potatoes as well as coal and silver, really

boomed with the discovery of gold in 1859. However, it wasn't admitted to the union as the thirty-eighth state until 1876.

2. For the annual spring picnic, the senior class voted to have a barbecue at Closter Lake, where there are facilities for swimming, a softball field, and a volleyball court. A committee was formed to organize the event, but no one could agree on a date for the picnic.

20.3 Vary Sentences (Expanding Short Sentences, Shortening Long Sentences) (Page 54)
Practice 2
Exercise 1 Adding Details
Sample sentences are given.

1. Having been thoroughly embarrassed, Selma looked incredulously at each of her friends to see each girl's reaction. (participial phrase/adverb/ infinitive phrase)
2. At our high school commencement, we, the graduates of 1998, wore our deep purple caps and gowns with great pride.(prepositional phrase/appositive phrase/adjective/adjective/ prepositional phrase)
3. While the graduates prepared to march onto the stage, confusion as well as excitement, on the part of the graduates and their relatives alike, filled the air. (adverb clause/prepositional phrase/prepositional phrase)
4. As the school band played a processional march, we, the graduates, filed in. (adverb clause/appositive)
5. Finally, the principal, in an especially dignified manner, called the first name. (adverb/ prepositional phrase)

Exercise 2 Adding Details and Combining Ideas
A sample rewritten passage is given.

(1) When the race was over, (2) Sally stumbled to the post. (3) It had been a long five miles. (4) No one had expected her to finish, or even "place," (5) but she had shown them. (6) She had worked out for weeks, (7) used her training, (8) depended on her confidence, (9) and given all of her energy to this goal. (10) She had now won a personal victory as well as a public one.

Exercise 3 Simplifying Long Sentences
A sample rewritten passage is given.

(1) In moving, almost everything that is familiar to a child, except members of the family, disappears. The child is left with a feeling of loss and perhaps without a sense of identity in the new surroundings. Many children at such times attach themselves to certain objects such as a blanket, stuffed animal, or favorite toy, which they have carried with them as a source of comfort and security.

(2) Such attachments can be sensitive stages in a child's development. When the child has become dependent on one particular object, he or she may then resist new things, often holding desperately to the familiar old ones, fearing the type of loss first felt during the move to a new home.

20.3 Vary Sentences (Using Different Sentence Openers and Structures) (Page 55)
Practice 1
Exercise 1 Writing Sentences with Different Openers
1. To get the number, Marni checked the telephone directory.

2. My new CD player, a compact model, has superb stereo speakers.
3. Although I disagreed, the committee approved the plan.
4. Smiling happily, Mary (or Accepting the award, Mary ...) accepted the award (or smiled happily).
5. Up the hill trudged the weary hikers.

Exercise 2 Varying Sentence Structure
Sample sentences are given.
1. Although the crowd was small, it inspired the team.
2. We knocked several times, but no one answered.
3. When I'm babysitting for Emma, she is a charming child, and we have fun together.
4. If you meet me at my locker, we can walk home together.

20.3 Vary Sentences (Using Different Sentence Openers and Structures) (Page 56)
Practice 2
Exercise 1 Using Different Sentence Openers
Sample openers are given.
1. In contrast, many new houses in the West do not have attics or basements. (transitional phrase)
2. At the fair, the child got lost in the crowd. (prepositional phrase)
3. Dashing for a bus, he sprained his ankle. (participial phrase)
4. Until they had fulfilled their obligations, they felt that they could not leave the place. (adverb clause)
5. In its Basic First Aid Course, the Red Cross teaches three methods to stop bleeding. (prepositional phrase)
6. To avoid rotting the plant's roots, Mavis was careful not to overwater the begonia. (infinitive phrase)
7. Not surprisingly, a six-cylinder engine uses less fuel than does one with eight cylinders. (adverb)
8. Lonely and sad, the dog watched me through the window. (adjective)
9. Because they appreciate in value rather than depreciate, antique jewelry and furniture are smart investments. (adverb clause)
10. Through the window appeared a faint glimmer. (inverted order)

Exercise 2 Using Different Sentence Structures
Sample sentences are given.

(1) I entered the forest as the sun began to set, amid long shadows. (complex) (2) ~~The Shadows were long.~~ (3) Following a seldom-used path (4) and feeling restless, (5) I had started walking. (simple) (6) The forest was cool, (7) and the dark branches dropped with the weight of green summer foliage. (compound) (8) As the leaves fluttered, (9) the brush crackled beneath my feet. (complex)

(10) I turned to the left, and I (11) walked into a clearing (12) that was blanketed by short grass and peppered with dark-colored flowers. (compound-complex) (13) Facing west, (14) I climbed onto a rock. (simple) (15) The sun was disappearing into a honey sunset swirl, (16) and the clouds shimmered orange. (compound) (17) As a cool breeze blew the leaves, my hair, and the grass, (18) the sun melted into the trees and soon dropped out of sight. (complex) (19) My restlessness was gone, and (20) I was at peace. (compound)

20.3 Vary Sentences (Using Different Types of Sentences) (Page 57)

Practice 1

Exercise 1   Identifying Different Types of Sentences

1. B
2. C
3. L
4. P
5. B

Exercise 2   Writing Different Types of Sentences

Sample sentences are given.

1. The draw bridge was stuck in the open position for thirty minutes.
2. If I study really hard, I should probably do quite well on the test.
3. We must first hike on the lower path, then proceed up the steep slope, and finally inch our way toward the peak.
4. We must irrigate the fields right now; that's the only way to save the crops.
5. You should search both the library book catalogue or the periodical index in order to find the best sources for your report on environmental pollution.

20.3 Vary Sentences (Using Different Types of Sentences) (Page 58)

Practice 2

Exercise 1   Identifying Types of Sentences

1. cumulative
2. balanced
3. periodic
4. loose
5. balanced

Exercise 2   Practicing with Different Types of Sentences

Students should be able to identify loose, periodic, balanced, and cumulative sentences in their outside sources. Students' sentences should illustrate an understanding of the four types of sentences.

20.3 Vary Sentences (Using Different Sentence Patterns and Professional Models) (Page 59)

Practice 1

Exercise 1   Writing Sentences with Parallel Structures

Sample sentences are given.

1. You'll find the container on the top shelf in the cabinet above the stove.
2. The lights in the auditorium dimmed, the audience quieted down, and the curtain went up.
3. Walking through the woods and admiring the various kinds of ferns, Jan spent a pleasant summer morning.
4. His tasks were to clean the stove, to take out the trash, and to prepare dinner.
5. She ventured where few people had gone before and where adventure beckoned at every turn.

Exercise 2   Writing a Paragraph with a Contrasting Structure

Students' paragraphs should illustrate proficiency in using sentences of various lengths.

20.3 Vary Sentences (Using Different Sentence Patterns and Professional Models) (Page 60)

Practice 2

Exercise 1   Using Structural Similarities

A sample passage is given.

The driver turned on the high-beam headlights, but that made the fog even more treacherous. He clicked on his low beams again, and that offered no relief from the lack of visibility. Fearfully, he hugged the right side of the road, and he proceeded at a very low speed.

Exercise 2   Using Structural Differences

A sample passage is given.

As the afternoon progressed, the overcast began to thicken and lower. A light breeze began fluttering the leaves of the tall trees along the coastal road. Soon the waves that had been gentle all morning began to swell and crash along the beach with an increasingly louder roar. Suddenly, the storm's fury struck!

Exercise 3   Using Models of Professional Writing

Students' source materials should contain recognizable sentence patterns. Students' passages should reflect the sentence patterns of the source materials.

20.4 Fragments and Run-ons (Fragments) (Page 61)

Practice 1

Exercise 1   Distinguishing Between Fragments and Complete Sentences

1. F
2. F
3. S
4. F
5. F
6. F
7. S
8. S
9. F
10. F

Exercise 2   Changing Fragments into Complete Sentences

Sample sentences are given.

1. Reaching a stop sign, I stopped.
2. We need a chisel, a hammer, and headless nails.
3. If you phone her, she will not answer.
4. This is strictly between you and me.
5. The fish were frozen together.
6. You will find it in the reference section of the school library.
7. Since she fell, she has been nervous.
8. I can fix it with rubber cement.
9. This is the book which Mother wanted.
10. He looked quickly in the file cabinet.

20.4 Fragments and Run-ons (Fragments) (Page 62)

Practice 2

Exercise 1   Distinguishing Between Fragments and Complete Sentences

1. F
2. S
3. F
4. S
5. F
6. F

7. S
8. F
9. F
10. F

Exercise 2   Identifying and Correcting Fragments
Sample sentences are given.
1. Their faces were shining with delight at seeing the movie star.
2. I wanted one thing: to take a long nap.
3. The committee was impressed by this application, which we received just yesterday.
4. correct
5. Traffic lights were flashing erratically as the cars jammed in the intersection, unsure whose turn it was to proceed.
6. The apples cooked with their sweet juices bubbling away.
7. She returned just as Mr. Chao said goodbye.
8. correct
9. I have a report to write and math to do before tomorrow.
10. He admired the silhouettes of the trees against the light of the moon.

20.4   Fragments and Run-ons (Run-ons) (Page 63)

Practice 1

Exercise 1   Distinguishing Between Run-ons and Properly Punctuated Sentences
1. RO
2. RO
3. S
4. RO
5. S
6. S
7. RO
8. RO
9. RO
10. RO

Exercise 2   Changing Run-ons into Properly Punctuated Sentences
Sample sentences are given.
1. There are two choices, and I will explain them both.
2. The new mall will contain sixty shops. Enclosed parking will be nearby.
3. Cabbage can be prepared many ways; my favorite is stuffed cabbage.
4. Carl Sagan wrote Cosmos; he also was the author of Broca's Brain.
5. Ice, of course, is dangerous. Last winter Father slipped and fell.

20.4   Fragments and Run-ons (Run-ons) (Page 64)

Practice 2

Exercise 1   Identifying and Correcting Run-ons
Sample sentences are given.
1. When I looked down, I saw that the well was apparently dry.
2. We read the Preamble to the Constitution, and our group felt anew the power of those words.
3. The boy had trouble with the decimal point. When multiplying he always put it in the wrong place.
4. When the thermometer broke, the mercury spilled onto the floor.

5. I mislaid my car keys; my house keys were also gone.
6. It is against the law to litter; nevertheless, people do it.
7. correct
8. I generally like the climate of the area where I live, but I do not enjoy the subfreezing temperatures of winter.
9. Everyone should be polite; however, many people are rude.
10. I made my own chili. To eat it one needs an iron stomach.

Writing Application
Avoiding Fragments and Run-ons
A sample corrected paragraph is given.

(1) Mosquitoes, those nasty little insects whose bites cause our skin to swell and itch, (2) inhabit every state in the Union and most areas of the world. (3) Actually, the bites should not be considered mere irritants since they lead to many deaths every year. (4) Theseinsects transmit many ailments (5) including temporary insanity, filariasis, and many types of viral and bacterial infections. (6) Of course, mosquitoes must bite to survive because the females need the protein from the blood to produce their eggs. (7) The females, which weigh one ten-thousandth of an ounce when unfed, triple that after a single bite. (8) Among nature's greatest achievements are the two intricate pumps inside the female's head. (9) Only one bite is necessary for them to draw enough blood to produce seventy-five eggs. (10) Much has been done to halt the growth of mosquitoes. Nothing, however, completely eradicates these insects.

20.5   Misplaced and Dangling Modifiers (Page 65)

Practice 1

Exercise 1   Recognizing Misplaced Modifiers
1. walking her dog
2. with remote control
3. that was stolen
4. noticeably upset
5. cooked well done
6. that come from California
7. with bifocals
8. with a forked trunk
9. frightened by the strange noise
10. with the large outdoor fruit and vegetable market

Exercise 2   Recognizing Dangling Modifiers
1. Closing the car trunk
2. correct
3. Reaching the intersection
4. While opening the package
5. correct

20.5   Misplaced and Dangling Modifiers (Page 66)

Practice 2

Exercise 1   Identifying and Correcting Misplaced Modifiers
Sample sentences are given.
1. Sitting at the sidewalk café, we saw the seagulls.
2. By phone, we arranged to have a pizza made.
3. We saw our clothes whirling round and round in the dryer.
4. Chiming out the hour, the grandfather clock awoke me.
5. He found the dollar under the couch.

Exercise 2   Identifying and Correcting Dangling Modifiers

Sample revised sentences are given.

1. To eat before the game, we must finish preparing dinner within fifteen minutes.
2. While laughing, she got a chicken bone stuck in her throat.
3. Checking all the stations, the foreman saw that the assembly line was running smoothly.
4. correct
5. Falling on the stairs, I dislocated my jaw.

Writing Application

Avoiding Misplaced and Dangling Modifiers

Sample phrases and clauses are given.

1. she cut her finger
2. Grinning broadly
3. that was rolling down the hill
4. he gulped
5. When Paula was young

20.6   Faulty Parallelism (Page 67)

Practice 1

Exercise 1   Recognizing Parallel Structure

1. who gives charity, who helps others
2. accountant, expediter, consultant
3. Growing very slowly, bursting into glorious color
4. since my daughter left, since my oldest son returned
5. sobbed, whimpered, collapsed
6. in the shower, at the breakfast table, at most other times
7. to jog daily, to hike on weekends
8. refinishing furniture, repairing clocks, constructing floral displays
9. Ms. Ames, Mr. Paulson, Dr. Phillips
10. that Joel writes sonnets, that I design mobiles

Exercise 2   Recognizing Faulty Parallelism

1. FP
2. FP
3. C
4. FP
5. FP

20.6   Faulty Parallelism (Page 68)

Practice 2

Exercise 1   Correcting Faulty Parallelism

Sample sentences are given.

1. The new employee was lazy, insolent, and often late.
2. I think the plants did well because I fertilized them rather than because I talked to them.
3. Ken will go either to the parade or to the Egyptian museum.
4. I hate weeding as much as having shots.
5. He wanted both to keep his job and to move to the country.
6. Going home is better than staying here.
7. I would choose reading a book over watching a television show.
8. His old tennis shoes were dirty, laceless, and smelly.
9. The coach tells me that I bat well, but field poorly.
10. Laughing together, sharing one another's problems, and overlooking faults—these make true friends.

Writing Application

Writing Sentences Containing Parallel Structures

Sample sentences are given.

1. Gathering honey and flying back to the hive, the bees worked diligently.
2. I listened to the melody floating through the air, and I was lulled by the sound.
3. I love gardening more than jogging.
4. I will participate in the log rolling contest, in the dance contest, and in the rodeo.
5. I was pleased by the game we played and by the strategy we used.

20.7   Faulty Coordination (Page 69)

Practice 1

Exercise 1   Recognizing Faulty Coordination

1. C
2. F
3. F
4. F
5. C

Exercise 2   Correcting Faulty Coordination

Sample sentences are given.

1. World War II, which lasted for half a decade, brought out a high degree of patriotism.
2. I have read a number of mystery stories, all of which have been popular for years.
3. Our principal, who is married and has two children, has just instituted a new behavior code.
4. Australia is located in the Southern Hemisphere. Most countries are located in the Northern Hemisphere.
5. I plan to study architecture in college. I also have a nervous stomach.

20.7   Faulty Coordination (Page 70)

Practice 2

Exercise 1   Recognizing Faulty Coordination

1. faulty
2. faulty
3. faulty
4. correct
5. faulty

Exercise 2   Correcting Faulty Coordination

Sample sentences are given.

1. I slowly climbed to the lookout point. Reaching the top provided me with a spectacular view.
2. The car, which is dented, has room for six.
3. Because the truck had a full load, it slowed down going uphill.
4. I turned on the television, and a commercial promptly showed up. When I turned the channel looking for something better, commercials were on wherever I turned.
5. Evan has a new wool pullover that he plans to wear to the beach where the wind can turn very cold.

Writing Application

Avoiding Faulty Coordination in Sentence Combining

Sample sentences are given.

1. I lost the gold charm, a gift from my father.
2. Daydreams invade the day; nightmares haunt the darkness.
3. Millions of bats, which inhabit one particular cave, journey each night to a distant lake.
4. I enjoy thumbing through encyclopedias because they contain fascinating articles.
5. The ice that was left out melted all over the countertop.

21.1 Verb Tenses (The Six Verb Tenses, The Four Principal Parts) (Page 71)

Practice 1

Exercise 1 Recognizing Tenses and Forms of Verbs

1. study, present basic
2. will be speaking, future progressive
3. arrived, past basic
4. did support, past emphatic
5. had been planning, past perfect progressive
6. has finished, present perfect basic
7. will have had, future perfect basic
8. do take, present emphatic
9. will promise, future basic
10. am having, present progressive

Exercise 2 Recognizing Principal Parts

1. study, present
2. speaking, present participle
3. arrived, past
4. support, present
5. planning, present participle
6. finished, past participle
7. had, past participle
8. take, present
9. promise, present
10. having, present participle

21.1 Verb Tenses (The Six Verb Tenses, The Four Principal Parts) (Page 72)

Practice 2

Exercise 1 Recognizing Verb Tenses and Their Forms

1. past emphatic
2. past progressive
3. past perfect progressive
4. future perfect
5. past
6. present perfect progressive
7. future
8. present
9. future perfect
10. present
11. past progressive
12. past perfect progressive
13. present emphatic
14. future perfect progressive
15. present perfect
16. present progressive
17. past
18. past perfect
19. future
20. future perfect
21. past emphatic
22. present progressive
23. past perfect progressive
24. future perfect
25. past
26. present perfect progressive
27. future
28. present
29. future perfect
30. present

Exercise 2 Recognizing Principal Parts

1. present
2. present participle
3. present participle
4. past participle
5. past
6. present participle

7. present
8. present
9. past participle
10. present
11. present participle
12. present participle
13. present
14. present participle
15. past participle
16. present participle
17. past
18. past participle
19. present
20. past participle
21. present
22. present participle
23. present participle
24. past participle
25. past
26. present participle
27. present
28. present
29. past participle
30. present

21.1 Verb Tenses (Regular and Irregular Verbs) (Page 73)

Practice 1

Exercise 1 Writing the Principal Parts of Irregular Verbs

1. drink, drank, (have) drunk
2. growing, grew, (have) grown
3. biting, bit, (have) bitten
4. fly, flying, (have) flown
5. hurt, hurt, (have) hurt
6. slay, slaying, slew
7. speak, spoke, (have) spoken
8. drawing, drew, (have) drawn
9. freeze, freezing, froze
10. ride, riding, (have) ridden

Exercise 2 Choosing the Correct Form of Irregular Verbs

1. fallen
2. shut
3. sent
4. gave
5. burst

21.1 Verb Tenses (Regular and Irregular Verbs) (Page 74)

Practice 2

Exercise 1 Learning the Principal Parts of Irregular Verbs

1. breaking, broke, broken
2. putting, put, put
3. ringing, rang, rung
4. teaching, taught, taught
5. choosing, chose, chosen
6. laying, laid, laid
7. spreading, spread, spread
8. tearing, tore, torn
9. biting, bit, bitten
10. shutting, shut, shut
11. fighting, fought, fought
12. eating, ate, eaten
13. swinging, swung, swung
14. shaking, shook, shaken
15. singing, sang, sung

16. binding, bound, bound
17. arising, arose, arisen
18. grinding, ground, ground
19. shining, shone *or* shined, shone *or* shined
20. striding, strode, stridden

Exercise 2 Choosing the Correct Forms of Irregular Verbs

1. crept
2. written
3. flung
4. sprang
5. ridden
6. come
7. broken
8. thrown
9. fallen
10. blown
11. gone
12. eaten
13. burst
14. worn
15. brought
16. bid
17. began
18. torn
19. sang
20. borne
21. froze
22. given
23. run
24. caught
25. taken

21.1 Verb Tenses (Verb Conjugation) (Page 75)
Practice 1
Exercise 1 Conjugating Basic and Progressive Forms

1. win (with *I*)
   I win
   I won
   I will win
   I have won
   I had won
   I will have won
   I am winning
   I was winning
   I will be winning
   I have been winning
   I had been winning
   I will have been winning
   I do win
   I did win
2. go (with *he*)
   he goes
   he went
   he will go
   he has gone
   he had gone
   he will have gone
   he is going
   he was going
   he will be going
   he has been going
   he had been going
   he will have been going
   he does go
   he did go
3. ride (with *we*)
   we ride
   we rode
   we will ride
   we have ridden
   we had ridden
   we will have ridden
   we are riding
   we were riding
   we will be riding
   we have been riding
   we had been riding
   we will have been riding
   we do ride
   we did ride
4. love (with *they*)
   they love
   they loved
   they will love
   they have loved
   they had loved
   they will have loved
   they are loving
   they were loving
   they will be loving
   they have been loving
   they had been loving
   they will have been loving
   they do love
   they did love

Exercise 2 Supplying the Correct Verb Form

1. has been
2. will be visiting
3. did promise
4. will have been living
5. slept

21.1 Verb Tenses (Verb Conjugation) (Page 76)
Practice 2
Exercise 1 Conjugating Verbs

1. plan (basic)
   I plan
   you plan
   he, she, it plans
   we plan
   you plan
   they plan
   I planned
   you planned
   he, she, it planned
   we planned
   you planned
   they planned
   I will plan
   you will plan
   he, she, it will plan
   I have planned
   you have planned
   he, she, it has planned
   we have planned
   you have planned
   they have planned
   I had planned
   you had planned
   he, she, it had planned
   we had planned
   you had planned
   they had planned
   I will have planned
   you will have planned

he, she, it will have planned
we will have planned
you will have planned
they will have planned
2. break (emphatic)
I do break
you do break
he, she, it does break
we do break
you do break
they do break
I did break
you did break
he, she, it did break
we did break
you did break
they did break

Writing Application
Using Different Tenses
Sample sentences are given.
1. I had borrowed the money to buy lunch.
2. The jetliner is landing on the runway nearest the terminal.
3. Before next year arrives that pipe will have sprung another leak.
4. Don't burst that water balloon.
5. I had been intending to visit the library since yesterday.
6. He will be wearing a blue shirt.
7. I really did try my best.
8. The detectives will investigate the crime scene.
9. They are swimming in the hotel pool.
10. He lost his wallet.

21.2 The Correct Use of Tenses (Present, Past, and Future Time) (Page 77)
Practice 1
Exercise 1   Identifying Tenses

1. (had studied)

2. (will have made)

3. (did try)

4. has been studying

5. have

6. (will be lying)

7. (was rolling)

8. (will make)

9. (had answered)

10. (will be leaving)

Exercise 2   Identifying Uses of Verbs
1. completed before another past event
2. future event before another future event
3. emphasized event
4. continuing to present
5. constant event
6. continuing future event
7. continuing past event
8. future event

9. completed before another past event
10. continuing future event

21.2 The Correct Use of Tenses (Present, Past, and Future Time) (Page 78)
Practice 2
Exercise 1   Identifying the Uses of Tense in Present Time
1. present event
2. long continuing event
3. completed before another past event
4. continuing event
5. recurring event
6. complete (indefinite time)
7. future event
8. present event
9. continuing event
10. recurring event

Exercise 2   Using Tense in Past Time
1. asked
2. has adopted
3. were discussing
4. has been
5. had written
6. has been studying
7. did insist
8. had left
9. has traveled
10. found

Exercise 3   Using Tense in Future Time
1. will have planted
2. will be
3. will motivate
4. will be allowed
5. will be
6. will have been exploring
7. will fly
8. will have been driving
9. will practice
10. will win

21.2 The Correct Use of Tenses (Sequence of Tenses, Modifiers That Help Clarify Time) (Page 79)
Practice 1
Exercise 1   Using the Correct Tense
Sample sentence completions are given.
1. he is doing a good job.
2. I wish
3. I was in Paris.
4. began to write.
5. I last saw a car like this one.

Exercise 2   Adding Modifiers to Help Clarify Tense
Sample modifiers are given.
1. tonight.
2. last year.
3. always
4. past three
5. On weekdays

21.2 The Correct Use of Tenses (Sequence of Tenses, Modifiers That Help Clarify Time) (Page 80)
Practice 2
Exercise 1   Using the Correct Forms of Subordinate Verbs, Participles and Infinitives
Sample additions and changes are given.
1. Having seen John run, our captain chose John for the team.

2. After he had tried many local sources, eventually he wrote to his congresswoman.
3. My plan is to have left before the evening train departs.
4. Because she has heard there will be a torna do, she is afraid.
5. Joel liked to watch the storm clouds gather.
6. Having danced for twenty years, the ballerina retired gracefully.
7. Although she earns only a small salary, Lisa is working industriously at her new job as a law clerk in the city.
8. She was glad to have gained experience in the field of electronics.
9. Having expected perfection, the conductor listened to the cacophony in angry silence.
10. If you have observed them before, you will notice the difference.

Exercise 2   Correcting Errors in Tense

A sample rewritten paragraph is given.

(1) In the mid-1870's, General George Custer received permission to explore the possibility of establishing a military post in the Black Hills. (2) The Northern Plains tribes owned the territory, which, according to rumor, was rich in gold. (3) With him Custer took geologists who did find this precious metal. (4) Soon after, hordes of prospectors invaded the land, violating the treaty. (5) The Indians objected and the government sent soldiers, supposedly to force the miners' departure.

21.3   The Subjunctive Mood (Page 81)
Practice 1
Exercise 1   Using the Subjunctive Mood

Verbs on the left should be changed to the forms on the right in student sentences.
1. keeps/keep
2. are/be
3. are/be
4. was/were
5. was/were

Exercise 2   Using Auxiliary Verbs to Express the Subjunctive Mood

Sample sentences are given.
1. If I could be neater, I would not have to rewrite this paper.
2. The kitchen would be cooler if you would turn off the oven.
3. If you should go to New York City, what would you want to see?
4. I would make a roast if you could stay for dinner.
5. We would not be so rushed if you could start earlier.

21.3   The Subjunctive Mood (Page 82)
Practice 2
Exercise 1   Using the Subjunctive Mood

1. He wishes that he were a few inches taller.
2. The judge insists that the reporter remain outside.
3. I prefer that she wait in the lobby.
4. They stared at me as if I were a ghost.
5. I move that the minutes from the meeting be read.

Exercise 2   Using Auxiliary Verbs to Express the Subjunctive Mood

Sample sentences are given.
1. This meeting would run more smoothly if he would be friendlier.
2. She wishes that Kate could be relaxed and comfortable.

3. If Noreen would invite you, would you attend?
4. The house would be warmer if you would heat it better.
5. I would go to the library if I could get home earlier.

Writing Application
Writing Sentences in the Subjunctive Mood

Sample sentences are given.
1. The rules require that you be here every morning.
2. I suggest that everyone be on the alert for more weather bulletins.
3. The balmy temperatures felt as if it were spring.
4. I demand that she be the one to carry out the assignment.

21.4   Voice (Page 83)
Practice 1
Exercise 1   Distinguishing Between Active and Passive Voice

1. passive
2. active
3. active
4. passive
5. active

Exercise 2   Using the Active and Passive Voice

1. acceptable
2. weak
3. acceptable
4. acceptable
5. weak

21.4   Voice (Page 84)
Practice 2
Exercise 1   Distinguishing Between the Active and Passive Voice

1. passive
2. active
3. passive
4. active
5. active
6. active
7. passive
8. passive
9. active
10. passive
11. active
12. passive
13. passive
14. active
15. active
16. active
17. passive
18. passive
19. active
20. passive

Exercise 2   Using the Active Voice

Sample sentences are given.
1. The judges selected the winning essays for their originality and lucidity.
2. The boss has chosen Murphy for the task.
3. Someone has reworded the last sentence in the contract.
4. Girls will wear formal gowns at the dance.
5. The owner was rewarding the dog for his quick response.
6. The agency received hundreds of applications.
7. The council is ignoring his numerous complaints.
8. The trainer will have fed the tigers by noon.

9. Her friends misconstrue Kate's seeming indifference.
10. The nurse quickly applied a cold compress to the wound.

22.1 Case (The Three Cases) (Page 85)
Practice 1
Exercise 1 Identifying Case
1. objective
2. nominative
3. nominative
4. possessive
5. possessive
6. possessive
7. possessive
8. possessive
9. objective
10. possessive

Exercise 2 Recognizing the Use of Nouns and Pronouns
1. object of a preposition
2. subject
3. predicate nominative
4. to show ownership
5. to show ownership
6. to show ownership
7. to show ownership
8. to show ownership
9. direct object
10. to show ownership

22.1 Case (The Three Cases) (Page 86)
Practice 2
Exercise 1 Identifying Case
1. possessive (to show ownership)
2. objective (indirect object)
3. nominative (predicate nominative)
4. objective (indirect object)
5. objective (object of a verbal)
6. possessive (to show ownership)
7. objective (direct object)
8. nominative (nominative absolute)
9. objective (indirect object)
10. objective (object of an infinitive)
11. possessive (to show ownership)
12. nominative (subject)
13. possessive (to show ownership)
14. objective (indirect object)
15. nominative (predicate nominative)
16. possessive (to show ownership)
17. nominative (subject)
18. objective (direct object)
19. nominative (subject)
20. nominative (subject)

Exercise 2 Using Pronouns in Different Cases
Sample pronouns are given.
1. We
2. me
3. my
4. His
5. She
6. him
7. I
8. him
9. your
10. his

22.1 Case (The Nominative Case, The Objective Case) (Page 87)
Practice 1
Exercise 1 Identifying Pronouns in the Nominative Case
1. she, PN
2. they, PN
3. he, S
4. He, NA
5. she, S

Exercise 2 Identifying Pronouns in the Objective Case
1. us, DO
2. me, OP
3. him, SI
4. her, SI
5. her, IO
6. them, OP
7. her, DO
8. them, SI
9. her, SI
10. me, IO

22.1 Case (The Nominative Case, The Objective Case) (Page 88)
Practice 2
Exercise 1 Identifying Pronouns in the Nominative Case
1. she (subject)
2. he (subject)
3. she (nominative absolute)
4. they (subject)
5. he (predicate nominative)
6. We (subject)
7. he (subject)
8. I (subject)
9. I (subject)
10. We (subject)

Exercise 2 Using Pronouns in the Nominative Case
Sample pronouns are given.
1. she (subject)
2. they (subject)
3. he (predicate nominative)
4. he (nominative absolute)
5. They (subject)
6. he (subject)
7. she (predicate nominative)
8. we (subject)
9. you (predicate nominative)
10. we (subject)

Exercise 3 Identifying Pronouns in the Objective Case
1. him (object of a verbal)
2. them (object of a preposition)
3. us (subject of an infinitive)
4. him (object of a verbal)
5. us (indirect object)
6. her (object of a verbal)
7. us (direct object)
8. me (indirect object)
9. us (subject of an infinitive)
10. me (object of a verbal)

22.1 Case (Errors to Avoid with Possessive Pronouns) (Page 89)
Practice 1
Exercise 1 Using Pronouns in the Possessive Case
1. his
2. theirs
3. his
4. its
5. my
6. hers
7. your
8. their
9. our
10. they're

Exercise 2 Using All Three Cases of Pronouns
1. I
2. His
3. her
4. its
5. me
6. yours
7. she
8. his
9. Their
10. she

22.1 Case (Errors to Avoid with Possessive Pronouns) (Page 90)
Practice 2
Exercise 1 Using Pronouns in the Possessive Case
1. its
2. Their
3. Your
4. its
5. my
6. yours
7. his
8. Hers
9. your
10. You're
11. You're
12. its
13. his
14. hers
15. their

Writing Application
Writing Sentences with Nominative, Objective, and Possessive Pronouns
Sample sentences are given.
1. He told us to leave the building.
2. Are you against my traveling to Chicago?
3. The best projects are yours and ours.
4. Beth seemed a bit bewildered, she having been away for so long.
5. The best actors in the play are he and I.
6. My season being over, I put my jersey in the hamper.
7. Jake sent her a greeting card.
8. Mr. Whitaker wanted him and me to come to his office after school.
9. The guests of honor are you and I.
10. The neighbor told us that our singing was too loud.

22.2 Special Problems with Pronouns (Page 91)
Practice 1
Exercise 1 Using Who and Whom Correctly
1. whoever
2. whom
3. whom
4. who
5. Whoever
6. whom
7. who
8. Whom
9. who
10. whom

Exercise 2 Using Pronouns in Elliptical Clauses
1. me
2. she
3. us
4. they
5. he

22.2 Special Problems with Pronouns (Page 92)
Practice 2
Exercise 1 Using Who and Whom Correctly in Questions
1. Who
2. Whom
3. Whom
4. Whom
5. whom
6. Who
7. Whom
8. whom
9. Who
10. Whom

Exercise 2 Using Who and Whom Correctly in Clauses
1. who won the election yesterday (subject)
2. whoever challenges your honesty (subject)
3. whom he likes (direct object)
4. who likes tennis (subject)
5. who, I think, carried messages (subject)
6. whoever sent the anonymous gift (subject)
7. whomever you approach (direct object)
8. whom I admire (direct object)
9. who plays lead guitar in the band (subject)
10. whoever applies for financial aid (subject)

Exercise 3 Identifying the Correct Pronoun in Elliptical Clauses
1. she is
2. we do
3. I did
4. they are to him
5. I did

23.1 Subject and Verb Agreement (The Number of Nouns, Pronouns, and Verbs; Singular and Plural Subjects) (Page 93)
Practice 1
Exercise 1 Determining the Number of Words
1. S
2. both
3. S
4. S
5. P
6. both
7. both
8. S
9. both

10. both

Exercise 2   Making Subjects and Verbs Agree
1. have
2. has
3. is
4. has
5. have

23.1   Subject and Verb Agreement (The Number of Nouns, Pronouns, and Verbs; Singular and Plural Subjects) (Page 94)
Practice 2
Exercise 1   Determining the Number of Nouns, Pronouns, and Verbs
1. singular
2. singular
3. singular
4. plural
5. both
6. singular
7. singular
8. plural
9. both
10. plural
11. singular
12. both
13. plural
14. both
15. singular
16. singular
17. singular
18. singular
19. both
20. both

Exercise 2   Making Subjects Agree with Their Verbs
1. results
2. provides
3. goes
4. fills
5. provoke

Exercise 3   Making Separated Subjects and Verbs Agree
1. evokes
2. is
3. serves
4. is
5. are

Exercise 4   Making Relative Pronouns Agree with Their Verbs
1. cost
2. ignores
3. appeal
4. were
5. was

23.1   Subject and Verb Agreement (Compound Subjects) (Page 95)
Practice 1
Exercise 1   Compound Subjects Joined by *Or* or *Nor*
1. takes
2. has
3. adds
4. accompanies
5. was
6. has
7. costs
8. makes
9. speak

10. helps

Exercise 2   Compound Subjects Joined by *And*
1. are
2. go
3. was
4. agree
5. close
6. are
7. is
8. are
9. has
10. enjoy

23.1   Subject and Verb Agreement (Compound Subjects) (Page 96)
Practice 2
Exercise 1   Making Compound Subjects Agree with Their Verbs
1. was
2. have
3. were
4. are
5. is
6. are
7. are
8. draw
9. causes
10. is
11. have
12. grow
13. were
14. are
15. was
16. helps
17. were
18. has
19. take
20. were

Exercise 2   Making Compound Subjects Agree with Their Verbs
1. are
2. were doing
3. was counted
4. were
5. appreciate
6. knows
7. keeps
8. complete
9. makes
10. enjoy

23.1   Subject and Verb Agreement (Confusing Subjects) (Page 97)
Practice 1
Exercise 1   Deciding on the Number of Subjects
1. P
2. S
3. S
4. P
5. S
6. S
7. S
8. S
9. S
10. S

Exercise 2   Choosing Verbs to Agree with Difficult Subjects
1. begins

2. are
3. are
4. are
5. meets
6. were
7. is
8. has
9. remains
10. are

23.1 Subject and Verb Agreement (Confusing Subjects) (Page 98)

Practice 2

Exercise 1 Making Confusing Subjects Agree with Their Verbs

1. are
2. is
3. is
4. seem
5. were
6. is
7. is
8. are
9. is
10. is

Writing Application

Applying the Rules of Subject and Verb Agreement
Sample sentences are given.

1. Neither of the boys is home.
2. The audience is applauding. *or* The audience are not in agreement over the quality of the performance.
3. Two dollars is not much money. *or* Two dollars are allocated for different purchases.
4. Genetics is an exciting field.
5. Next to the desk is where I want you to sit. *or* Next to the desk are the books that I want to read.
6. Each of the club members is assigned a different task.
7. Most of the cement is being poured today.
8. Spaghetti and meatballs is a delicious meal. *or* Spaghetti and meatballs are of different consistencies.
9. Either she or her parents are meeting with the principal.
10. Some of the children are playing in the yard.

23.2 Pronoun and Antecedent Agreement (Agreement Between Personal Pronouns and Antecedents) (Page 99)

Practice 1

Exercise 1 Choosing Personal Pronouns to Agree with Antecedents

1. their
2. its
3. his
4. her
5. her

Exercise 2 Pronoun-Antecedent Agreement in Sentences

1. his
2. it
3. her
4. their
5. his
6. his
7. their

8. your
9. her
10. his

23.2 Pronoun and Antecedent Agreement (Agreement Between Personal Pronouns and Antecedents) (Page 100)

Practice 2

Exercise 1 Making Personal Pronouns Agree With Their Antecedents

1. their
2. it
3. their
4. their
5. his
6. its
7. their
8. their
9. her
10. her

Exercise 2 Avoiding Shifts in Person and Gender

1. Each girl must submit her report before leaving.
2. Those hikers will soon realize that they cannot walk for miles in shoes meant for dress wear.
3. The welders wear goggles so that their eyes will be shielded from the sparks.
4. Trying to protect its calf, the cow disregarded its own safety as the coyotes approached.
5. We learned in chemistry that we should often try again.
6. The students want to know what they should bring to class on Monday.
7. As hurricane Donna swept along the predicted path, it left destruction in its wake.
8. All the team members learned that they have to practice hard to win.
9. That nation has strengthened its economy, and now it has solid social programs.
10. Anyone can use his tickets for this ride.

23.2 Pronoun and Antecedent Agreement (Agreement with Indefinite and Reflexive Pronouns) (Page 101)

Practice 1

Exercise 1 Making Personal Pronouns Agree with Indefinite Pronouns

1. them
2. it
3. their
4. her
5. her
6. their
7. it
8. his
9. their
10. them

Exercise 2 Using Reflexive Pronouns Correctly

1. herself /she
2. yourself /you
3. myself /I
4. ourselves /we
5. yourself /you

23.2 Pronoun and Antecedent Agreement (Agreement with Indefinite and Reflexive Pronouns) (Page 102)
Practice 2
Exercise 1 Making Personal Pronouns Agree with Indefinite Pronouns
1. his
2. their
3. their
4. they
5. her
6. her
7. their
8. their
9. them
10. their
11. them
12. their
13. his
14. her
15. their

Exercise 2 Using Reflexive Pronouns Correctly
1. Scott and I were the first ones to arrive.
2. To whom other than her should the award be given?
3. Mary and Jean forgot to invite John and me.
4. Andrea and he were the most popular couple there.
5. The only person who can convince them is you.
6. Carmen looked at them in the photograph.
7. May Jerry and I have a piece of your pizza?
8. Who besides you can stay late today?
9. The person who has the best batting average is he.
10. The teacher and she will hand out the books.

23.3 Special Problems with Pronoun Agreement (Vague Pronoun References) (Page 103)
Practice 1
Exercise 1 Correcting Vague Pronoun References
Sample sentences are given.
1. Jeff needs to improve his average and pass the final. His doing either one seems unlikely.
2. The boys promptly wrote thank-you notes, an act that shocked their mother.
3. Missy's boutique is the most successful shop in town. She deserves her success.
4. Occasionally, we have a power failure or a bad storm. Both of them frighten the children.
5. Many valuables were broken and some were lost. Both the damages and the losses make me angry.

Exercise 2 Solving More Problems with Pronoun References
Sample sentences are given.
1. The annual picnic always features barbecued chicken.
2. In that game, a player can only reach "home" with an exact roll of the dice.
3. Bostonians often drop their r's.
4. correct
5. The article suggests that Perkins is guilty.

23.3 Special Problems with Pronoun Agreement (Vague Pronoun References) (Page 104)
Practice 2
Exercise 1 Correcting Vague Pronoun References
Sample corrected sentences are given.
1. To stake a claim on the frontier, a person had to live there.
2. We grumbled about the work done on the house because the builders left the roof open and the floor warped.
3. I quickly shifted to a more neutral topic, and this move prevented the inevitable argument over politics.
4. She wore a sweater over her blouse and a vest over the sweater. The look was too bulky.
5. Valery is self-disciplined and energetic. These two characteristics will be useful throughout life.
6. We are adding to our small ranch, and the changes should help everyone feel less cramped.
7. After waxing his new car, Jack polished the chrome and cleaned the interior. These chores became a monthly project.
8. When my father spoke angrily, we listened.
9. Near the East River in New York City a person can see the United Nations Headquarters.
10. George was too busy and involved with his own work, factors that made it possible for him to ignore other people.

Exercise 2 Correcting Vague Pronoun References
Sample corrected sentences are given.
1. Sam worked in a music store last summer and enjoyed the experience very much.
2. Managers sometimes have to discipline or even fire employees. These duties might make the managers uncomfortable.
3. We found spilled milk on the counters and broken dishes on the floor. This mess was our first clue.
4. I could never figure out why the station manager took my favorite program off the air.
5. correct

23.3 Special Problems with Pronoun Agreement (Page 105)
Practice 1
Exercise 1 Recognizing Problems of Pronoun Reference
1. FR
2. FR
3. FR
4. approaches
5. FR

Exercise 2 Correcting Problems of Pronoun Reference
Sample sentences are given.
1. (1) After Nancy spoke to Laura, Nancy felt much calmer.
2. (2) Mr. Pardi asked Tom to repeat the experiment Tom had just completed.
3. (3) The still life was a masterpiece. The wine seemed to sparkle in the goblet, and the fruit looked real enough to eat. The painting made me gasp.
4. (5) The coach told Hankins that he would not renew Hankin's contract.

23.3 Special Problems with Pronoun Agreement (Page 106)

Practice 2

Exercise 1 Correcting Ambiguous Pronoun References

1. The flight attendant told the woman that the flight attendant would ask someone to help her find the missing luggage.
2. This bonsai is growing in a container that discourages root growth, but the bonsai still seems too large.
3. Stephanie asked Betty Jane for help with the cooking.
4. While Barney wheeled his small son around the park, Barney was very contented.
5. Craig would have to leave soon, he informed Harry.

Exercise 2 Correcting Distant Pronoun References

1. In many stories by Ray Bradbury, the Martians are described as gentle, highly intelligent creatures who are destroyed by people from earth. The stories are written so skillfully that readers truly feel they have entered another world.
2. Not far from the shore, a small sailboat seemed motionless, its mast like a needle. Red and white buoys dotted the horizon. There was no one on the boat to unfurl the sail.
3. We plunged our hands into the huge mound of popcorn. Before us on the screen were the faces of the men, women, and children starving in Africa. Once the popcorn was gone, we guiltily put the box under the seat.
4. Muffins fresh from the oven, their smell filling the air, lay in wicker baskets. Jars of homemade jam, the fruit glistening along the glass sides, made our mouths water.
5. The meeting had gone badly, Mr. Snelling reflected, as he loosened his tie. It had been given to him by his daughter and was a conservative brown. He had forgotten to bring his notes, and he felt that he was not dressed appropriately.

24.1 Degrees of Comparison (Recognizing Degrees of Comparison, Regular Forms) (Page 107)

Practice 1

Exercise 1 Recognizing Degrees of Comparison

1. comp.
2. pos.
3. sup.
4. sup.
5. comp.
6. sup.
7. pos.
8. sup.
9. comp.
10. pos.

Exercise 2 Comparing Adjectives and Adverbs

1. cleverer, cleverest
2. soft, softer
3. unusual, most unusual
4. friendlier, friendliest
5. more awkwardly, most awkwardly

24.1 Degrees of Comparison (Recognizing Degrees of Comparison, Regular Forms) (Page 108)

Practice 2

Exercise 1 Recognizing Positive, Comparative, and Superlative Degrees

1. comparative
2. positive
3. superlative
4. positive
5. superlative
6. comparative
7. comparative
8. positive
9. superlative
10. comparative

Exercise 2 Forming Regular Comparative and Superlative Degrees

1. luckier, luckiest
2. more pleasing, most pleasing
3. sooner, soonest
4. stranger, strangest
5. thicker, thickest
6. more pretentious, most pretentious
7. more heavily, most heavily
8. fonder, fondest
9. cleverer, cleverest
10. curlier, curliest
11. more rapid, most rapid
12. more rapidly, most rapidly
13. tastier, tastiest
14. wider, widest
15. greener, greenest
16. more safely, most safely
17. colder, coldest
18. more hopeful, most hopeful
19. harder, hardest
20. more proudly, most proudly
21. more shocking, most shocking
22. more delightful, most delightful
23. more stunning, most stunning
24. more carefully, most carefully
25. shorter, shortest

24.1 Degrees of Comparison (Irregular Forms) (Page 109)

Practice 1

Exercise 1 Forming Irregular Comparative and Superlative Degrees

1. best
2. farther
3. worse
4. least
5. latest
6. further
7. best
8. worse
9. worst
10. more

Exercise 2 Using Adjectives and Adverbs to Make Comparisons

Sample sentences are given.

1. This is the worst meal I have ever eaten.
2. Vic played worse today than yesterday.
3. Vanilla ice cream tastes better than chocolate.
4. This new recipe requires more yeast than my old one.

5. I play tennis best.

24.1 Degrees of Comparison (Irregular Forms) (Page 110)
Practice 2
Exercise 1   Forming Irregular Comparative and Superlative Degrees
1. better
2. farther
3. best
4. less
5. more
6. further
7. more
8. worse
9. later
10. worse

Writing Application
Using Adjectives and Adverbs to Make Comparisons
Sample sentences are given.
1. This is the clearest water in the state.
2. No one is more trustworthy than Nick.
3. You must stay alert when you drive on the highway.
4. This is the best steak I've ever eaten.
5. I have bad news to tell you.
6. This is the worst snowstorm of the winter so far.
7. We have to travel far.
8. This prank was more malicious than his last one.
9. It's windier today than yesterday.
10. She is the most secretive person I've ever met.

24.2   Clear Comparisons (Using Comparative and Superlative Degrees) (Page 111)
Practice 1
Exercise 1   Using the Comparative and Superlative Degrees Correctly
1. least
2. oldest
3. more
4. coldest
5. more
6. most
7. more
8. fewest
9. fastest
10. most

Exercise 2   Recognizing Inappropriate Comparisons
Students should replace the underlined modifiers with those to the right.
1. happiest /happier
2. brightest /brighter
3. friendlier /friendliest
4. correct
5. safest /safer

24.2   Clear Comparisons (Using Comparative and Superlative Degrees) (Page 112)
Practice 2
Exercise 1   Using the Comparative and Superlative Forms Correctly
1. nicer
2. more likely
3. worse
4. youngest
5. farther
6. more viable
7. better

8. best
9. louder
10. brighter
11. most talented
12. most violent
13. later
14. more bewildered
15. most brilliant

Exercise 2   Supplying the Comparative and Superlative Degrees
1. muddier
2. best
3. clearer
4. warmer
5. better
6. oldest
7. more
8. heavier
9. more susceptible
10. more
11. rudest
12. more beneficial
13. most casual
14. more familiar
15. most impressive

24.2   Clear Comparisons (Logical Comparisons) (Page 113)
Practice 1
Exercise 1   Making Balanced Comparisons
Sample corrections are given.
1. ... better than my mother's.
2. ... bigger than his father's.
3. ... more complicated than those for that model.
4. ... higher than the one Judy took.
5. ... less expensive than at this store.

Exercise 2   Using *Other* and *Else* in Comparisons
Sample corrections are given.
1. ... farther than anyone else on his team.
2. ... than anyone else's.
3. ... more fluently than anyone else.
4. ... prettier than any other flowers on this street.
5. ... better than any other football team.

24.2   Clear Comparisons (Logical Comparisons) (Page 114)
Practice 2
Exercise 1   Making Balanced Comparisons
Sample corrections are given.
1. ... more legible than Linda's.
2. ... calmer than those on the perimeter.
3. ... more fun than feeding the alligators.
4. ... bigger than a deer's.
5. ... similar to those on a bobcat.
6. ... as much as contact with poison oak.
7. ... longer than Richard's.
8. ... fewer than those in last year's
9. ... more relaxing than watching a television show.
10. ... healthier than those in Ms. Patterson's garden.

Exercise 2   Using *Other* and *Else* in Comparisons
Sample corrections are given.
1. ... more fascinating than anyone else's.
2. ... more respected than any other person who lived there.
3. ... of any of the other contestants.
4. ... more thorough than anyone else.
5. ... more tricks than anyone else we ever saw.

24.2 Clear Comparisons (Absolute Modifiers) (Page 115)

Practice 1

Exercise 1 Correcting Illogical Comparisons
Sample corrections are given.
1. This model comes in a wider range of colors ...
2. ...are perpendicular.
3. That snake has the most dangerous venom.
4. ... treat us equally.
5. ... lines parallel.

Exercise 2 Writing Clear Comparisons
Sample sentences are given.
1. Nutrimax is more nutritious than Sugar Puffs.
2. Janie is slightly heavier than Carol.
3. Of *The Twilight Zone*, *I Love Lucy*, and *The Honeymooners*, my favorite show is *The Twilight Zone*.
4. I like dancing bears much more than roaring lions.
5. I had more to eat for dinner than Chris did.

24.2 Clear Comparisons (Absolute Modifiers) (Page 116)

Practice 2

Exercise 1 Avoiding Absolute Modifiers in Comparisons
Sample corrections are given.
1. ... more thorough than mine.
2. ... more suitable than my Uncle Walter's.
3. ... more significant than the last one.
4. ... more overburdened with math homework than Keith was.
5. ... less unusual than Aunt Mary's.
6. ... more directly to their destination.
7. ... more similar than those two gray ones.
8. ... more unlike mine was than his was.
9. ... more dangerous than a rattlesnake's.
10. ... less wilted than the ones you picked.

Writing Application

Writing Effective Comparisons
Sample sentences are given.
1. Of ounces, pounds, and tons, tons are the heaviest.
2. Physicians are more educated than most accountants.
3. Of Cary Grant, James Stewart, and Humphrey Bogart, Humphrey Bogart may be the best.
4. A saxophone is a larger instrument than a clarinet.
5. *It's a Wonderful Life* has a happier ending than *Citizen Kane*.

25.1 Negative Sentences (Recognizing Double Negatives, Forming Negative Sentences Correctly) (Page 117)

Practice 1

Exercise 1 Recognizing Double Negatives
1. C
2. DN
3. C
4. C
5. DN
6. DN
7. C
8. DN
9. DN
10. DN

Exercise 2 Correcting Double Negatives
Sample corrected sentences are given.
1. (2) The guard had seen nothing suspicious.
2. (5) At first we couldn't see anything in the darkness.
3. (6) They don't have any more morning papers at the candy store.
4. (8) The baby can't eat any more of those apples.
5. (9) Neither of the boys had done anything wrong.
6. (10) Ms. Martinez won't accept any late papers.

25.1 Negative Sentences (Recognizing Double Negatives, Forming Negative Sentences Correctly) (Page 118)

Practice 2

Exercise 1 Avoiding Double Negatives
1. any
2. ever
3. anywhere
4. no one
5. any

Exercise 2 Avoiding Problems with Negatives
Sample sentences are given.
1. Phil never did anything to antagonize the crew members.
2. You should not drive that car anywhere without snow tires.
3. Hardly anyone knew the answers on the exam.
4. I can't find my address book anywhere.
5. We never saw the bear tracking us.

Exercise 3 Correcting Double Negatives
Sample sentences with corrected phrases are given.
1. She would hardly try to finish the project on time.
2. When he went to the park there was nobody there.
3. After the long hike, I could scarcely walk.
4. There were but a few blossoms on the apple tree.
5. While recovering from the accident, Stacy didn't want any pity.

25.1 Negative Sentences (Understatement) (Page 119)

Practice 1

Exercise 1 Using Understatement
1. The new crop of rookies was not unpromising.
2. The climb is difficult, but not impossible.
3. The judge was not unsympathetic ... decision.
4. The extra cost of air conditioning is not insignificant.
5. The reviews of the critics were not unenthusiastic.

Exercise 2 Writing Negative Sentences
Sample sentences are given.
1. It is not easy for me to read the small print on the bottle.
2. None of these pictures are mine.
3. Will wasn't finished with his project.
4. Nobody came to the Millers' surprise party.
5. None of the students bought the book.

25.1 Negative Sentences (Understatement) (Page 120)

Practice 2

Exercise 1 Using Understatement
1. Interruptions from inquisitive children were not infrequent.
2. This dime store trinket is not inexpensive.

3. I am not unimpressed by your fluency in Russian.
4. The sentimental value of the ring is not unimportant.
5. Taking some time for yourself is not unessential.
6. Her opinion is not irrelevant.
7. Tad is certainly not a nonconformist.
8. His prose style was not displeasing.
9. Considering the barbaric manners of his guests, I think Bob's conduct was not dishonorable.
10. The findings from the study were not insignificant.

Writing Application
Writing Negative Sentences
Sample sentences are given.
1. Your constant disruptions are not appreciated.
2. I can see nothing through this telescope.
3. Henry never bothered to report the incident to the police.
4. As a student she is not unintelligent.
5. The face in this blurry photograph is barely recognizable.
6. The dinner has hardly begun, and the guests are already complaining about the quality of the food.
7. There are but two possibilities, victory or defeat.
8. I scarcely noticed that the new freeway entrance had opened.

25.2 Common Usage Problems (Page 121)
Practice 1
Exercise 1 Avoiding Common Usage Problems
1. besides
2. because of
3. taught
4. from
5. eager
6. regardless
7. effect
8. Leave
9. adapt
10. principle

Exercise 2 Correcting Common Usage Problems
Students should replace words on the left with those on the right in sentences.
1. real/very
2. done/have done
3. healthy/healthful
4. This here/This
5. very unique/unique

25.2 Common Usage Problems (Page 122)
Practice 2
Exercise 1 Avoiding Usage Problems
1. effect
2. already
3. isn't
4. except
5. much
6. somewhere
7. all together
8. among
9. all right
10. anxious
11. very
12. blond
13. a while
14. are
15. because
16. can
17. can't help admiring
18. burst
19. advertisement
20. continual
21. dived
22. immigrated
23. enthusiastic
24. Because of
25. former

Exercise 2 Avoiding Usage Problems
1. friendly
2. hung
3. earned
4. Regardless
5. Lay
6. may be
7. somewhat
8. loose
9. ought
10. Admit only

26 Capitalization (First Words, Proper Nouns, Proper Adjectives) (Page 123)
Practice 1
Exercise 1 Using Capitals for First Words
1. The, Tell, In
2. We, But
3. What, Golly
4. Resolved, That
5. The, Wow, That

Exercise 2 Capitalizing Proper Nouns and Proper Adjectives
1. Halbert Clinic, Blue Cross, Medicare
2. Alhambra, Granada, Moorish
3. Republican, Democratic, New York
4. Metroliner, Metro Park, New Jersey
5. Ellen Blair, Surephoto, Unilens

26 Capitalization (First Words, Proper Nouns, Proper Adjectives) (Page 124)
Practice 2
Exercise 1 Capitalizing First words
1. Your
2. I, Instead, And, A
3. Resolved, That
4. The, He
5. Oh, This

Exercise 2 Using Capitals for Proper Nouns
1. Army, Cumberland, Georgia, Tennessee, Kentucky, Civil War
2. Spanish, French, Italian
3. Old Testament, New Testament, Koran
4. Declaration of Independence, Constitution, Bill of Rights
5. South America, Pacific Ocean, Chile, Peru
6. New York State Regents Scholarship, Westinghouse Science Award
7. Skyliner Tristar
8. Big Dipper
9. correct
10. Nash Rambler, Customer Relations Department, Unity Motor Company, Dearborn, Michigan.

Exercise 3 Using Capitals for Proper Adjectives
1. correct
2. Bible study
3. First and Second avenues
4. correct

5. correct
6. Lake Erie
7. correct
8. Himalayan village
9. Boice automobile
10. correct

26 Capitalization (Titles, Letters) (Page 125)
Practice 1
Exercise 1 Using Capitals in Titles
1. Sergeant
2. "The Dry Salvages," *Four Quartets*
3. Senator
4. M.F.A.
5. Aunt, General
6. *Mona Lisa, The Last Supper*
7. Saint, Pastor
8. *Consumer Reports, Penny Power*
9. *Annie,* "Tomorrow"
10. Mr., Poetry

Exercise 2 Using Capitals for Salutations and Closings
1. Dear Rabbi Hartman,
2. Your grateful neighbor,
3. With deep regret,
4. My dear Ethel,
5. Sincerely yours,
6. Dear Chairman Gott:
7. Your friend always,
8. Dear Sir or Madam:
9. Dearest Cousin,
10. With warm regards,

26 Capitalization (Titles, Letters) (Page 126)
Practice 2
Exercise 1 Using Capitals in a Business Letter

43 berry hill lane
cornwall, new york 12518
november 5, 2001

director of admissions
fairleigh dickinson university
1000 river road
teaneck, new jersey 07666

dear director:

after speaking with my college adviser, i may be interested in enrolling in the college of business administration at fairleigh dickinson university in september of next year.

would you please send me your catalog for the college of business administration? i am also interested in your admission requirements and details of the financial aid package provided by the university.

since i live some distance from teaneck, i would also like information about on-campus housing or housing in the area.

thank you very much for your assistance.

yours truly,
elizabeth green

Writing Application
Using Capitalization Rules in Original Sentences
Sample sentences are given.
1. William Golding's Lord of the Flies is Tom's favorite novel.

2. Governor Dexter Hamilton has been in politics for a long time.
3. Go east on Route 14, north on Route 9, and east on Maple Avenue.
4. The New York Yankees have won many championships through the years.
5. Barbara can speak French and German.
6. The Lincoln Memorial is a quiet place of contemplation.
7. The Atlantic Ocean and the Pacific Ocean seemingly stretch infinitely from the east and west coasts respectively of the United States.
8. My favorite courses are American History 2, French 4, and Calculus 2.
9. I attended Monroe Junior High School, and Franklin Regional High School.
10. She said "I won't be able to come over for dinner today."

27.1 End Marks (Page 127)
Practice 1
Exercise 1 Using End Marks for Sentences and Phrases
1. (!)
2. (?)
3. (.)
4. (!)
5. (!)
6. (.)
7. (!)
8. (.)
9. (.)
10. (?)

Exercise 2 Using End Marks in Your Own Sentences
Sample sentences are given.
1. Wendy saw Dr. Farley yesterday.
2. Wow! Did you see that?
3. A ticket to Houston costs $250 over the Internet.
4. He asked if we were leaving soon.
5. Don't quit!

27.1 End Marks (Page 128)
Practice 2
Exercise 1 Using End Marks
1. Whew! What a scare that was. *or* !
2. How many times have you tried to win a race?
3. Fowler's book on English usage is a very useful reference book.
4. Watch out for that car!
5. She asked if I had achieved my goal.

Exercise 2 Using End Marks in Other Situations
1. Confucius, who died in 470 (?) B.C., was a philosopher.
2. correct
3. correct
4. The calendar page gave the following date: Oct. 26.
5. The package was addressed to Mr. Luis Ramirez, 23 Grove St., St. Paul, Minn.
6. At 10:30 P.M. the baby finally fell asleep.
7. I. Vitamin A
   A. Sources
      1. Milk, butter, eggs
      2. Green and yellow vegetables
   B. Value
      1. Preserves health of skin
      2. Preserves health of mucous membranes

8. His train is due to arrive on Sat., Apr. 17, at 8 A.M.
9. Jeannette Rankin was the first woman elected to the U.S. Congress.
10. correct

27.2 Commas (That Separate Basic Elements) (Page 129)
Practice 1
Exercise 1   Using Commas Correctly
1. none
2. We requested the book weeks ago, yet it hasn't come back so far.
3. The cookies should be cooled, drizzled with melted chocolate, and sprinkled with chopped nuts.
4. The fish was served with a rich, tangy sauce.
5. none
6. Paula tried to reach Jack all day, but she had no luck.
7. Potted palms, Easter lilies, and pink azaleas banked the stage.
8. My first job was a happy, rewarding experience.
9. We had hoped to see that new musical, but no tickets were available.
10. Mr. Hawkins has a large collection of rare, valuable coins.

Exercise 2   Recognizing Rules for Commas
1. cumulative adjectives
2. compound sentence
3. series
4. coordinate adjectives
5. cumulative adjectives
6. compound sentence
7. series
8. coordinate adjectives
9. compound sentence
10. coordinate adjectives

27.2 Commas (That Separate Basic Elements) (Page 130)
Practice 2
Exercise 1   Punctuating Simple and Compound Sentences
1. My mother and father arrived on time, but we had to wait for the other relatives.
2. correct
3. Leslie will graduate from high school this June, and several of her other friends will graduate with her, but her best friend will not graduate until next year.
4. These customers want their merchandise delivered today, or they plan to cancel their orders.
5. correct
6. Our car needs a complete tune up, for it has been over six months since it has had one.
7. We neither wanted their assistance now, nor would we accept it at some future time.
8. correct
9. Join us at the meeting this evening, for it promises to be dramatic and exciting.
10. correct

Exercise 2   Punctuating Items in a Series and Coordinate Adjectives
1. The leader of the rock group was a friendly, attractive youth.

2. Fresh fruit, green vegetables, lean meat, and grain products were part of her diet.
3. correct
4. Our advisor planned the trip, chartered the bus, and arranged the hotel reservations.
5. A well-planned, thoughtful speech followed the introduction.
6. Battles were fought in New Jersey, New York, Pennsylvania, Delaware, and Virginia during the Revolutionary War.
7. These hardy plants grow equally well in window boxes, in home gardens, and in open fields.
8. The survey of the city showed that many buildings were abandoned, that many small businesses had closed, and that the streets needed repair.
9. correct
10. The vessel slipped into port on a rainy, moonless night.

27.2 Commas (That Set Off Added Elements) (Page 131)
Practice 1
Exercise 1   Using Commas with Added Elements
1. dinner, Mom
2. happening, I
3. that, in addition, we
4. safety, the
5. principal, not the class advisor, will
6. teachers, moreover, have
7. owner, I assure you, took
8. think, Ellen, that
9. over, I
10. is, without a doubt, a

Exercise 2   Distinguishing Between Essential and Nonessential Elements
1. none
2. I, which
3. none
4. none
5. sweater, which … aunt, was
6. Dickinson, who … Amherst, became
7. none
8. President, speaking … reporters, deplored
9. Jeremy, a … person, surprised
10. none

27.2 Commas (That Set Off Added Elements) (Page 132)
Practice 2
Exercise 1   Setting Off Introductory Material
1. To practice my speech I rehearsed it in front of a mirror.
2. Cautioned by her mother and warned by her friends, Betsy drove slowly through the busy intersection.
3. At the supermarket, checkout counters always seem to have long lines.
4. correct
5. If the weather is pleasant, we hope to attend a concert in the park tonight.
6. George, will you help at the bazaar on Saturday?
7. Of course, the judge will punish the offenders.
8. Weakened by the storm, the battered merchant ship limped into port two weeks late.
9. Delightedly, Steve opened the door and greeted his cousins.

10. No, I never thought I would have a chance to win first prize.

Exercise 2 Setting Off Parenthetical Expressions
1. There are five houses on that street now, not the two you remember.
2. You must, nevertheless, do the assignments.
3. Professor Watkins is, I believe, one of the top economic experts in the country.
4. The results, we hope, will be beneficial to everyone.
5. You know, Mrs. Grey, we will do whatever we can to help.

Exercise 3 Distinguishing Between Essential and Nonessential Material
1. correct
2. O'Hare Airport, which is one of the busiest airports in the world, handles many daily arrivals and departures.
3. correct
4. Dr. Stevenson, whom you heard lecture last week, will speak again today.
5. Heinrich Schliemann, who unearthed the ruins of Troy and Mycenae, wanted to excavate the Minoan ruins on Crete.
6. correct
7. correct
8. The Interstate Commerce Commission, which was authorized by Congress in 1887, has the power to regulate commerce among the states.
9. The original Fort Laramie, built by fur traders William Sublette and Robert Campbell, was established in 1834 near the junction of the North Platte and Laramie rivers in what is now the state of Wyoming.
10. correct

27.2 Commas (Other Uses) (Page 133)
Practice 1
Exercise 1 Adding Commas to Sentences
1. Coburn, M.D., appeared
2. Dad's, pancakes
3. 1,238
4. wonder," Joyce said, "if
5. Court, Dover, Delaware 19901
6. Peggy, Anne
7. June 20, 1986, my
8. $14,000
9. wing," the guide continued, "were
10. coffee, cake

Exercise 2 Punctuating a Letter
672 Pondfield Road
Bronxville, New York 10708
October 25, 2001

Dear Gerri,

Well, it looks as if I will see you this fall after all. My family and I will be coming to Bronxville next Saturday, November 2, to visit Sarah Lawrence College. It has been a busy fall with all this college shopping going on. My current favorite is Rutgers in New Brunswick, New Jersey. In addition, we have visited Drew, St. Johns, and Seton Hall. I am applying to all of them, but I haven't made any firm decision yet.

My parents would like to take us out to lunch when we are in town next Saturday, so think of some likely places. It will be good to see you again.

Your old friend,
Sal

27.2 Commas (Other Uses) (Page 134)
Practice 2
Exercise 1 Using Commas in Other Situations
1. Mail entries by May 30, 2000, to Box 5, Troy, Iowa 52537.
2. Harold Andre, Sr., lives in Santa Barbara, California.
3. In 1978 the United States imported 8,230,000 barrels of oil.
4. In one day 5,675 people called the toll-free phone number (800) 555-0220 to pledge money for the charity drive.
5. Jim spent his savings on a new bicycle; Pat, on a CD player.
6. "We'll be late," Virginia worried, "unless we hurry."
7. In the dark, stairways can prove hazardous.
8. Karen Wilson, D.D.S., will open an office in this building.
9. Paul said, "On Saturday I will mow the lawn."
10. In what encyclopedia did you read that Montreal, Quebec, Canada, has about 1,214,300 people?

Exercise 2 Using Commas in a Social Letter
736 Williams Avenue
Dayton, Ohio 45402
August 5, 1997

Dear Margaret,

Well, after almost six weeks of travel, my family and I have returned from our exciting trip to Egypt. Returning to the United States, we were struck by the difference in cultures. It felt, I think, like going from an old world to a new.

Naturally, we saw all the famous sights: the Pyramids and Sphinx at Giza, the temples of Karnak and Luxor, the Aswan Dam, and, of course, Cairo. Much to my surprise, I was fascinated by Cairo, the capital city of Egypt. I visited the Egyptian Museum, the Cairo Tower, Mohammed Ali Mosque, and other places.

My mother bought an old, expensive bracelet. As if that weren't enough, she also invested in a caftan called a galabias and two brass trays.

I'm looking forward to your visit next week, and I'll tell you about the rest of my experiences then.

Affectionately,
Brad

Writing Application
Student sentences should illustrate various rules of comma usage.

27.3 Semicolons and Colons (Page 135)
Practice 1
Exercise 1 Using Semicolons Correctly
1. merchants; however,
2. overslept; as
3. elective; but
4. footsteps; he

Exercise 2 Using Colons Correctly
1. poisonous: holly
2. table: "I
3. 11:215
4. plain: We
5. *History: Connections*

27.3 Semicolons and Colons (Page 136)
Practice 2
Exercise 1 Using Semicolons
1. The committee was unhappy with the decision; nevertheless, they understood why it had been made.
2. Ben struggled up the steep, rocky hill; and when he reached the top, Ben collapsed in a heap on the ground.
3. The clipper ship, battered by the vicious storm, fought a losing battle; the main mast, weakened by the winds, broke.
4. We have invited cousin Hank, who is an attorney in Atlanta; my friend Betty, who lives next door; and Betty's brother, who is home from college for the weekend.
5. The storm washed out the road; therefore, it took us an additional hour to reach the cabin.

Exercise 2 Using Colons
1. The office manager gave us a list of needed supplies: paper clips, correction fluid, rubber bands, and brass fasteners.
2. Warning: This product is for external use only.
3. The coach's explanation was simple and direct: The team had decided to try to rebuild by using the younger players.
4. His historical research took him to a number of countries: England, Belgium, France, Austria, and Germany.
5. The book you need is called The Revolution Remembered: Eyewitness Accounts of the War for Independence.

Exercise 3 Using Semicolons and Colons Correctly
1. Joanne purchased all the picnic supplies: soda, potato chips, frankfurters, rolls, and fresh fruit.
2. The family agreed with the doctor's prognosis; nevertheless, they decided to get another opinion.
3. The United States Postal Service issued an unusually attractive commemorative stamp: It depicts General Bernardo de Galvez at the Battle of Mobile in 1780.
4. The first CD contains selections from the group's concert; the second CD is a compilation of old hits.
5. The host was a well-known scientist and author: Carl Sagan.
6. The President welcomed the foreign dignitary: "The people of the United States welcome you and hope that your visit will be a pleasant and productive one."
7. This is her plan: She wants to visit Milan and then Rome.
8. Mary Ellen invited Bill, who enjoyed playing cards: Sue, who loved to dance; and Glen, who didn't enjoy parties at all.
9. The flight to Ireland left at 11:30 P.M.
10. Six pupils took the state scholarship examination today; the rest decided to wait for the next test.

27.4 Quotation Marks and Underlining (Quotation Marks for Direct Quotations) (Page 137)
Practice 1
Exercise 1 Distinguishing Between Direct and Indirect Quotations
1. I
2. I

3. D
4. I
5. D
6. D
7. I
8. I
9. D
10. D

Exercise 2 Using Quotation Marks Correctly
Location of quotation marks are indicated for sentences marked D in Exercise 1; sample rewritten indirect quotations are given.

1. "You really should try out for the part," Louise suggested.
2. "If your grades don't get better, you'll be grounded for a month," said Frank's mother.
3. * "What ... up?"
4. "I am sure that Mr. Hawkins will give me a good reference," Don said.
5. * "Get ... Street," Bill explained, "and ... Market."
6. * "That ... house,"
7. "The harpist was exceptionally good," Warren remarked.
8. "Jill, may I borrow your notes on Chapter 15?" I asked.
9. * "Oh, my gosh!" Phil exclaimed. "That jump was incredible!"
10. * "Without a doubt," the owner stated, "we will surpass last year's sales."

27.4 Quotation Marks and Underlining (Quotation Marks for Direct Quotations) (Page 138)
Practice 2
Exercise 1 Enclosing Direct Quotations in Quotation Marks
1. "I am going to take my driver's test today," said Gloria.
2. My father replied, "I will be happy to help you."
3. "Tell me what happened," I pleaded. "I can't bear to be in suspense any longer."
4. correct
5. The bus driver sighed, "Don't you have the correct change?"
6. correct
7. "I know," she answered, "I just heard the news on the radio."
8. My little brother says I am "the world's bossiest sister."
9. The judge rapped the gavel: "I want order in the courtroom."
10. "I am so pleased you can visit us," wrote Joyce. "We have all missed you since you moved away."
11. "How many times have I told you," sighed Margaret, "that you must not track mud into the house?"
12. "This is the hardest thing I have ever had to do," said my boss ominously.
13. correct
14. Katherine announced, "I have registered to vote in the next election."
15. "Please leave the house right now," said Paulette. "I need some peace and quiet."

Exercise 2 More Work With Direct and Indirect Quotations
1. "Karen thinks we should go on a picnic," announced Rick. D

2. Dorian warned, "Mr. Dombrowski frowns on tardiness." D
3. Skip told us that he had just learned three new songs. I
4. "The movie was excellent," said Angelo. "You really should go see it." D
5. The woman at the ticket counter said, "That will be forty-five dollars, please." D
6. The acrobat told us that he practiced for several hours each day. I
7. "You are wrong," said Marco. "I have been there, and I can tell you the sand is really white." D
8. Margaret says that you were mean to her, Jason. I
9. Darlene stood straight and tall: "I passed my driving test." D
10. "We are looking forward to meeting you in person," wrote Allan. "Letters and photographs are not really enough." D

27.4 Quotation Marks and Underlining (Other Punctuation Marks with Quotation Marks, Quotation Marks in Special Situations) (Page 139)

Practice 1

Exercise 1 Punctuating Direct Quotations
1. "Are ... Take ... 7A'?" Jane asked.
2. me, "The ... Thursday"; but
3. "We all hope," Sally wrote, "that ... soon."
4. "Have ... cut?"
5. exclaimed, "What ... is!"
6. said, "I ... immediately"; then
7. "Can't you see," Josh pleaded, "that ...quickly?"
8. asked, "Who ... begins, 'Whose ...'?"
9. plan: "I ... pool."
10. "Wow!" Harvey said. "We ... team."

Exercise 2 Paragraphing Dialogue
Students' dialogues should demonstrate a thorough understanding of the use of quotation marks.

27.4 Quotation Marks and Underlining (Other Punctuation Marks with Quotation Marks, Quotation Marks in Special Situations) (Page 140)

Practice 2

Exercise 1 Using Other Punctuation Marks Correctly with Quotations
1. According to H. L. Mencken, William Jennings Bryan was "the national tear duct."
2. Did they ask, "What can we do to help?"
3. "I think you can be whatever you want to be," Father said.
4. Emma Lazarus described the poor people of the world as "huddled masses yearning to breathe free."
5. She agreed to work "day and night"; we never believed her.
6. When she saw the new car, she screamed, "Hooray!"
7. Oscar Wilde commented about a famous contemporary: "Mr. Henry James writes fiction as if it were a painful duty."
8. "Is that clear?" she asked.
9. In the bottle were his "secret ingredients": frog legs, talcum powder, and an old arrowhead.
10. Gertrude Stein gave the following advice to Ernest Hemingway: "Remarks are not literature."

Exercise 2 Punctuating with Ellipsis Marks and Single Quotation Marks
1. "Then the president turned to us and said, 'I'm afraid I must decline,' and walked from the room."
2. Robert Benchley once jested, "I haven't been abroad in so long that I almost speak English without an accent."
3. A quotation from Katherine Mansfield begins, "I want, by understanding myself, to understand others. ..."
4. "Later they studied Hamlet's famous soliloquy, which begins, 'To be, or not to be, that is the question.'"
5. Catherine Drinker Bowen has written: "All artists quiver under the lash of adverse criticism.... When Beethoven heard that a certain conductor refused to perform one of his symphonies, he went to bed ... until the symphony was performed."
6. "She asked, 'How did it happen?' and burst into tears."
7. Mark Twain ends his criticism of Scott with these words: "... He did measureless harm; more real and lasting harm, perhaps, than any other individual that ever wrote."
8. My mother said, "I always wanted to sing professionally."
9. About Bernhard Shaw, Oscar Wilde said that he "... hasn't an enemy in the world, and none of his friends like him."
10. "What did he mean when he said, 'You'll be sorry'?"

27.4 Quotation Marks and Underlining (Underlining and Quotation Marks) (Page 141)

Practice 1

Exercise 1 Using Underlining and Quotation Marks
1. "Moon River" Breakfast at Tiffany's
2. none
3. a, o
4. Long Day's Journey into Night, tour de force
5. imply

Exercise 2 More Work with Underlining and Quotation Marks
1. The Spirit of St. Louis
2. "The Fox and the Grapes"
3. Guernica, chef-d'oeuvre
4. "Soups and Stews"
5. The Sound and the Fury, Macbeth

27.4 Quotation Marks and Underlining (Underlining and Quotation Marks) (Page 142)

Practice 2

Exercise 1 Using Underlining and Quotation Marks
1. The French expression le style c'est l'homme was one of her favorite sayings.
2. The train called the Twentieth Century Limited traveled between New York and Chicago.
3. "Wilkommen," the opening song in the musical Cabaret, is considered a most effective opening number.
4. I just read the poem "Wild Swans" by Edna St. Vincent Millay.
5. The Daily Times has great political influence.

Exercise 2 Applying the Rules Governing the Use of Quotation Marks and Underlining

1. Two of romantic painter John Constable's works are Salisbury Cathedral and Haystacks.
2. Chaucer's Canterbury Tales begins with the following words: "When in April the sweet showers fall …"
3. "She had bought," Flannery O'Connor wrote, "a new dress for the occasion."
4. In his essay "Dunkirk," Winston Churchill describes the most famous retreat in history.
5. "What factors led you to that conclusion?" she asked.
6. I enjoyed Emily Brontë's novel, Wuthering Heights.
7. Bill continued, "Then my sister said, 'I am going to enlist!' and my mother began to cry."
8. In Shakespeare's Romeo and Juli et, Romeo sighs, "… O! that I were a glove upon that hand …"
9. "That's my final offer," he blurted. "Take it or leave it."
10. Remember to cross your t's and dot your i's.

Writing Application

Using Quotation Marks and Underlining Correctly in Your Own Writing

Sample sentences are given.

1. Everyone in the family enjoyed The Spirit of St. Louis, a film about the American aviator Charles Lindbergh.
2. Grandmother often says, "Get up early and get things done."
3. I enjoyed reading the poem "Birches" by Robert Frost.
4. The Crestview Times includes only the news of the immediate area.
5. Stop saying furthermore before every sentence.

27.5 Dashes, Parentheses, Brackets, and Hyphens (Dashes, Parentheses) (Page 143)
Practice 1
Exercise 1 Using the Dash

1. trucks—all
2. right—now
3. acclaim—all
4. me—this is just between us, of course—that
5. stadium—it … dome—seats

Exercise 2 Using Parentheses

1. Odyssey, (andra, meaning "man") suggests
2. Stanton (1815–1902) was
3. camel (also called a dromedary) has
4. (a), (b), (c)
5. General Widget (the price was the lowest in years) and

27.5 Dashes, Parentheses, Brackets, and Hyphens (Dashes, Parentheses) (Page 144)
Practice 2
Exercise 1 Using the Dash

1. Athletics—that is, winning athletics—can inspire college alumni to contribute large sums of money to their universities.
2. Once a year—no more than that—I like to visit my aunt in her house by the beach.
3. What would you do if someone like Albert Einstein—that genius—wanted to have a talk with you?

4. The delayed—I should say three hours overdue—train will arrive soon.
5. The flowers in the vases—roses carnations and lilies—certainly do cheer up this room.
6. Boots, jeans, cowboy hats, and belts—Jake had all the trappings of the urban cowboy.
7. Alex—the one who had given her the locket—would be arriving in twenty minutes.
8. To dance, to sing, to laugh—these were Sally's only ambitions.
9. In her entire life—all ninety-two years—my great-grandmother never traveled out of New York.
10. Her house—or should I say cottage?—was decorated in a very unusual manner.

Exercise 2 Enclosing Material in Parentheses

1. Florence Nightingale (1820–1910) is regarded as the founder of modern nursing.
2. She served as a nurse during the Crimean War (1854–1856).
3. For dinner we had steak, baked potatoes, and broccoli. (I have always disliked broccoli.) A homemade apple pie was served for dessert.
4. Built in 1826, the stone barn (a Hancock Shaker Village landmark) housed fifty-two cows.
5. Estoril (we drove there from Lisbon) is a popular tourist resort in Portugal.
6. Mystic Village in Connecticut and Sturbridge Village in Massachusetts (Have you ever visited either of them?) recreate life of an earlier period.
7. Her plan is to create a garden of (1) lilacs, (2) roses, (3) tulips, and (4) daffodils.
8. The firm's New Jersey phone number is (201) 555-4678.
9. Because of the storm (What a blizzard!), school was canceled.
10. When you apply to a college, be sure you send (a) the completed application, (b) your high school transcript, (c) your SAT scores, (d) several references, and (e) the registration fee.

27.5 Dashes, Parentheses, Brackets, and Hyphens (Brackets) (Page 145)
Practice 1
Exercise 1 Using Brackets Correctly

1. championship [Bobby Fischer] eventually
2. "It [experience] is
3. Brittanico [sic].
4. novel [Pudd'nhead Wilson], the
5. of [sic]."

Exercise 2 Using Dashes, Parentheses, and Brackets
Placement of needed dashes, parentheses, and brackets is shown.

1. (a), (b), (c)
2. allegory [sic] on
3. crowd—Tompkins
4. Wilkes (Wasn't … birds?) is
5. to—oh,

27.5 Dashes, Parentheses, Brackets, and Hyphens (Brackets) (Page 146)
Practice 2
Exercise 1 Enclosing Material in Brackets

1. "Fourscore and seven years ago [87 years], our fathers brought forth on this continent a new nation …"
2. "We the people of the United States, in order to form a more perfect Union [of the thirteen former

colonies], establish justice, insure domestic tranquility, provide for the common defense ..."

3. "No perking [sic]" was written on the sign at the corner.

4. "The figures [sculptures made of ice] melted in the heat."

5. "Who won it [the World Series]?" asked the little boy.

6. "It is well-known fact [according to whom?] that our team will win," boasted Scott.

7. "That restaurant [Susanne's] has live jazz every Friday and Saturday, during dinner," said Stan.

8. According to Alma, "You could have knocked her over with a fender [sic]."

9. The reporter wrote, "They [the family of the victim] are not going to forget this sight for as long as they live!"

10. Darlene wrote, "I am too ill to go to Helen's [her friend's] birthday party."

Writing Application
Using Dashes, Parentheses, and Brackets in Your Own Writing
Sample sentences are given.

1. The car flew over the cliff—to this day I have difficulty describing what I saw.

2. The jetliner—a wide-body aircraft with one engine under each wing and another in the tail—quickly climbed into the sky.

3. The immense size of the building—as I would find out once I started work—made leaving at the end of the day quite an ordeal.

4. In order to learn how to play tennis, you need (1) a tennis racquet, (2) some tennis balls, and (3) lots of time to practice.

5. My friend said, "It [the movie] is one of the worst films I have ever seen."

6. The newspaper editorial went on to say, "We must not approve construction projects that will endanger the environmint [sic] by causing pollution."

7. Her phone number is (274) 555-0793.

8. Mark Twain (1835–1910) was one of America's foremost writers and humorists.

9. His back yard—a gently sloping rectangle about one hundred feet wide—contains both flower and vegetable gardens.

10. Her duties included (a) keeping inventory, (b) selling jewelry, and (c) cleaning the display cases.

27.5 Dashes, Parentheses, Brackets, and Hyphens (Hyphens) (Page 147)
Practice 1
Exercise 1 Using Hyphens
1. great-grandfather
2. jack-o'-lantern
3. ninety-six
4. self-explanatory
5. none
6. fire-resistant
7. head-on
8. none
9. five-story
10. Senator-elect

Exercise 2 Hyphenating Words
1. mis-spell
2. el-bow
3. erase
4. in-ter-fere

5. all-impor-tant
6. length
7. Belgium
8. dis-a-gree
9. around
10. cir-cum-spect

27.5 Dashes, Parentheses, Brackets, and Hyphens (Hyphens) (Page 148)
Practice 2
Exercise 1 Using Hyphens to Join Words
1. thirty-first floor
2. semi-invalid
3. ex-Senator
4. self-adjusting
5. pre-American
6. well-intentioned advice
7. correct
8. correct
9. two-thirds cup
10. all-around athlete
11. twenty-six students
12. correct
13. correct
14. much-sought-after painting
15. pre-Columbian art
16. a comic-strip character
17. out-of-date styles
18. three-fourths cup
19. a well-decorated room
20. re-examination
21. ex-roommate
22. de-emphasize
23. president-elect
24. a five-year-old girl
25. thirty-seven new homes

Exercise 2 Using Hyphens at the Ends of Lines
1. Spanish
2. sister-in-law
3. excite-ment
4. correct
5. correct
6. frisky
7. correct
8. American
9. correct
10. self-interest
11. vi-brant
12. great-grandmother
13. correct
14. correct
15. correct
16. aban-don
17. clas-sify or classi-fy
18. correct
19. mot-to
20. correct
21. correct
22. correct
23. ninth
24. correct
25. unde-cided

27.6 Apostrophes (Page 149)
Practice 1
Exercise 1 Writing Possessive Forms
1. dress's
2. children's

3. anyone's
4. boys'
5. days'
6. each other's
7. players
8. Smiths'
9. its
10. brother-in-law's
11. women's
12. geese's
13. Andy and Steven's
14. minutes'
15. our
16. one another's
17. Lois's
18. mice's
19. motorists'
20. passer-by's

Exercise 2 Using Apostrophes in Other Ways
1. *A*'s
2. We've
3. shouldn't, *and*'s
4. here's, they've
5. o'clock, what's, what's

27.6 Apostrophes (Page 150)
Practice 2
Exercise 1 Using Apostrophes
1. the man's computer
2. two o'clock
3. James's *or* James' book
4. '95
5. the Joneses' house
6. the babies' cribs
7. the women's sports
8. each other's stories
9. 12's
10. who's
11. won't
12. Whose sandwich is it?
13. the Department of Defense's advice
14. Pat and Mike's comedy act
15. they're
16. someone's report
17. Queen Elizabeth II's son
18. a two weeks' vacation
19. Jane's and Mike's bicycles
20. its tail

Writing Application
Using the Rules for Apostrophes in Original Sentences
Sample sentences are given.
1. Ken's glasses were on the kitchen table.
2. The childrens' laughter echoed through the school playground.
3. His two pet cats' purring emanated from the living room.
4. George is taking a week's vacation.
5. I would like four dollars' worth of the fruit.
6. Bill's and Sam's bicycles are in the garage.
7. I just found somebody's notebook on the floor.
8. Lillian said that she wouldn't complete the work until tomorrow.
9. The 1930's were a time of massive unemployment in America.
10. There are too many *and*'s in your sentences.

Diagraming Basic Sentence Parts (Subjects, Verbs, and Modifiers)Answer (Page 151)

Exercise 1 Diagraming Subjects, Verbs, and Modifiers
1.
2.
3.

Exercise 2 More Work with Diagrams
1.
2.

Diagraming Basic Sentence Parts (Subjects, Verbs, and Modifiers)Answer (Page 152)

Exercise 1 Diagraming Subjects, Verbs, and Modifiers
1.
2.

3.

4.

5.

6.

Diagraming Basic Sentence Parts (Adding Conjunctions) (Page 153)

Exercise 1 Diagraming Sentences with Conjunctions

1.

2.

3.

Exercise 2 More Work with Conjunctions

1.

2.

Diagraming Basic Sentence Parts (Adding Conjunctions) (Page 154)

Exercise 1 Diagraming Sentences with Conjunctions

1.

2.

3.

4.

5.

© Prentice-Hall, Inc.

Answers • 211

6.

Diagraming Basic Sentence Parts (Complements) (Page 155)

Exercise 1 Diagraming Sentences with Complements

1.

2.

Exercise 2 More Work with Complements

1.

2.

Diagraming Basic Sentence Parts (Complements) (Page 156)

Exercise 1 Diagraming Complements

1.

2.

3.

4.

Louis Armstrong was \ musician
a jazz

5.

6.

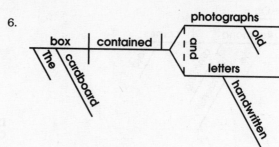

Diagraming Phrases and Clauses (Prepositional Phrases) (Page 157)

Exercise 1 Diagraming Prepositional Phrases

1.

2.

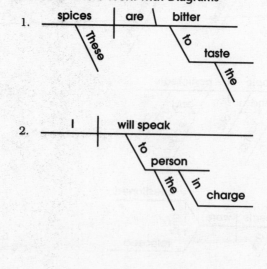

Exercise 2 More Work with Diagrams

1.

spices are \ bitter
These to taste the

2.

I | will speak
to person
the in charge

Diagraming Phrases and Clauses (Prepositional Phrases) (Page 158)

Exercise 1   Diagraming Prepositional Phrases

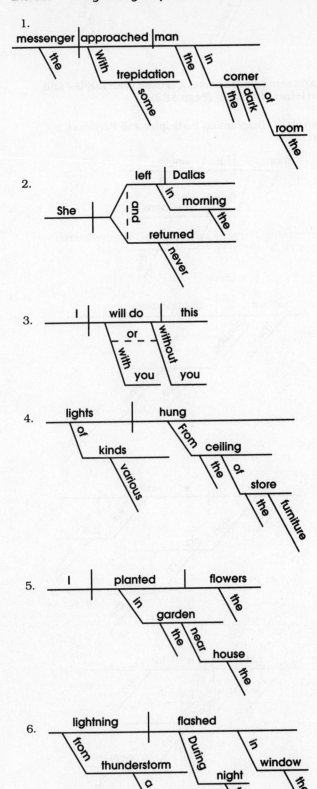

Diagraming Phrases and Clauses (Appositives and Appositive Phrases) (Page 159)

Exercise 1   Diagraming Appositives and Appositive Phrases

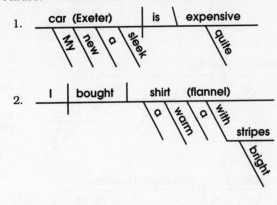

Exercise 2   More Work with Diagrams

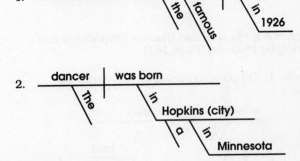

Diagraming Phrases and Clauses (Appositives and Appositive Phrases) (Page 160)

Exercise 1   Diagraming Appositive Phrases

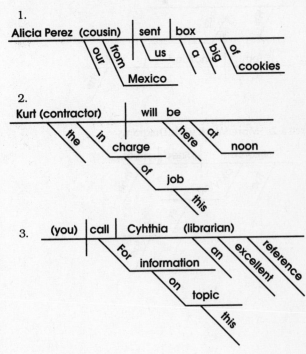

4.
Mr. Collins (teacher) | is

5.
Frank (neighbor) | walks

6.
guide (person) | described | paintings

Diagraming Phrases and Clauses (Participles and Participial Phrases) (Page 161)

Exercise 1 Diagraming Participles and Participial Phrases

1.
woman | called

2.
car

Exercise 2 More Work with Diagrams

1.
children | ruined | shoes

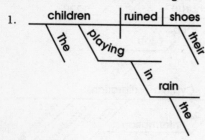

2.
turkey | was | ready

Diagraming Phrases and Clauses (Participles and Participial Phrases) (Page 162)

Exercise 1 Diagraming Participles and Participial Phrases

1.
man | is | uncle

2.
jetliner | disappeared

3.
lady | is | waiting

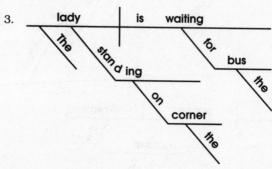

4.
girl | is | friend

5.

6.

Diagraming Phrases and Clauses (Gerund and Gerund Phrases) (Page 163)

Exercise 1   Diagraming Gerunds and Gerund Phrases

1.

2.

Exercise 2   More Work with Diagrams

1.

2.

Diagraming Phrases and Clauses (Gerund and Gerund Phrases) (Page 164)

Exercise 1   Diagraming Gerund Phrases

1.

2.

3.

4.

5.

Exercise 1   Diagraming Infinitives and Infinitive Phrases

1.

6.

2.

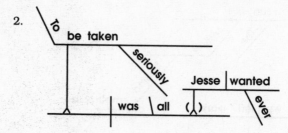

Diagraming Phrases and Clauses (Infinitives and Infinitive Phrases) (Page 165)

Exercise 1   Diagraming Infinitives and Infinitive Phrases

1.

3.

2.

4.

Exercise 2   More Work with Diagrams

1.

5.

2.

6.

Exercise 1   Diagraming Compound Sentences

1.

2.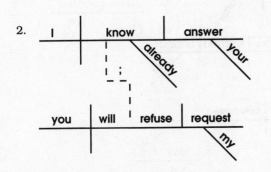

Exercise 2   More Work with Diagrams

1.

2.

Exercise 1   Diagraming Compound Sentences

1.

2.

3.

4.

5.

6.

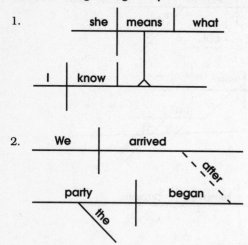

Diagraming Phrases and Clauses (Complex Sentences (Page 169)

Exercise 1   Diagraming Complex Sentences

1.

2.

Exercise 2   More Work with Diagrams

1.

2.

Diagraming Phrases and Clauses (Complex Sentences) (Page 170   Exercise 3   Diagraming Complex Sentences

1.

2.

3.

4.

5.

6.

Diagraming Phrases and Clauses (Compound-Complex Sentences) (Page 171)

Exercise 1   Diagraming Compound-Complex Sentences

1.

2.

1.

2.

Diagraming Phrases and Clauses (Compound-Complex Sentences) (Page 172)

Exercise 1   Diagraming Compound-Complex Sentences

1.